ALICYCLIC COMPOUNDS

Alicyclic Compounds

by

DOUGLAS LLOYD

B.Sc., F.R.I.C.

*Senior Lecturer in Chemistry in the
United College of St. Salvator and
St. Leonard in the University of
St. Andrews*

LONDON

EDWARD ARNOLD (PUBLISHERS) LTD

Made and printed in Great Britain by
William Clowes and Sons, Limited, London and Beccles

PREFACE

IN presenting a text on alicyclic compounds it is first necessary to define what types of compounds are covered by this term. A classification of organic compounds which has been made [see, e.g. Gilman, *Organic Chemistry*, Vol. I, p. 66 (Wiley, New York, 1938)] divides carbocyclic compounds into 'aromatic' and 'alicyclic' compounds. Until the later 1940s this classification was straightforward, for 'aromatic' carbocyclic compounds meant 'derivatives of benzene', and 'alicyclic' compounds meant all other carbocyclic compounds. With the realisation that aromatic properties were not restricted to compounds which were structural derivatives of benzene a new class of compounds was recognised, known as non-benzenoid aromatic compounds. These compounds might be classified either as alicyclic or as aromatic compounds, particularly as some of their properties resemble those of benzene whilst others are those of olefinic compounds. In fact it is frequently impossible to define a compound specifically as 'aromatic' or 'non-aromatic'; in any case, as discussed in the text, the chemical differences between 'aromatic' and 'olefinic' compounds are differences of degree rather than of kind. Consequently in the present text the author has preferred to classify carbocyclic compounds into *benzenoid* compounds and *alicyclic* compounds, which is unequivocal and in fact restores the earlier mode of sub-division of carbocyclic compounds. The term *aromatic* then refers to certain properties of compounds rather than to their molecular structure.

Of the four main classes of organic compounds, aliphatic, benzenoid, alicyclic and heterocyclic, only the first two classes normally receive extensive coverage in standard text-books of organic chemistry. Despite their wide occurrence alicyclic and heterocyclic compounds are frequently relegated to one chapter and a few pages each. In the past few years the position with regard to heterocyclic compounds has been eased by the publication of a number of student texts devoted exclusively to them but alicyclic compounds still remain the poor relation. The present text is humbly offered as a remedy for this neglect.   It is aimed at the Honours undergraduate student or the non-specialist postgraduate.

Alicyclic chemistry repays its study, for in many ways it is a microcosm of organic chemistry as a whole.   A survey of alicyclic chemistry includes accounts of fundamental aspects of organic chemistry such as synthetic methods, reaction mechanisms, stereochemistry, and aromatic character. Some of the most interesting recent developments in organic chemistry, e.g. conformational analysis, or the investigation of new aromatic systems, have derived in great measure from the study of alicyclic compounds.

Additionally alicyclic compounds are widely distributed in nature and have a wide range of uses.   However, in order to keep the present text within reasonable limits, it does not deal with natural products (except as examples) but rather describes the fundamental chemistry of alicyclic compounds.   Also for the sake of imposing some limit on its range, the discussion is for the most part restricted to monocyclic compounds.   The most important group of polycyclic compounds, those having the cyclopentanoperhydrophenanthrene nucleus, is in any case dealt with adequately in other special texts.

Except where reaction mechanisms are essential to the discussion of a topic, e.g. of molecular rearrangement reactions, they are not normally mentioned.   Partly this was done because it was felt to be more useful and also clearer not to labour descriptions of reactions with such discussions when the important point was the reaction itself; and partly because the mechanisms are for the most part straightforward and are readily available elsewhere, and, if required, can easily be found by consulting one of the many texts on reaction mechanisms.

In discussions with colleagues in this and other universities there was a large measure of agreement that so long as suitable references to further reading material were provided, references to original papers were unnecessary in a non-specialist text, and that their absence made the reading of the text easier.   Additionally detailed references increase the cost of a book, a result which all authors might seek to avoid.   In consequence references to original papers are not given in the present text, but at the end of each chapter a list of references to further suitable review articles is provided.   Additionally the names of workers are frequently given accompanied by a date, especially where recent work is concerned.   This should assist any reader who wishes to do so to track down the original papers describing the work in question.

It is a pleasant duty to thank friends who have helped in the preparation of the text.   Especial thanks are due to Dr. J. F. W. McOmie (University of Bristol) for a detailed appraisal of the first version of the manuscript and for many most helpful and constructive comments and criticisms.   Professor R. A. Raphael (University of Glasgow) was also kind enough to read

through the manuscript and offer valuable criticisms. Many mistakes
have been eliminated thanks to the co-operation of these colleagues, but
undoubtedly others remain, for which the author must take complete
responsibility. Perfection is beyond the achievement of a mere human,
and the author hopes that he at least fulfils the latter qualification. He
would appreciate it if errors are pointed out to him and would also be glad
to receive any other comments which might lead to improvement of the
book. He hopes that no worker will feel slighted by omission of his
particular contribution to the knowledge of any topic; in preparing a text
of this length selectivity is obviously essential and much valuable work
inevitably gets insufficient or no mention.

Finally thanks are due to my wife and Mrs. P. A. Sugden for their
assistance in reading the proofs, and to Messrs. Edward Arnold for their
co-operation and assistance at all stages in the production of the book.

St. Andrews 1963   DOUGLAS LLOYD

CONTENTS

I

INTRODUCTION;
STRAIN THEORY; STEREOCHEMISTRY

ORGANIC compounds may be classified into two main types: (*a*) open-chain or aliphatic; and (*b*) closed chain or cyclic compounds. The latter group may be subdivided into *carbocyclic* compounds, in which the rings of atoms consist exclusively of carbon atoms, and *heterocyclic* compounds, wherein one or more atoms of elements other than carbon—most commonly nitrogen, oxygen or sulphur—are also found in the ring.

A large number of carbocyclic compounds are derivatives of benzene (C_6H_6) or fused-ring analogues of benzene (e.g. naphthalene, anthracene, etc.). Such compounds may be termed *benzenoid* compounds; all other carbocyclic compounds are then classified as *alicyclic* compounds. This may be represented diagrammatically as follows:

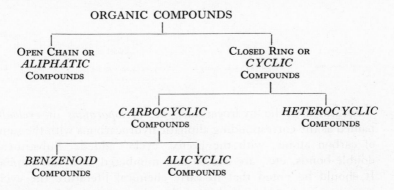

The term *benzenoid* is used rather than the more usual one *aromatic*, because aromatic character is not restricted to benzenoid compounds. Other cyclic compounds are known, not derived from benzene structurally, whose chemical properties, like those of benzene, cannot be adequately represented by formulae consisting of alternating double and single bonds (as in the Kekulé formulae for benzene). They have properties somewhat

1

akin to those of benzene, for example behaving sometimes as saturated compounds rather than as unsaturated. Examples of such compounds are discussed in Chapters X–XIII.

Rings of any size from three upwards may (and do) exist. It is convenient to represent saturated hydrocarbon rings by short-hand formulae,

cyclopropane cyclobutane cyclopentane cyclohexane cycloheptane

become respectively:

etc.

Note that a plain hexagon always represents cyclohexane and *never* benzene, which is always represented as either

or

[In accordance with the recommendations of the Publications Committee of The Chemical Society (London), the first of these formulae is normally used rather than the inscribed circle formula.]

Double-bonds and substituent groups are shown in the usual way, e.g.

cyclohexene cyclohexa–1,3–diene 1–cyanocyclopropane– 2–methylcyclohexene–
             –1–carboxylic acid   carboxylic acid

Saturated cyclic hydrocarbons, i.e. *cycloparaffins* or *cycloalkanes*, are named as the corresponding aliphatic hydrocarbons with the same number of carbon atoms, with the prefix 'cyclo' added. Substituent groups, double-bonds, etc., are named and numbered as in the aliphatic series. It should be noted that in early chemical literature the cycloparaffins were known as *polymethylenes* and cyclopropane, cyclobutane, etc., were described as trimethylene, tetramethylene, etc.

Compounds containing two fused rings are named after the corresponding aliphatic hydrocarbon containing the same number of carbon atoms as the total number of carbon atoms making up the two rings, with the prefix 'bicyclo' added. Between this prefix and the main name numbers are written, enclosed in square brackets, indicating the number of carbon atoms contained in each bridge of the compound, but excluding the atoms common to both rings, e.g.

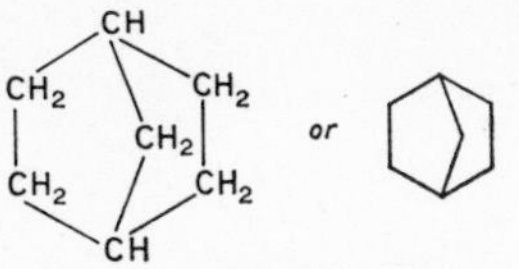

bicyclo- [2,2,1] -heptane 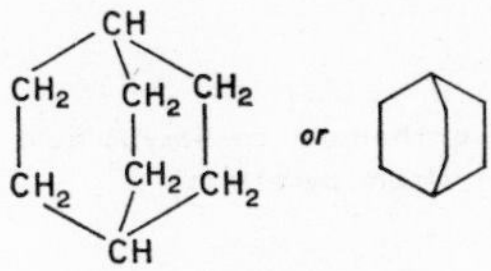   bicyclo- [2,2,2] - octane 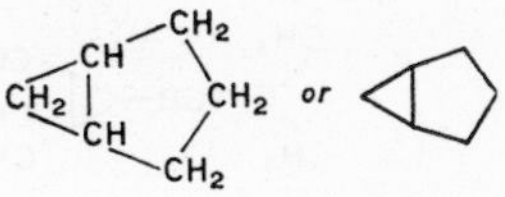   bicyclo- [3,1,0] -hexane

The numbers within the brackets are conventionally written in descending numerical order.

The first and second examples given above are also sometimes known (and especially in early literature) as 1,4-endomethylenecyclohexane and 1,4-endoethylenecyclohexane.

To locate substituent groups, the carbon atoms are numbered, starting from a carbon atom at which the bridges join, and proceeding around the bridges in the order of decreasing length (in number of carbon atoms) of bridge, e.g.

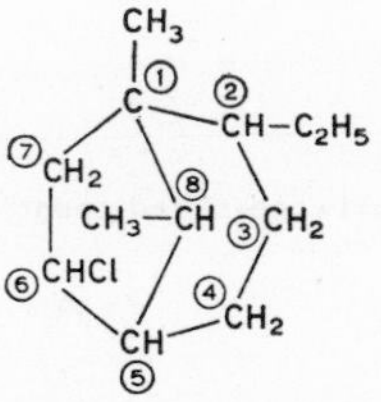

6-chloro-2-ethyl-1,8-dimethyl-
bicyclo- [3,2,1] - octane

(The bridges are thus numbered in the same order as they are designated by the numerals within the square brackets of the formula.)

For fuller details of nomenclature, and for the nomenclature of compounds with more than two rings, the publication entitled *Handbook for Chemical Society Authors, 1960* (Chemical Society, London, 1960), should be consulted.

Alicyclic compounds in nature

Compounds of the alicyclic series are widely distributed in nature, the largest group being cyclohexane derivatives. Thus many terpenes have this structure, e.g.

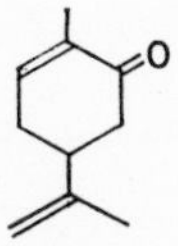

carvone 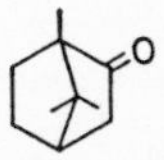   camphor

Other examples of naturally-occurring alicyclic compounds with rings of various sizes are:

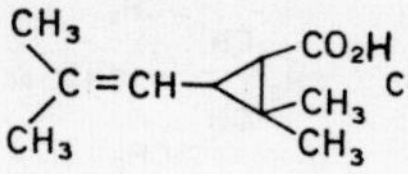

$$CH_3\text{-}C(CH_3)=CH\text{-}\triangle(CH_3)(CH_3)CO_2H$$ Chrysanthemum carboxylic acid (from pyrethrin)

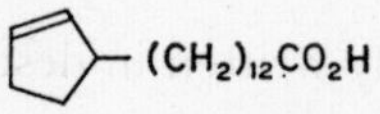

$$\bigcirc\!\!-(CH_2)_{12}CO_2H$$ Chaulmoogric Acid (from chaulmoogra oil)
(used in the treatment of leprosy)

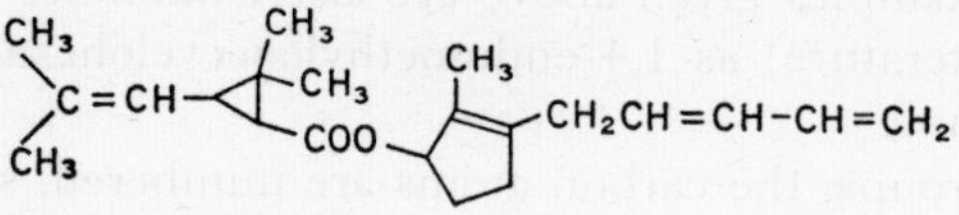

Pyrethrin I (from pyrethrum)
(Insecticide)

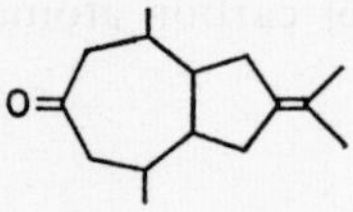

β - Vetivone (from oil of vetiver)

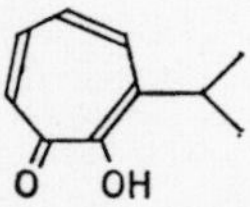

α - Thujaplicin (from heartwood of red cedar)

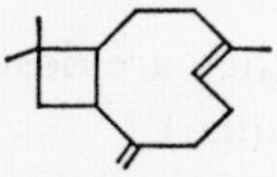

Caryophyllene (from oil of cloves)

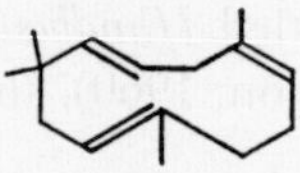

Humulene (from hops)

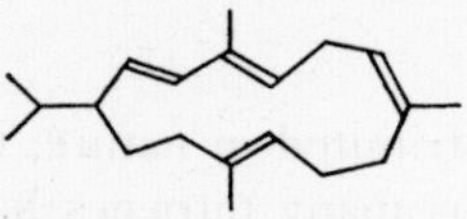

Cembrene (in exudate from pine trees)

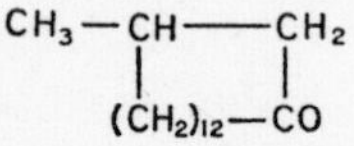

$$CH_3\text{-}CH\text{----}CH_2$$
$$\quad\;\;|\qquad\qquad|$$
$$\quad(CH_2)_{12}\text{-}CO$$

Muscone (from the musk deer)
(Perfume)

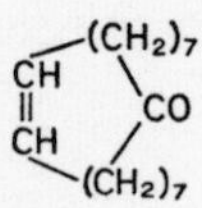

Civetone (from the civet cat)
(Perfume)

Also there are many compounds such as the steroids which contain the cyclopentanoperhydrophenanthrene nucleus, e.g. cholesterol:

HO

cyclopentanoperhydrophenanthrene   cholesterol

Very many other alicyclic compounds are found naturally, in plants and animals, and among the constituents of crude petroleum oils. This account does not, however, deal specifically with natural products, but discusses rather the fundamental properties of alicyclic compounds.

Strain theory

Before the early 1880s the only known alicyclic compounds were all derivatives of cyclohexane. Some distinguished chemists (e.g. V. Meyer in 1876) suggested strongly that rings other than six-membered could not be formed and were indeed incapable of existence. In 1881, however, Markovnikov prepared a cyclobutane derivative and Freund prepared cyclopropane, while in 1883 W. H. Perkin began his important series of researches on small-ring compounds and soon produced pure samples of cyclobutane, cyclopropane and cyclopentane derivatives.

It was soon evident that the small-ring compounds were in some respects more reactive than cyclohexane derivatives. In general alicyclic compounds resemble the corresponding open-chain compounds in their chemical and physical properties, with the cyclic compounds usually having somewhat higher boiling-points, but cyclopropane and cyclobutane derivatives show differences in both chemical and physical properties from their open-chain analogues.

Cyclopropane tends towards ethylene in its properties. Some chemists have formally regarded ethylene as a two-membered ring (dimethylene), and have thus seen this tendency towards unsaturation in the small-ring compounds as a logical transition towards the properties of the 'two-membered ring'.

Cyclopropane is reduced by hydrogen in the presence of a nickel catalyst at 120° to propane. The ring is also broken by bromine, hydrogen bromide, hydrogen iodide and sulphuric acid, giving addition products, e.g.

$$\triangleleft \quad \begin{array}{l} \xrightarrow{\text{Br}_2} \text{BrCH}_2\text{CH}_2\text{CH}_2\text{Br} \\ \xrightarrow{\text{HBr}} \text{CH}_3\text{CH}_2\text{CH}_2\text{Br} \end{array}$$

Furthermore a rule similar to Markovnikov's may be applied to these addition reactions when substituted cyclopropane rings are involved. The ring breaks between the most heavily and the least heavily substituted carbon atoms in the ring.   If the reagent has the formula HX, the hydrogen atom adds to the least substituted carbon atom and the group —X to the most substituted, e.g.

$$ \begin{array}{c} CH_3 \\ CH_3 \end{array}\!\!>\!\!\triangleleft\!\!-\!CH_3 \quad\xrightarrow{\ HBr\ }\quad (CH_3)_2CBr-CHCH_3-CH_3 $$

In contrast to olefinic compounds, however, the cyclopropane ring is unaffected by ozone or by permanganate, e.g.

$$ \begin{array}{c} CH_3 \\ CH_3 \end{array}\!\!>\!\!\triangleleft^{CH=C(CH_3)_2} \quad\xrightarrow{\ KMnO_4\ }\quad \begin{array}{c} CH_3 \\ CH_3 \end{array}\!\!>\!\!\triangleleft^{CO_2H} $$

Various chemical properties and spectral evidence also indicate that an α,β-double-bond can partially conjugate with a cyclopropane ring.   For example the position of the maximum in the spectrum of phenylcyclopropane is intermediate between those of ethylbenzene and styrene:

	$\lambda_{max.}$
$PhCH_2CH_3$	2060
$Ph-\triangleleft$	2200
$PhCH=CH_2$	2455

Cyclobutane shows less tendency to undergo addition reactions than cyclopropane, but will react with hydrogen in the presence of a nickel catalyst at 200°, and also, on heating, with hydrogen iodide.   Other halogen acids and bromine do not open the cyclobutane ring.   The larger ring hydrocarbons are stable and closely resemble aliphatic paraffin hydrocarbons in their properties.

Baeyer (1885) put forward his famous *Strain Theory* to explain these variations in properties with ring-size.   He pointed out that if the normal angles between the four valencies of a tetrahedral carbon atom are assumed to be 109° 28', i.e. the valencies are equally spaced about the atom, then in three- and four-membered rings severe distortion of the normal valency angles must be involved.   Thus in a cyclopropane ring each bond must be distorted from the tetrahedral angle by 24° 44':

If all the rings are assumed to be planar, the distortions for each ring-size are as follows:

No. of atoms in ring	Angle between Valency Bonds	Distortion from normal Valency Angle *
(2) (ethylene)	0°	54° 44'
3	60°	24° 44'
4	90°	9° 44'
5	108°	0° 44'
6	120°	−5° 16'
7	128° 34'	−9° 33'
8	135°	−12° 46'
etc.		

* = 1/2 [Normal Valency Angle − Actual Angle between bonds]. (The distortion caused is assumed to be equally shared between the two bonds. See diagram above.)

This distortion in the smaller rings was said to cause strain in the molecule and hence cause their enhanced reactivity. It should be noted that this theory was originally based on a geometric and mechanical idea of valency bonds, but there seems no reason why it should not equally apply to electrical distortions.* The presence of 'strain' and hence of decreased stability has also been shown by the enhanced values of the molecular heat of combustion per methylene group of cyclopropane and cyclobutane compared to the values for the larger rings:

No. of carbon atoms in ring	2	3	4	5	6	7
Mol. ht. of combustion per CH_2 group (kcal.)	170	166·6	163·95	158·7	157·4	158·3

Thorpe and Ingold (1921 *et seq.*) pointed out that the bond-angles around a tetrahedral carbon-atom would all be equal only if the four atoms or

* Quantum mechanical calculations stipulate that the orbitals about any first-row element may not form an angle of less than 90°. To reconcile this concept with the known molecular structure of cyclopropane it has been suggested that bonding orbitals between the ring atoms are directed not at each other, but at angles γ, = 22°, outside the equilateral triangle, giving an angle between the orbitals of 104°. (See diagram.) This means in effect that the ring bonds are 'bent'; they have been called 'bent bonds' or 'banana bonds'. The bonds in cyclobutane are thought to be similarly bent, although to a lesser extent. The reduced overlap of the orbitals consequent upon their not being directed at each other is held to be responsible for the carbon–carbon bond being weaker than normal.

2—A.C.

groups of atoms attached to it were identical. If, however, there are groups of different sizes attached to these bonds then variations in bond-angle will be caused by this alone, large groups tending to be separated by angles exceeding the mean tetrahedral angle and smaller groups being consequently forced closer to each other. This can be shown diagrammatically in one plane by the following representations of neopentane and propane:

$$
\begin{array}{ccc}
\text{CH}_3\diagdown\diagup\text{CH}_3 & & \text{H}\diagdown\diagup\text{CH}_3 \\
\text{C} & \textit{but} & \text{C} \\
\text{CH}_3\diagup\diagdown\text{CH}_3 & & \text{H}\diagup\diagdown\text{CH}_3 \\
\end{array}
$$

Although this modification to the original strain theory cannot be applied quantitatively it has been used to interpret certain points of detail in alicyclic chemistry.

A more serious difficulty with the original strain theory was its failure to account for the stability of rings larger than five-membered. According to the theory such rings should also be strained and thus might be expected to show properties comparable with those of the small rings. But this is not the case; for instance the larger rings have none of the additive properties associated with the small rings.

To explain the stability of cyclohexane and its derivatives, Sachse (1890) suggested that their rings were non-planar. This suggestion remained largely overlooked until it was restated by Mohr in 1918. By maintaining the tetrahedral angles for the carbon valencies two unstrained ring forms could be postulated, the 'chair' form (I) and 'boat' form (II)

(I)   (II)

The failure to discover two forms of cyclohexane at first caused non-acceptance of this theory, but Mohr pointed out that the two forms would be readily interconvertible simply by rotation about the single-bonds. The energy of interconversion (5 kcal./mole) is much too small to allow separation of the two forms.

Mohr further suggested that if such rings were non-planar, then decalin (III) should exist in two forms, *cis*, (IV), and *trans*, (V), which at the time he formulated as follows (but see pp. 20 ff.):

(III)   (IV) (cis)   (V) (trans)

In 1925, Hückel obtained two different isomers of decalin. They require drastic conditions for interconversion.

It is worth noting that there had already been earlier evidence available supporting the concept of non-planarity of rings made up of more than five carbon atoms. For instance,

(a) both *cis-* and *trans-*cycloheptane-1,2-diols give complexes with boric acid and with acetone;

(b) both *cis-* and *trans-*hexahydrohomophthalic acids [(2-methylcyclohexyl)-acetic acid] form intramolecular anhydrides;

(c) two isomeric β-decalones were known to exist.

Such facts were difficult to explain without assuming the rings to be non-planar and puckered.

The occurrence and stability of bridged-rings (e.g. camphor, see p. 3) also accords with the idea of buckled rings. It is difficult to envisage compounds with skeletons such as (VI) and (VII) without assuming that they have non-planar structures.

(VI)   (VII)

Since 1925 very large rings have both been made synthetically and found to occur naturally (e.g. in civetone and muscone, see p. 4). Their properties closely resemble those of aliphatic compounds and are thus in accord with those predicted for buckled rings. For example, Ruzicka has prepared compounds having up to 34 carbon-atoms in the ring, and for all of these large-ring compounds, the heat of combustion per methylene group remains almost constant. (But note the discussion on pp. 74 ff.)

Stereochemistry of alicyclic rings

Alicyclic compounds having substituents at only one ring carbon atom can exist in only one stereochemical form, but if substituents are present at more than one of the ring carbon atoms then more than one stereoisomer may exist. Thus in the case of cyclopropane-1,2-dicarboxylic acid (VIII), there is one isomer (IX) with both carboxyl groups on the same side of the ring and another (X) with one carboxyl group on each side of the ring.

CO_2H CO_2H CO_2H

CO_2H CO_2H CO_2H

(VIII)   (IX)   (X)

This may be compared with the situation which exists in the case of

substituted olefins (e.g. maleic and fumaric acids) and a similar nomenclature is used. Compound (IX) is described as the *cis*-isomer and
compound (X) as the *trans*-isomer; they are geometrical isomers of each
other. Similar considerations apply to rings of all sizes and increasing
numbers of substituents will usually lead to increasing numbers of geometrical isomers. For example there are four possible isomers (XI),
(XII), (XIII) and (XIV) of 1,2,3,4-tetramethylcyclobutane.

(XI)   (XII)   (XIII)   (XIV)

However, disubstitution by two identical groups at one carbon atom
lowers the number of possible geometrical isomers; for example, only one
geometrical isomer of cyclopropane-1,1,2-tricarboxylic acid is possible,
and there are only three geometrical isomers of 1,1,2,3,4-pentamethyl-
cyclobutane.

In addition to geometrical isomerism, optical isomerism is possible in
the case of many polysubstituted alicyclic compounds. Thus of the two
cyclopropane-1,2-dicarboxylic acids, the *cis*-isomer has a plane of symmetry
in the molecule and therefore cannot be resolved, but the *trans*-isomer has
no such plane of symmetry and can therefore be resolved into *d*- and
l-forms. Similarly cyclopropane-1,1,2-tricarboxylic acid is resolvable
into stereoisomers, but all four of the 1,2,3,4-tetramethylcyclobutanes have
planes of symmetry in their molecules and are consequently not resolvable.

Methods of distinguishing between alicyclic *cis*- and *trans*-isomers

Many ways of distinguishing between alicyclic *cis*- and *trans*-isomers
are possible, and two simple examples must serve to illustrate some of the
methods used.

1 In the case of the two cyclopropane-1,2-dicarboxylic acids mentioned
above, recognition of their identity is simple since:

(i) For steric reasons only the *cis*-isomer can form an intramolecular
anhydride. (Under forcing conditions the *trans*-acid might form the *cis*-
anhydride, but hydrolysis of the anhydride formed would give a different
acid (*cis*-) from the starting acid, showing that such a change had taken
place.)

(ii) The *cis*-acid has a plane of symmetry in the molecule whereas the
trans-acid has not. The latter acid, unlike the former, is therefore
resolvable into *d*- and *l*-forms.

(iii) *Trans*-acids have higher melting points than their *cis*-isomers.

2 An example of a more complicated case, from work by Wislicenus, and more recent work by Jacobs, concerns the two possible geometric isomers of 2,5-dimethylcyclopentane-1,1-dicarboxylic acid and the three geometric isomers of 2,5-dimethylcyclopentane-1-carboxylic acid. If the two dicarboxylic acids are formulated as (A) and (B) (see below), it can be seen that one isomer (A) will give only one monobasic acid (C) on decarboxylation, whereas (B) will give two isomers [(D) and (E)].

Of the three monobasic acids (C), (D) and (E), (D) and (E) have a plane of symmetry through the molecule whereas (C) has not, and the structure of (C) has been confirmed by its partial resolution. The acids (D) and (E) have been distinguished since:

(i) (E) is esterified more rapidly than (D), and is therefore presumably less sterically hindered,

(ii) (D) is the main product obtained by catalytic hydrogenation of 2,5-dimethylcyclopentene-1-carboxylic acid, and is therefore presumably the *cis*-isomer,

(iii) (D) is isomerised to (E) on heating with hydrogen chloride in acetic acid. This indicates that (E) is the more stable isomer, i.e. the *trans*-isomer. (See next chapter, p. 27, for an explanation of this difference in stability between the *cis*- and *trans*-isomers.)

All these facts are consistent with (D) and (E) being the *cis*- and *trans*-isomers respectively.

FOR FURTHER READING

Raphael, R. A. (1953). In *Chemistry of Carbon Compounds*, Vol. IIA, edited by E. H. Rodd. Chapter I. Elsevier.

Fuson, R. C. (1942). In *Organic Chemistry*, Vol. I, edited by H. Gilman. Chapter II. Wiley.

Eliel, E. L. (1962). *Stereochemistry of Carbon Compounds*, Chapter VII. McGraw-Hill.

For a review of recent ideas on the structure of cyclopropane see:
Lukina, M. Y. (1962). *Russ. Chem. Rev.*, 419.

II

THE CONFORMATION OF ALICYCLIC RINGS

Conformation of compounds

It is first necessary to define the term *conformation*. It was first coined by W. N. Haworth in 1929. It may be defined as *The different possible arrangements in space of the atoms of a single classical organic structure (or configuration) which can be produced by the rotation about the single bonds in that structure.* In German usage the term *constellation* is frequently used with the same meaning.

Let us consider such arrangements, and for a first example consider tartaric acid. We also need to consider means of projecting these 'conformations' because normal projection formulae such as:

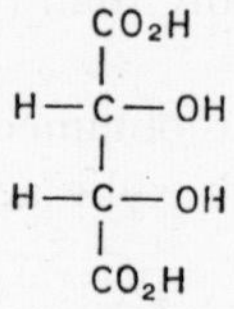

$$
\begin{array}{c}
CO_2H \\
| \\
H-C-OH \\
| \\
H-C-OH \\
| \\
CO_2H
\end{array}
$$

will not suffice.

A first rule to be noted is that all fully saturated (i.e. sp^3) carbon atoms always seek to take up an arrangement of their valency bonds such that there is the normal tetrahedral angle between these bonds. Thus tartaric acid might be represented as:

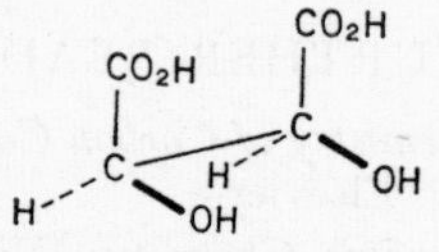

This gives a truer picture than the projection formula and is sometimes called a perspective formula. Perspective formulae are frequently of great assistance in assessing the behaviour of molecules.

However, owing to the rotations about single bonds, molecules will not

12

necessarily remain static in any one such form.   Thus *meso*-tartaric acid might equally be represented by the following formulae:

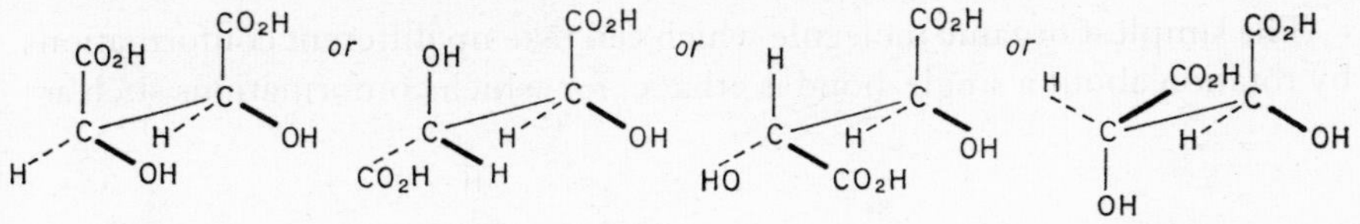

(a) (b) (c) (d)

These variants are obtained merely by rotation of the molecule about the central carbon–carbon bond.

Alternative ways of representing these different *conformations* are:

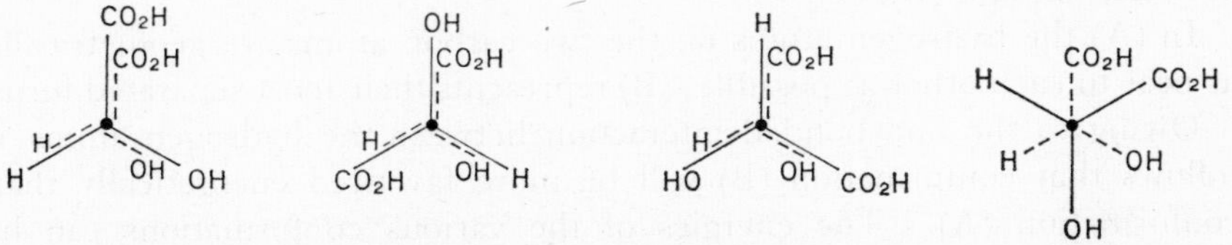

(a) (b) (c) (d)

or

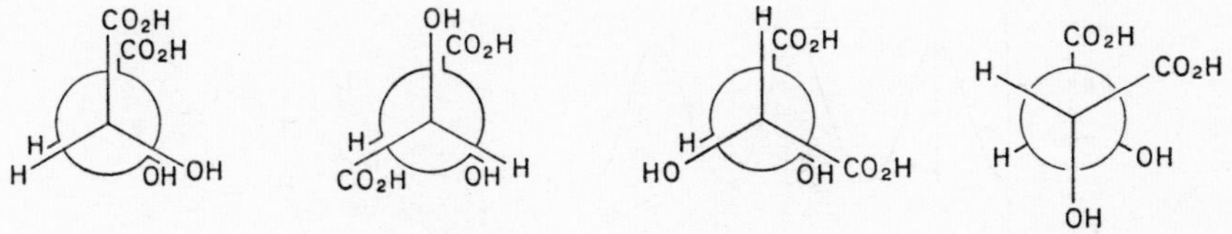

(a) (b) (c) (d)

In both systems the molecule is viewed along the line of a valency-bond —in this instance the central carbon–carbon bond—and the formulae then indicate the correct angles between the various bonds as seen from that direction.   Each of these types of formulation will be used in this book, as suits best for the particular occasion.

Note that *all* the formulae given above represent the *same molecule* and the *same isomer* of that molecule.   Differences of conformation and not of configuration or structure are involved.

It is next necessary to consider whether all of these conformations are equally preferred, i.e. if there is 'free' rotation about a single-bond.

When one is considering the interactions between atoms spaced at intramolecular distances, it is of course necessary to distinguish between atoms which are bonded directly to each other and atoms which are not so linked, i.e. *non-bonded* atoms.   If two atoms are non-bonded, then even if both are neutral, at these distances they will repel one another due to their interaction.   This repulsion increases with decreasing separation of the atoms.

The simplest organic molecule which can take up different conformations by rotation about a single-bond is ethane, for which conformations such as:

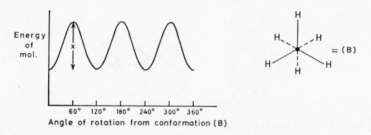

can be realised, with, of course, all the various intermediate arrangements between (A) and (B).

In (A) the hydrogen atoms on the two carbon atoms are geometrically as near to each other as possible; (B) represents their most separated form.

Owing to the non-bonded interaction between the hydrogen atoms it follows that conformation (B) will be more favoured energetically than conformation (A).   The energies of the various conformations can be represented graphically as functions of rotation about the carbon–carbon bond as follows:

In other words there is a potential barrier, equal to x, acting against completely free rotation in the molecule.   In ethane this is considered to be one of the magnitude of 3 kcal./mole.   This figure may be compared with the value of 20–30 kcal., which is the order required to inhibit rotation completely.

Thus it is seen that although rotation is not completely restricted, it is not entirely free, and the molecules will tend to take up preferentially the (B) or *staggered* type of conformation rather than the (A) or *eclipsed* type.

Let us now consider n-butane in a similar way.   The picture is now rather more complicated.   As the central carbon–carbon bond is rotated, conformations such as (I)–(VI) are possible.

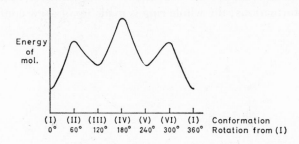

There are now two types of eclipsed conformations—those where a methyl group eclipses another methyl group (IV) and those where a hydrogen atom is eclipsed by a methyl group [(II) and (VI)]. Similarly two types of staggered conformation are possible, the fully staggered conformation (I), sometimes described as *transoid* (or even, quite incorrectly as *trans*); or the partially staggered conformations (with respect to the positions of the methyl groups) (III) and (V), known sometimes as *skew* or *gauche*.

We have seen already that staggered conformations are more favoured than eclipsed ones. The eclipsing or *opposition* of two methyl groups, as in (IV), leads to more repulsions within the molecule than the opposition of a methyl group and the smaller hydrogen atom. Similarly the transoid conformation will be more favoured than the skew conformation as in the former case the two methyl groups have the greatest possible distance of separation. Thus the energy–rotation relationship for n-butane has the form:

Therefore n-butane and other open-chain hydrocarbons will tend to take up the completely staggered form:

giving rise to the well-known zigzag arrangement of carbon chains in aliphatic compounds, which has been recognised for many years from physical studies on these compounds.

Conformation of cyclohexane and its derivatives

After Sachse and Mohr's suggestion that cyclohexane rings were non-planar, chemical evidence accumulated to confirm this idea, and more recently it has been confirmed by physical evidence, notably by X-ray diffraction studies by Hassel. As pointed out by Mohr, the tetrahedral angles may be maintained by buckling the ring in either of two ways, to give a 'boat' or 'chair' form.

If we apply conformational analysis (i.e. an analysis of the conformational factors involved) to these structures, we find that in the boat form carbon atoms 2 and 3, and 5 and 6 have eclipsed conformations; the remaining conformations are skew. In the chair form, however, there are no eclipsed conformations; the whole ring is made up of skew conformations:

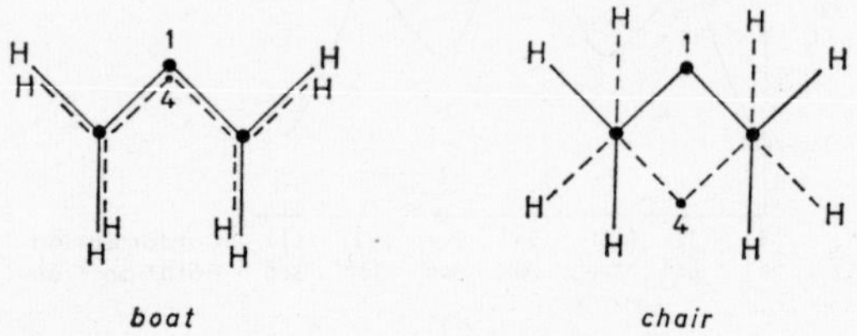

It is now realised that whereas the chair form is a definite and rigid form which resists distortion, the so-called boat form is but one possible shape of a mobile or flexible form which can be readily distorted into a variety of shapes. (This can be best appreciated by the study of the appropriate molecular models.) The classical boat form is not even the most energetically favoured conformation of the flexible form, which is represented rather by the *skew* or *twist* conformation:

In this skew conformation, atoms 1, 2, 4 and 6 are coplanar, while atoms 1, 3, 4 and 5 lie in another plane. Substituents at atoms 2, 3, 5 and 6 take up approximately axial or equatorial positions (*see* p. 11), but the positions of the substituents at atoms 1 and 4 relative to neighbouring substituent atoms are more like those in cyclopentane derivatives.

Since the chair form, unlike the flexible forms, involves neither angle strain nor eclipsed conformations, it follows that it is energetically favoured with respect to other possible conformations. Consequently the majority of cyclohexane molecules take up a chair conformation. This has been confirmed by physical measurements.

If a full picture of the chair form of the cyclohexane ring is drawn, it may be seen that the hydrogen atoms fall into two groups, those on bonds represented by continuous lines being roughly perpendicular to the general plane of the ring, and those on bonds represented by dotted lines being arranged around the ring, roughly in the general plane of the ring.

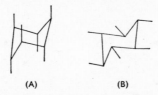

The former are described as *axial* (*a*) bonds, the latter as *equatorial* (*e*) bonds. It may further be noted that whereas the axial substituents tend to be crowded together [see (A)] the equatorial ones are spread out around the ring, and are more readily accessible [see (B)].

(A)   (B)

Because of this difference in spacing, axial and equatorial substituents differ in their reactivity.

For any cyclohexane ring *two* chair forms are possible, each being convertible into the other by rotation about the valency bonds of the rings, viz.

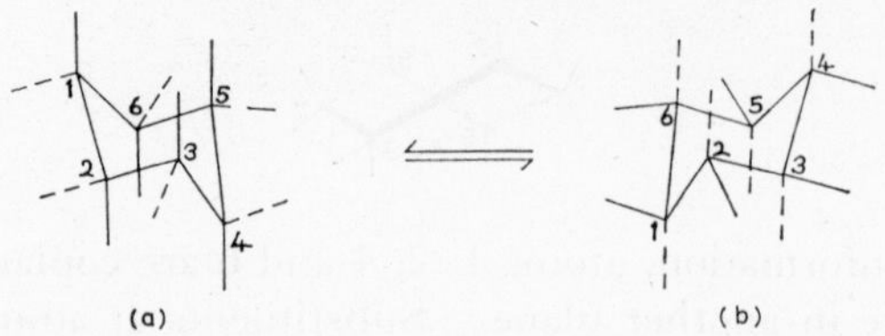

[Chair form (*a*) is converted into form (*b*) in the above diagram by rotation of carbon atom no. 1 downwards and carbon atom no. 4 upwards (and vice versa).]

In passing from one chair form to the other, the axial groups in the one form become equatorial in the other and vice versa. The energy barrier between the two forms is high enough to ensure that the forms are discrete entities but insufficient to prevent their rapid interconversion at normal temperature. Consequently no one hydrogen atom in cyclohexane can be definitely assigned to any one conformation but is equally likely (since the molecule is symmetrical) to be found in either an equatorial or axial conformation. [In this simplified discussion no account is taken of the intermediate conformations between (*a*) and (*b*) (above) through which the molecule may pass in changing from one chair form to the other.]

Owing to the less crowded situation of the equatorial positions, bulky groups will predominantly tend to take up equatorial conformations. Thus methylcyclohexane will be predominantly in form (i) rather than form (ii):

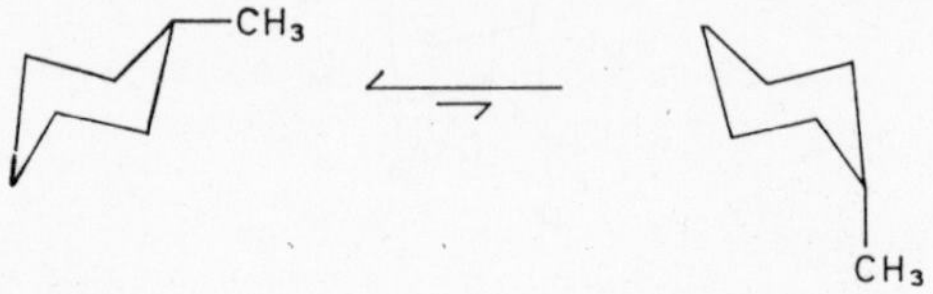

By viewing the molecule along the axis of the appropriate ring bonds it is easily seen that in the axial form the methyl group has a skew conformation with respect to one of the ring bonds whilst in the equatorial form it is transoid:

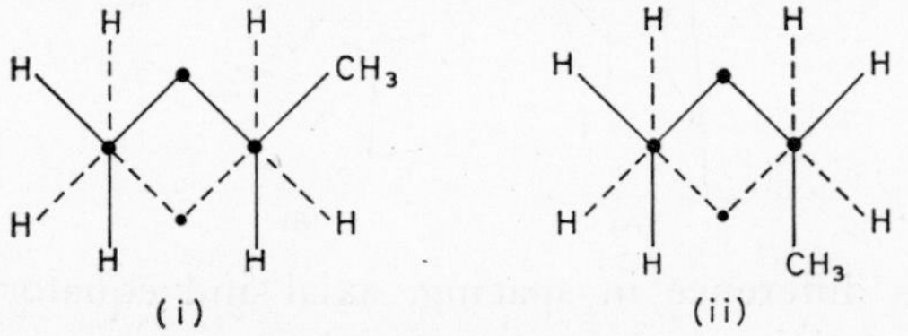

As rotation about single bonds is not prohibited, even if it is to some extent restricted, a methylcyclohexane molecule will not exist exclusively in one form. By simple rotations about the ring valency bonds forms (i)

and (ii) will be interchangeable.   But at any moment the molecules will be for the greater part in conformation (i).   This has been shown to be indeed the case by physical studies (I.R. spectra, etc.).

Another illustration of the fact that the equatorial conformation is the preferred one is the observation that if a mixture of carvomenthone (U) and isocarvomenthone (W) is equilibrated, the equilibrium mixture contains 80% of carvomenthone, which can take up a conformation with both the methyl and isopropyl groups equatorial.

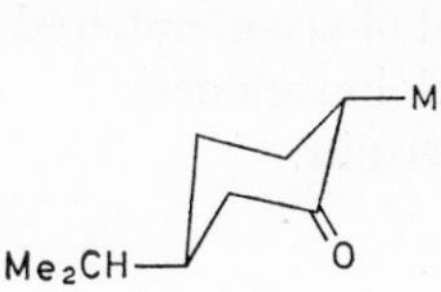

(U) 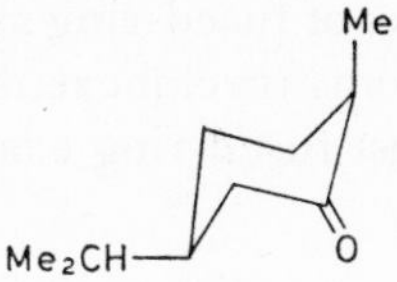   (W)

(It is assumed that the large isopropyl group, rather than the smaller methyl group, will take up an equatorial conformation in isocarvomenthone.)

It will now be well to translate the conventional *cis* and *trans* description of the stereochemistry of cyclohexane derivatives into conformational terms.   If we flatten out the chair form of cyclohexane (X) we get the flat planar representation (Y)—a representation frequently used for cyclohexane compounds.

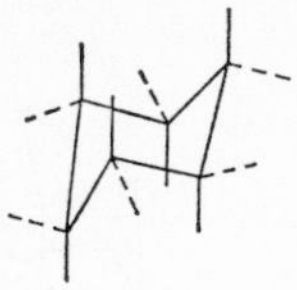

(X) 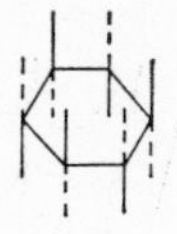   (Y)

If two groups are attached to one ring atom, it is obvious that one group must be equatorial and the other must be axial.

Now consider two groups attached to adjacent ring atoms.   From the above diagram of (X) and (Y) it may be seen that if two such groups are *cis* to each other, then one must be equatorial and the other axial; if the two groups are *trans* to each other, then they must be either both axial or both equatorial.   It further follows that for 1,3- and 1,4-substituents the relationships must be:

	cis	*trans*
1,3	*e,e* or *a,a*	*a,e*
1,4	*a,e*	*e,e* or *a,a*

Where two substituents can be either *e,e* or *a,a* they will, in the case of a simple cyclohexane ring where interconversion of conformations is not totally restricted, preferentially take up the di-equatorial form. It has already been shown that an equatorial position is energetically more stable than an axial position. Hence a *cis*-1,3-disubstituted (*e,e*) cyclohexane will be more stable than the corresponding *trans*-1,3-isomer, which must be *a,e*. Similarly in the case of 1,2- and 1,4-substituted cyclohexanes the *trans*-isomer is the more stable one.

Now let us consider the conformations of more complex cyclohexane derivatives, i.e. of fused-ring systems and of six-membered rings including sp^2 carbon-atoms (cyclohexenes and cyclohexanones).

The simplest fused-ring example is decalin:

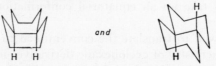

Two isomers of this compound have been isolated and were for a long time ascribed the conformations:

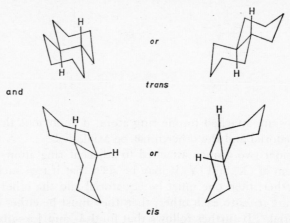

Following the recognition that the chair form of cyclohexane was more stable than the boat form, it was realised that *cis*- and *trans*-forms of decalin could be constructed in both cases made up only from chair forms:

or

and   *trans*

or

cis

These structures have in fact been confirmed by electron diffraction measurements by Bastiansen and Hassel (1946). In the case of the *cis*-form the two rings are joined by one *e*- and one *a*-bond. One consequence of this is that the *cis*-form can be turned 'inside-out' like a simple cyclohexane ring:

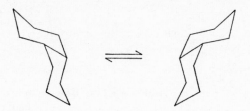

As in the case of cyclohexane it is not possible to isolate separate forms owing to their ease of interconversion. Thus in the case of the *cis*-decalins, substituent groups are not rigidly constrained to an *a*- or *e*-position, but will tend, as in the case of the simple cyclohexane ring, to assume the *e*-conformation. Therefore *cis*- and *trans*-decalols derived from *cis*-decalin (i.e. hydroxy-*cis*-decalins, with the hydroxyl group respectively *cis*- and *trans*- to the *cis*-ring junction) may have either *e*- or *a*-hydroxyl groups, although the *e*-conformation will predominate:

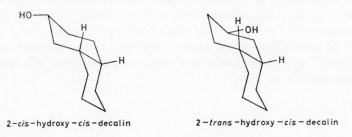

2 –*cis*–hydroxy –*cis*–decalin   2 –*trans*–hydroxy –*cis*– decalin

In *trans*-decalin the rings are joined by two *e*-bonds and, in contrast to the *cis*-isomer, the molecule is rigidly constrained to one form and exists in one discrete conformation. In consequence substituent groups attached to a *trans*-decalin skeleton are strictly confined to either an *a*- or *e*-conformation and may be assigned a quite definite conformation. Thus we can have the following two isomeric 2-decalols derived from *trans*-decalin, which can be definitively described as 2-*e*-*trans*-decalol and 2-*a*-*trans*-decalol (or 2-*e*- and 2-*a*-hydroxy-*trans*-decalin). See p. 22.

Similar considerations apply if more than two rings are fused together, as in the steroids and triterpenoids, and the application of the tenets of conformational analysis to the investigation of the precise stereochemistry of these molecules has been of paramount importance. The same principles apply as in the case of the simple cyclohexane rings, e.g. equatorial substituents are the most stable, etc., and since in the case of these fused-ring compounds substituent groups are rigidly constrained to one conformation, these principles can give an exact picture of the stereochemistry of the molecule.

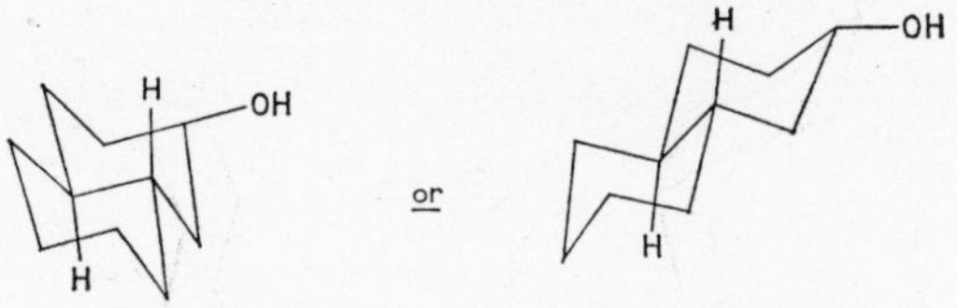

cis (to ring junction) or *e* (2 - *e* - *trans* - decalol)

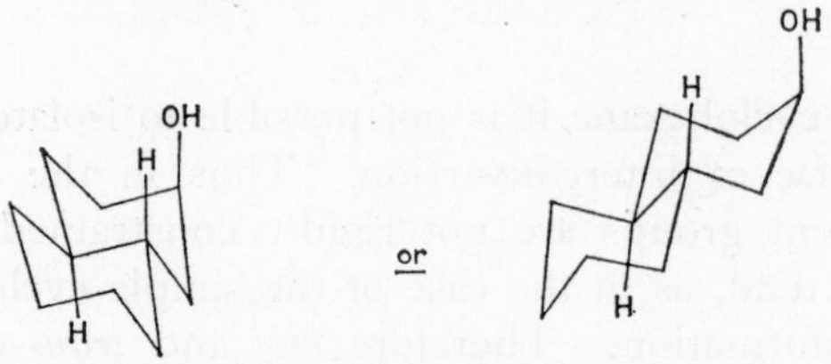

trans (to ring junction) or *a* (2 - *a* - *trans* - decalol)

In the case of cyclohexene derivatives, it is once again possible to draw up two forms, both of which satisfy the requirements as regards valency angles, corresponding to the chair and boat (or flexible) forms of cyclohexane. In the case of cyclohexene there is the additional geometric requirement that the four carbon atoms flanking the double-bond (positions 1, 2, 3, 6) must all be in one plane. The two forms, to which the terms 'half-chair' and 'half-boat' have been applied, may be represented diagrammatically as:

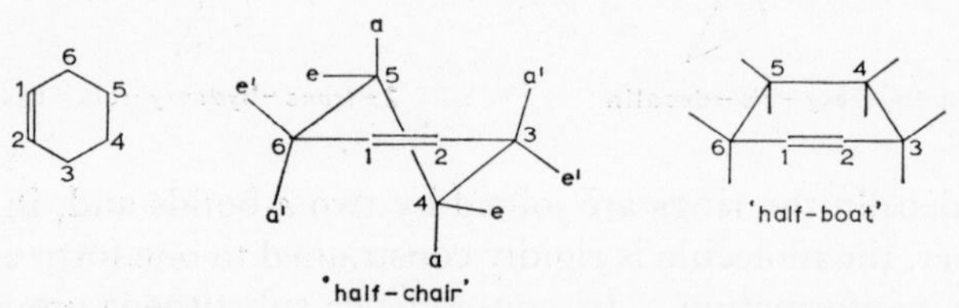

Once again it may be shown that the chair-like form is the favoured conformation; this has also been proved to be the case in the cyclohexene derivatives which have been studied by X-ray analysis.

The non-allylic carbon atoms are completely staggered with respect to each other and their exocyclic valencies may fairly be described as equatorial and axial. In the case of the allylic carbon atoms, however, the exocyclic bonds only correspond approximately to axial and equatorial, owing to the distortion caused by the geometry of the ethylenic bond. They have been designated 'quasi-axial' (a') and 'quasi-equatorial' (e').

In the case of cyclohexanones, the presence of the carbonyl carbon atom has little effect on the overall shape of the molecule. Again chair and boat forms are possible, and again the chair-form is the more stable. But owing to the different steric structure of a carbonyl group (sp^2) as compared to a methylene group (sp^3), the oxygen atom of the carbonyl-group is in an eclipsed or 'opposed' conformation with respect to the two adjacent equatorial hydrogen atoms:

In such carbonyl compounds the 2-equatorial isomer is not always the most stable. Thus in the case of 2-bromocyclohexanone, I.R. studies have shown that the axial conformation predominates. This has been ascribed to the effect of the dipolar interaction of the carbonyl group, which would repel the bromine atom; this repulsion will be greater in the eclipsed equatorial structure than in the staggered axial conformation.

This example has been introduced purposely as a warning against considering only one set of influences, conformational or otherwise, and not taking into account all the factors involved.

It is of interest to note that when a second bromine atom is introduced into the *cis*-6-position, then the two bromine atoms take up equatorial rather than axial conformations, presumably because in the axial conformation there is repulsion, both steric and dipolar, between the two adjacent axial bromine atoms.

There are many other examples of disubstituted cyclohexane derivatives for which the diequatorial form, for reasons other than conformational, is not the preferred conformation. Two simple examples are (i) *trans*-1,2-dibromocyclohexane, where, owing to electrical repulsions between the two bromine atoms, the diaxial and diequatorial forms are present in approximately equal amounts, and (ii) *cis*-1,3-dihydroxycyclohexane, where the diaxial conformation is actually the predominant one, being stabilised by hydrogen bonding between the two hydroxyl groups, which is possible in the diaxial but not in the diequatorial conformation.

Apart from the difference in stability between the axial and equatorial conformations, substituents in axial or equatorial positions frequently have substantially different reactivity. These differences have been utilised to investigate the stereochemistry of cyclic molecules, the technique being described as conformational analysis. Use may be made of these concepts both in synthesis, to ensure formation of the desired isomer, or in assigning the spatial formulae of molecules on the basis of their reactivity.

It should be mentioned again that strict application of these rules should be reserved for fused-ring systems wherein interchange between *a*- and *e*-conformations is impossible. None the less the rules apply in a less rigid form to monocyclic compounds, especially if the latter are heavily substituted or substituted by large groups.

3—A.C.

Examples of the effect of conformation on chemical reactions and reactivity are:

(i) In reductions of carbonyl compounds, oximes, conjugated dienes, $\alpha\beta$-unsaturated carbonyl compounds, etc., by means of alkali metals, lithium aluminium hydride, sodium and potassium borohydride, the more stable (e-) isomer is usually formed, e.g.

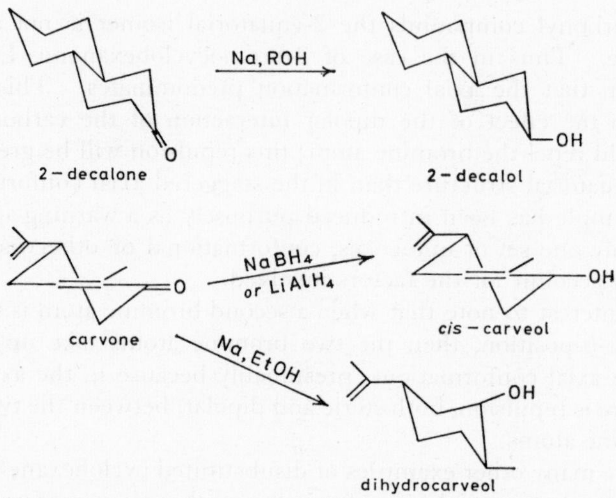

(ii) e-Hydroxyl groups are more readily esterified, and e-ester groups more easily hydrolysed than the corresponding a-isomers. Thus trans-4-tert.-butylcyclohexanol, which has an e-hydroxyl group, is esterified faster than the cis-isomer, which has an a-hydroxyl group. (In each case the large tert.-butyl group takes up almost exclusively an e-conformation.) Likewise the ethyl ester of trans-4-tert.-butylcyclohexane carboxylic acid is saponified twenty times as fast as the corresponding cis-isomer.

Similarly, e-amino groups are more readily acylated than a-amino groups.

(iii) The oxidation of alcohols with chromic acid or hypobromous acid proceeds faster in the case of a-hydroxy-compounds than for the e-isomers. For example cis-4-tert.-butylcyclohexanol is oxidised much faster than its trans-isomer.

(iv) a-Groups are more readily replaced in S_N2 reactions than are e-groups. Thus in the reaction of the tosyl derivatives of 4-tert.-butyl-cyclohexanol with PhS^- the cis-isomer reacts nineteen times faster than the trans-isomer:

(v) In elimination reactions of the type

$$\begin{matrix} X & H \\ | & | \\ -C-C- \\ | & | \\ H & Y \end{matrix} \longrightarrow -CH=CH- + XY$$

it is necessary for all the four atoms or groups involved (i.e. X, Y and the 2 carbons) to be coplanar. In the case of cyclohexane derivatives this can only be achieved if the two eliminated groups are both axial. This is exemplified by the fact that menthyl chloride gives only one olefin on dehydrohalogenation, since only one adjacent hydrogen atom can be in an axial position when the chlorine atom is also in an axial position, whereas neomenthyl chloride can and does form two olefins. Furthermore the neomenthyl compound reacts forty times faster than the menthyl chloride, since the former has its chlorine atom axial in the most favourable conformation (with the isopropyl group equatorial), whereas the most favourable conformation of the latter has all three substituent groups equatorial.

Similarly, of the two isomers of 2-chlorocyclohexanol, only the *trans*-isomer forms an epoxide on treatment with sodium hydroxide, for only in this one can both the chlorine atom and hydroxyl group be axial and coplanar.

(vi) In addition reactions of olefins, both carbon atoms involved and the two entering atoms (or groups of atoms) must be coplanar, thus resulting in a di-axial product. (In the case of a simple cyclohexane ring the latter can, of course, easily revert to a diequatorial conformation.) Thus chlorine adds on to cyclohexene to give exclusively *trans*-1,2-dichlorocyclohexane.

(vii) In halogenation of cyclohexanones, the 2-*a*-derivative is always formed more readily than the 2-*e*-isomer. (Again in the case of simple cyclohexane rings the *a*- and *e*-positions will, however, be easily inter-changeable.)

(viii) The action of nitrous acid on an *e*-NH_2 group gives predominantly substitution of the group by a hydroxyl group, without inversion, whereas in the case of an *a*-NH_2 group, mostly olefin is obtained, together with some inverted alcohol, e.g.

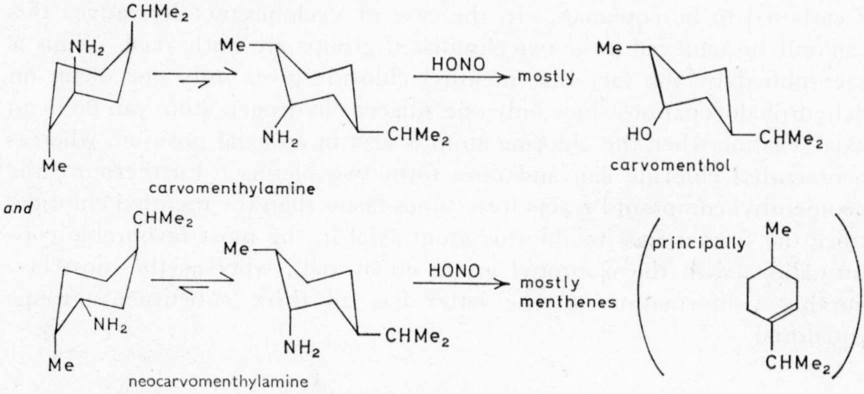

carvomenthylamine

and

neocarvomenthylamine

Conformations of other alicyclic rings

The cyclopentane ring, once regarded as planar, is now thought to be distorted. Although there is almost no angle strain in the planar model, there is conformational strain caused by the completely eclipsed con-formations:

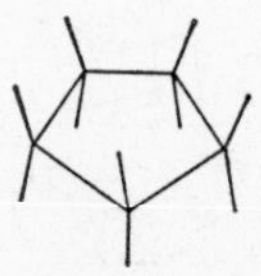

By distorting the ring from the planar form, this conformational strain is relieved. In one possible conformation of cyclopentane, at any one instant one atom is markedly out of plane with the other four, which may them-selves be slightly distorted out of a truly planar form. Rather than one particular ring atom always being the one most out of plane, the different atoms in turn take up this conformation:

This has been called the 'envelope' form of cyclopentane. An alternative conformation is the 'half-chair' form, in which three atoms of the ring are more or less coplanar and the other two atoms are out of this plane, the puckering again being mobile, as in the 'envelope' form.

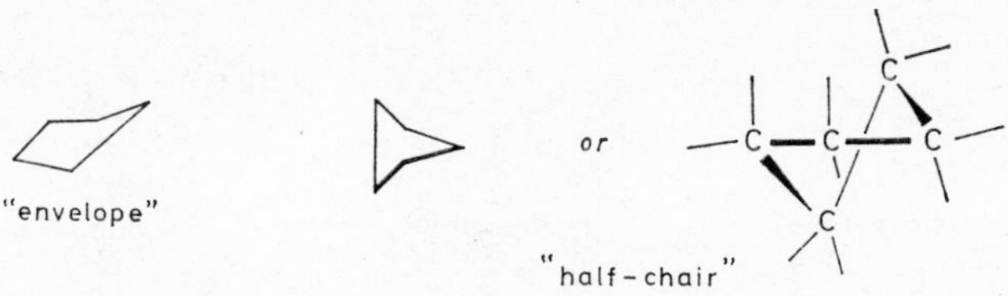

"envelope"

"half-chair"   or

It is considered that either the 'envelope' or 'half-chair' conformation may be preferred, depending upon the particular substituted cyclopentane compound in question.

The somewhat higher value for the heat of combustion per methylene group obtained for cyclopentane (as compared with cyclohexane or cycloheptane; see table, p. 7) is ascribed to the conformational strain in the molecule.

The cyclopropane ring must inevitably be rigid and planar and made up from completely eclipsed conformations. The cyclobutane ring seems to deviate somewhat from planarity, thereby relieving to some extent both conformational strain and also the crowding between substituents on the 1- and 3-positions of the ring.

If two substituent groups are present on adjacent atoms of these small ring compounds, these groups will eclipse one another if they are *cis* to each other, but if they are *trans* to each other, they will be eclipsed by hydrogen atoms:

cis   trans

In consequence the *cis* isomer is conformationally the less stable of the two.

Seven-membered and larger rings have been shown to be puckered. Very large rings tend to take up an elongated conformation in which two sides of the ring lie parallel to each other in the same way as aliphatic chains would:

Medium-sized rings (i.e. 7–12-membered) are puckered and have more complicated conformations of considerable flexibility which have only recently begun to be studied in detail.   Suggested preferred conformations for some of them are approximately as shown in the following diagrams.

cycloheptane   cyclooctane   cyclodecane

It is thought that rings of more than nine carbon atoms are virtually free from conformational strain.

In conclusion the contrast should be noted between, on the one hand, the chair form of cyclohexane, where there is a considerable energy barrier to be overcome in converting the molecule to another conformation, and, on the other hand, cyclopentane, the flexible (or boat) forms of cyclohexane, and the higher cycloalkanes, where there are ring systems of considerable flexibility, making it extremely difficult, or sometimes impossible, to define particular preferred conformations.

Some consequences of these variations in conformation with ring-size are discussed in more detail in Chapter VII.

Despite the non-planarity of six-membered and larger rings, *cis-* and *trans-* are still the best terms in which to discuss and define the stereo-chemistry of the various isomers.   This is especially so in the case of seven-membered and larger rings where the full conformational structures have yet to be elucidated, and where, in any case, the ring systems have considerable flexibility, making it difficult or perhaps even impossible to define particular conformations.   In the case of three-, four-, and five-membered rings, however, the terms *cis-* and *trans-* have a precise meaning strictly comparable to the usage employed for ethylenic compounds; this arises from the planarity or near-planarity of these ring systems.

FOR FURTHER READING

GENERAL

Eliel, E. L. (1962).   *Stereochemistry of Carbon Compounds*, Chapters VIII and IX.   McGraw-Hill.

Barton, D. H. R. (1956).   In *Perspectives in Organic Chemistry*, edited by A. Todd, p. 68.   Interscience.

Barton, D. H. R. (1953).   *J. Chem. Soc.*, 1027.

Barton, D. H. R. and Cookson, R. C. (1956).   *Quart. Rev.*, **10**, 44.

Dauben, W. G. and Pitzer, K. S. (1956).   In *Steric Effects in Organic Chemistry*, edited by M. S. Newman.   Chapter I.   Wiley.

Lau, H. H. (1961).   *Angew. Chem.*, **73**, 423.

CYCLOHEXANE DERIVATIVES

Klyne, W. (1954). In *Progress in Stereochemistry* Vol. I, edited by W. Klyne. Chapter 2. Butterworth.

Orloff, H. D. (1954). *Chem. Rev.*, **54**, 348.

MEDIUM-SIZED RINGS

Dunitz, J. D. and Prelog, V. (1960). *Angew. Chem.*, **72**, 896.

Raphael, R. A. (1962). *Proc. Chem. Soc.*, 97.

III

PREPARATION OF ALICYCLIC COMPOUNDS

MOST methods for the preparation of alicyclic compounds inevitably involve a reaction leading to ring-closure.   Exceptions are the formation of cyclohexane derivatives by the reduction of benzenoid compounds.

It has long been recognised that two factors contribute to the ease with which ring-closure may be effected, namely,

(i) the strain in the ring formed—'Strain Factor';

(ii) the chance of near approach of the groups which must interact to close the ring—'Distance Factor'.

In general the tendency to ring-closure increases from cyclopropane to cyclopentane derivatives, and is at a maximum for five- and six-membered rings.   Ruzicka (1926)† suggested that the strain and distance factors could be summed empirically to give results which correspond closely to those

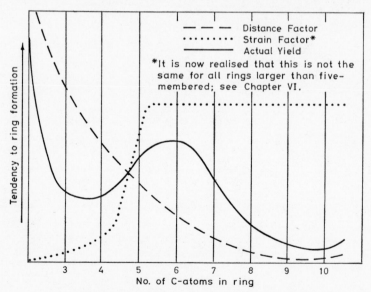

†Ruzicka *et al*; *Helv. chim. acta.* (1926), **9**, 499

30

obtained in practice.   This is shown graphically opposite; it was based on what might be termed classical puckered-ring strain theory, and takes no account of the more recent studies on the conformations involved in the fine structures of ring compounds.

It is now thought that the distance factor is probably the more important of the two, except in the case of the medium-sized rings (7–12 membered rings).   Two carbon atoms which have to interact to effect ring-closure, have the greatest opportunity of approaching one another if they are 1,5 or 1,6 atoms, i.e. to form five- or six-membered rings.

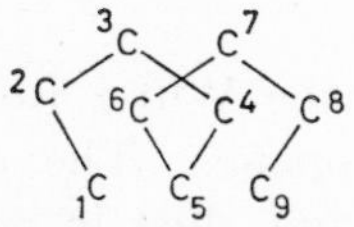

$$C_1 - C_2 \;=\; 1.54 \,\text{Å}$$
$$C_1 - C_3 \;=\; 2.51 \,\text{Å}$$
$$C_1 - C_4 \;=\; 2.52 \,\text{Å}$$
$$C_1 - C_5 \;=\; 1.67 \,\text{Å}$$
$C_1 - C_6$, etc., depends on the flexing of the chain

An obviously related fact is that only 1,4- and 1,5-dibasic acids readily form cyclic anhydrides, and that only γ- and δ-hydroxyacids readily form lactones.

In the case of the smaller rings the observed ease or difficulty of ring-closure agrees very well with the distances separating the atoms in a flexed chain of carbon atoms (see diagram above), except that the cyclo-butane ring appears to be more difficult to obtain in practice than the cyclopropane ring.   This could be partly due to the fact that for ring-closure to take place the four carbon atoms forming the ring must take up a folded conformation (A) rather than the normally preferred staggered conformation (B) which keeps the 1- and 4-atoms well separated from each other.

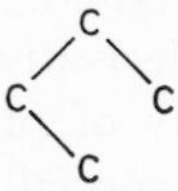

(A) 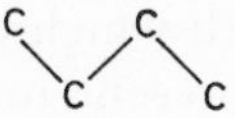   (B)

This difference is paralleled by the relative ease with which epoxides may be got from 1,2-halohydrins and the relative difficulty with which tri-methylene oxides are got from 1,3-halohydrins.

In all reactions involving two reactive centres in one molecular species there must always be competition between intermolecular and intramole-cular reaction.   In particular when very long chains separate the reacting groups intermolecular reactions are favoured.   Hence special techniques are required in the preparation of large-ring compounds, such as high-dilution techniques or reactions taking place at metal surfaces.   Each of these methods increases the opportunity of intramolecular reaction relative to that of intermolecular reaction.

Conformational strain in medium-sized rings (7–12-membered) makes them particularly difficult to prepare.

The various reactions used to effect ring-closure are, in general, adaptations of standard condensation reactions of aliphatic compounds. Some of these methods are now described.

I. Elimination of Halogen from α,ω-dihalogencompounds

1 Cyclisation of α,ω-dihalocompounds

This reaction is an intramolecular adaptation of the Wurtz Reaction, first used by Freund in 1881 to prepare cyclopropane. The dihalo-compound is cyclised by means of sodium, or by zinc dust in aqueous alcohol, e.g.

$$CH_2 \underset{CH_2Br}{\overset{CH_2Br}{<}} \xrightarrow{Na} \triangleright$$

or, in general,

$$(CH_2)_n \underset{CHRBr}{\overset{CHRBr}{<}} \xrightarrow{Na} (CH_2)_n \underset{CHR}{\overset{CHR}{<}} |$$

The commercial preparation of cyclopropane uses this method, starting from 1,3-dichloropropane derived from the chlorination of propane obtained from natural gas. Cyclopropane and cyclohexane derivatives may be prepared in this way in reasonable yield, especially the former. Owing to the ease with which cyclohexane derivatives can be obtained by other methods, the present method is really of practical value only for cyclopropane derivatives. Secondary and especially tertiary halides give large quantities of olefins as by-products (and sometimes as the only products) unless the reaction is carried out at a low temperature.

Cyclopentane derivatives can be obtained in low yield, whilst cyclobutane derivatives are obtained, if at all, only in very small yield. Thus tetramethylene dibromide gives cyclobutane in only 7% yield. In attempted preparations of rings larger than six-membered, inter- rather than intramolecular condensation takes place, e.g.

$$Br(CH_2)_{10}Br \xrightarrow{Na} Br(CH_2)_{20}Br + Br(CH_2)_{30}Br, etc.$$

If the halogen atoms are adjacent to activating groups, milder reagents may bring about ring-closure of a dihalogen compound, e.g.

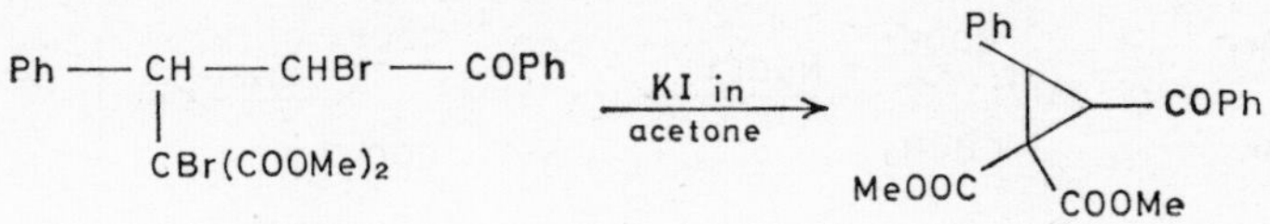

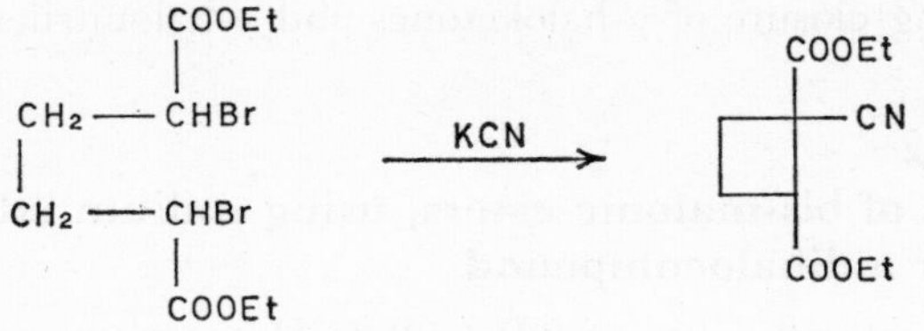

Ph —— CH —— CHBr —— COPh $\xrightarrow[\text{acetone}]{\text{KI in}}$ [cyclopropane structure with Ph, COPh, MeOOC, COOMe]

| CBr(COOMe)$_2$

[structure: CH$_2$—CHBr / CH$_2$—CHBr with COOEt groups] $\xrightarrow{\text{KCN}}$ [cyclobutane ring with COOEt, CN, COOEt]

II. Ester Condensations

2 Elimination of hydrogen halide from ω-halomalonic esters

In this method, akin to method 1, ω-halomalonic esters are first prepared from an α,ω-dihalocompound and malonic ester, and then the resultant esters are ring-closed with alkali, e.g.

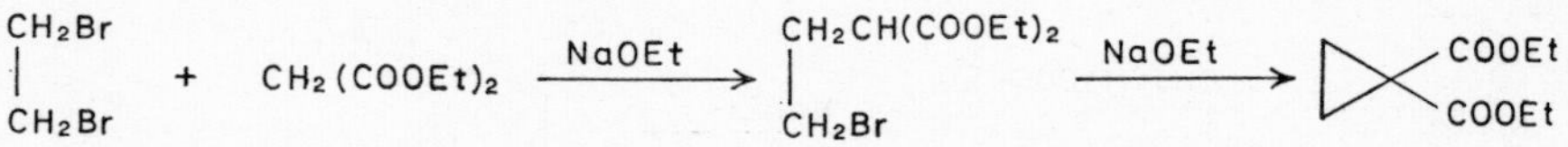

[CH$_2$Br / CH$_2$Br] + CH$_2$(COOEt)$_2$ $\xrightarrow{\text{NaOEt}}$ [CH$_2$CH(COOEt)$_2$ / CH$_2$Br] $\xrightarrow{\text{NaOEt}}$ [cyclopropane with COOEt, COOEt]

In fact the reaction can be done in one step, using appropriate molar proportions (1:1) of malonic ester and dihalocompound. This method was first used by W. H. Perkin in 1883 for the preparation of a cyclobutane derivative:

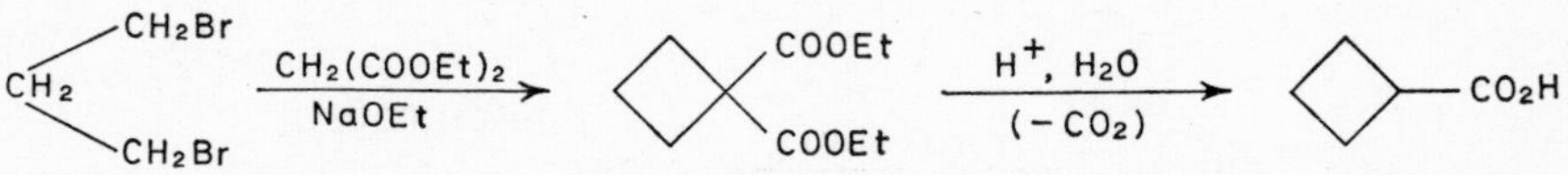

[CH$_2$(CH$_2$Br)$_2$] $\xrightarrow[\text{NaOEt}]{\text{CH}_2(\text{COOEt})_2}$ [cyclobutane with COOEt, COOEt] $\xrightarrow[(-\text{CO}_2)]{\text{H}^+,\ \text{H}_2\text{O}}$ [cyclobutane with CO$_2$H]

Acetoacetic ester, cyanacetic ester and other similar compounds may be used in place of malonic ester, except that four-membered ring compounds cannot be obtained from condensations involving acetoacetic ester; pyran derivatives are obtained instead in this case. The use of acetoacetic ester provides a convenient route for the synthesis of cycloalkylmethylketones, e.g.

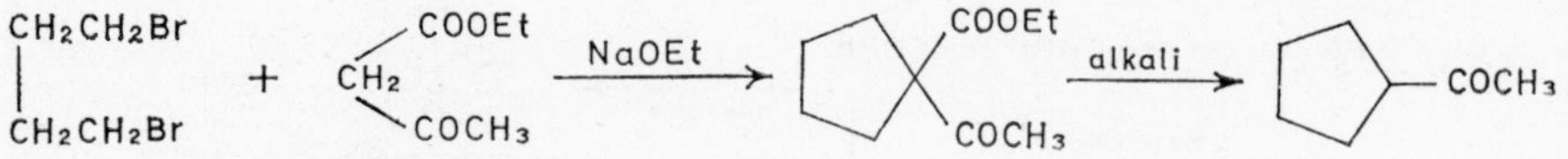

(Note also the ring-closure of γ-haloketones and γ-halonitriles, p. 47.)

3 Ring closures of bis-malonic esters, using sodium ethoxide and a halogen or a dihalocompound

A bis-malonic ester has two —$CH(COOC_2H_5)_2$ groups and can thus form a di-sodio derivative, which reacts with bromine or iodine to form a ring-compound:

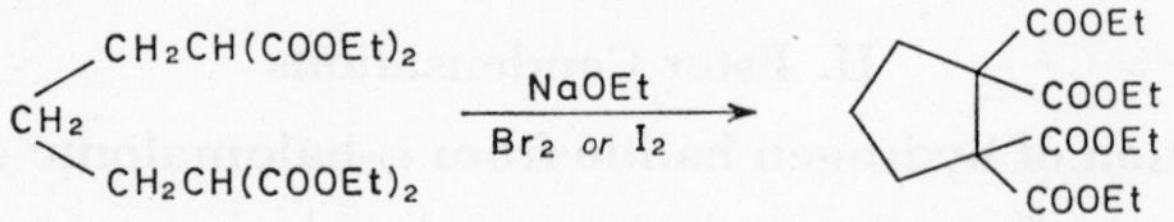

Instead of using the halogen to effect ring-closure, a dibromo- or diiodo-compound may be used:

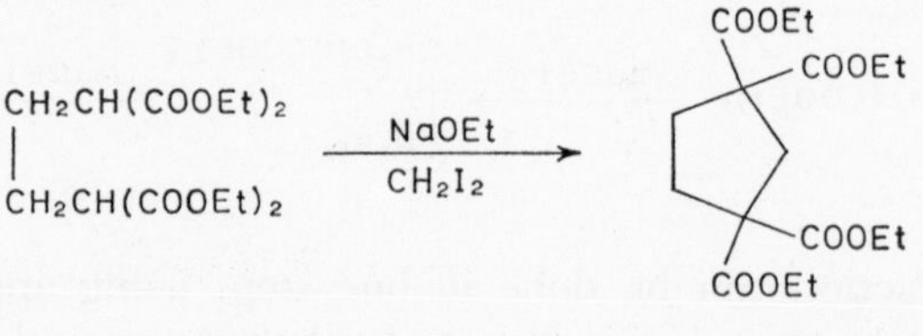

Bis-malonic esters are prepared either (i) by the reaction of an α,ω-dihalo-compound with *two* moles of malonic ester, of (ii) by condensation of malonic ester with an aldehyde in the presence of an alkaline catalyst:

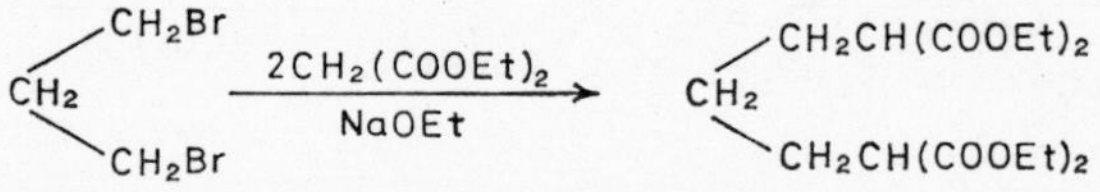

4 Dieckmann reaction

The Dieckmann Reaction is an intramolecular Claisen Condensation, an example being:

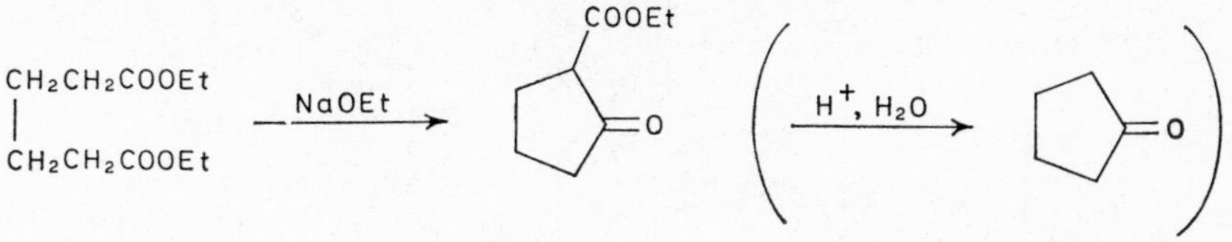

This reaction can be reversible. It can be applied to esters of adipic, pimelic and suberic acids (and substituted analogues), giving respectively 5, 6, and 7-membered rings, although the latter are obtained only in low yield. (Large rings have also been prepared; see page 40.) The products are β-ketoesters and can therefore be alkylated or acylated at the activated β-carbon atom, and then hydrolysed and decarboxylated to give 2-alkyl- or 2-acyl-cycloalkanones (cf. acetoacetic ester condensations), e.g.

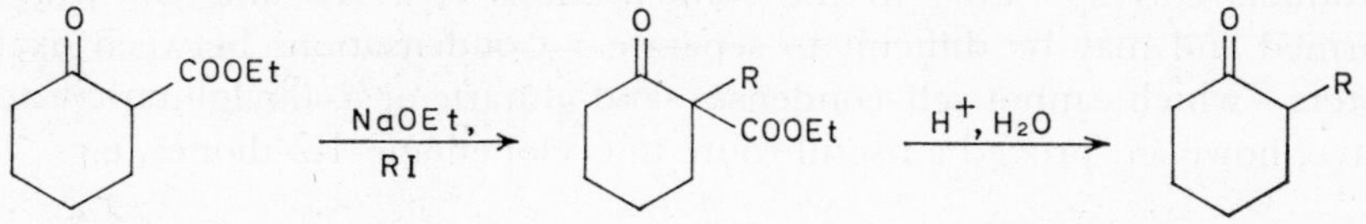

It is not possible to get three- and four-membered rings by this reaction. Esters of glutaric and succinic acids give instead intermolecular condensation products. Thus from diethyl succinate 2,5-dicarbethoxycyclohexane-1,4-dione is obtained:

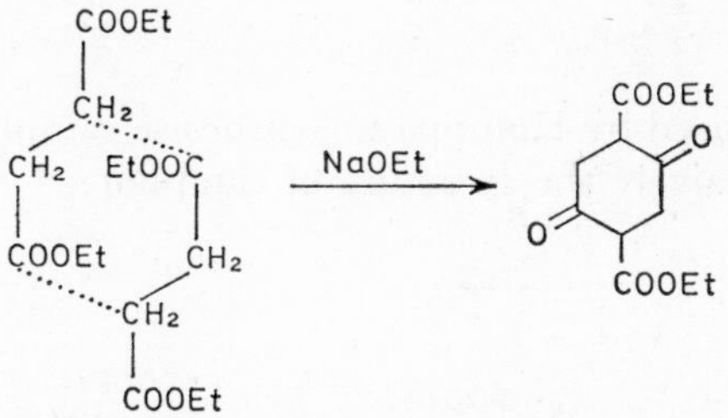

An interesting example of the application of the Dieckmann reaction is in the preparation of dimedone, 5,5-dimethylcyclohexane-1,3-dione, used for the identification and estimation of aldehydes (see Chapter VI):

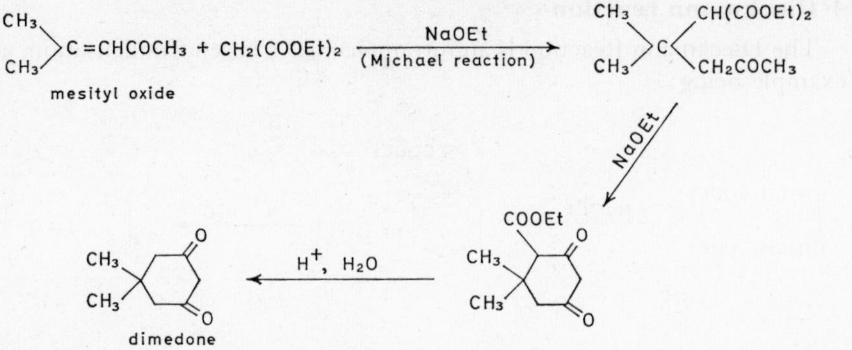

mesityl oxide

dimedone

5 Intermolecular condensations of esters

The bimolecular condensation of succinic ester, considered in the previous section, is really an example of an intermolecular condensation involving two separate ester molecules. Condensations between two *different* ester molecules are not in general satisfactory, owing to the variety of products obtainable; thus if two esters A and B are reacted together, products corresponding to the condensations AA, AB and BB will be formed and may be difficult to separate. Condensations between oxalic esters—which cannot self-condense—and glutaric or β-alkylglutaric esters have, however, proved a useful route to cyclopentane-1,2-diones, e.g.

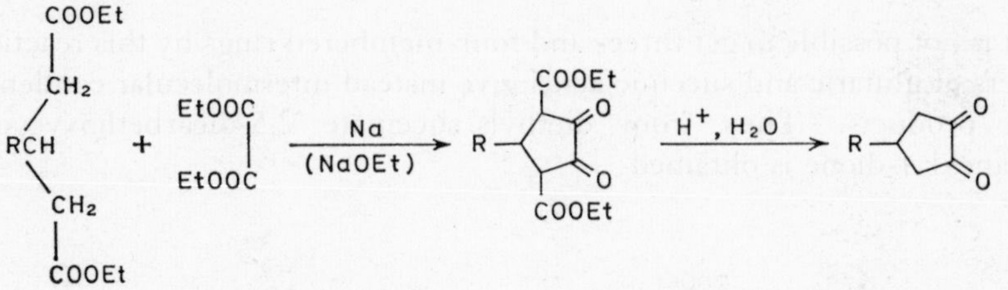

This method was used by Komppa to synthesise camphoric acid and thus to establish conclusively the structure of camphor:

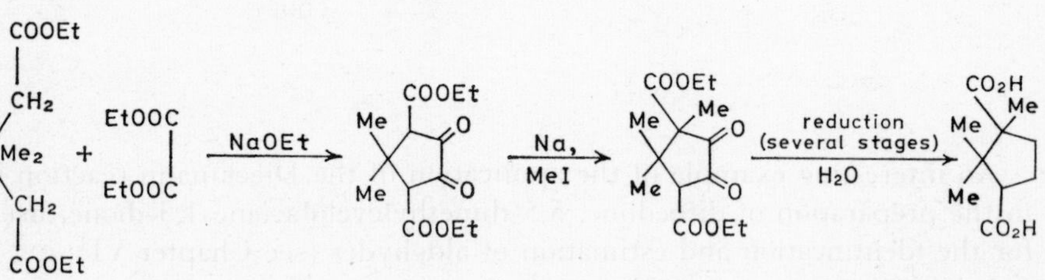

III. Ring-closure Reactions involving Ketones

6 Intramolecular elimination of water from diketones

In a suitable diketone the methylene or methyl group adjacent to one of the keto-groups will condense with the other keto-group in the molecule under the influence of acid or alkali. The method is only applicable to the formation of five- and six-membered rings. Examples are:

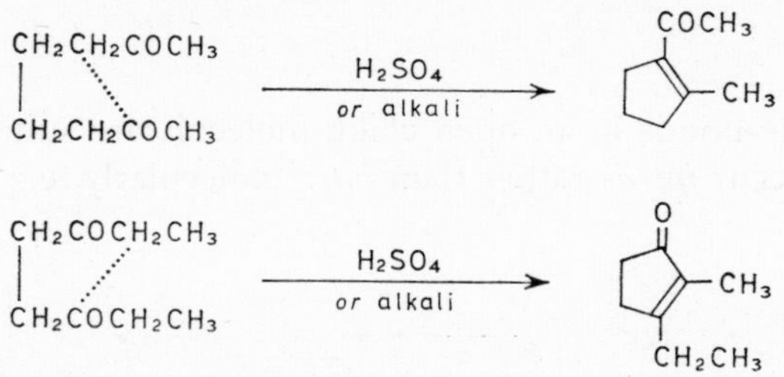

Note that in both of these cases a five-membered ring is formed, although on paper a seven-membered ring in the first case, and a three-membered ring in the second case, could also be formed; neither is.

7 Pinacone reduction of diketones

1,4- 1,5- 1,6- and 1,7-diketones have been reduced in such a way as to produce the appropriate cyclic 1,2-diols, e.g.

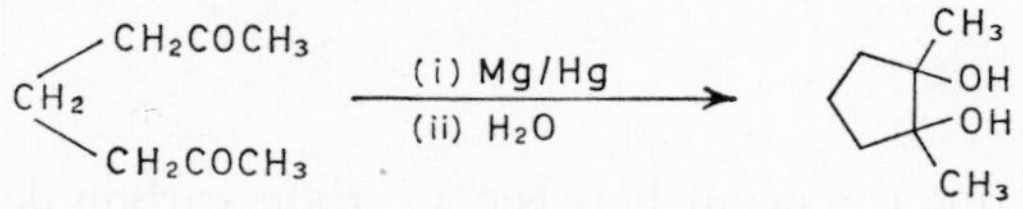

8 Intramolecular condensation of haloketones

δ- and ε-haloketones form respectively cyclopentanols and cyclohexanols on treatment with magnesium in ether. Presumably a Grignard compound is formed first which then reacts intramolecularly with the sterically adjacent carbonyl group. An example is:

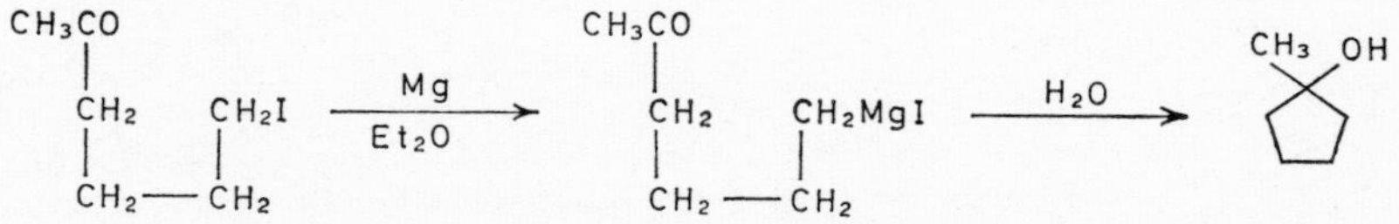

(Note also the condensations described in method 15.)

IV. Ring-closure of Olefins

9 Ring-closure of diolefins by acid-catalysed additions to C=C

Acid catalysis brings about the polymerisation of certain olefins, e.g. isobutylene, $(CH_3)_2C{=}CH_2$. The reaction mechanism is:

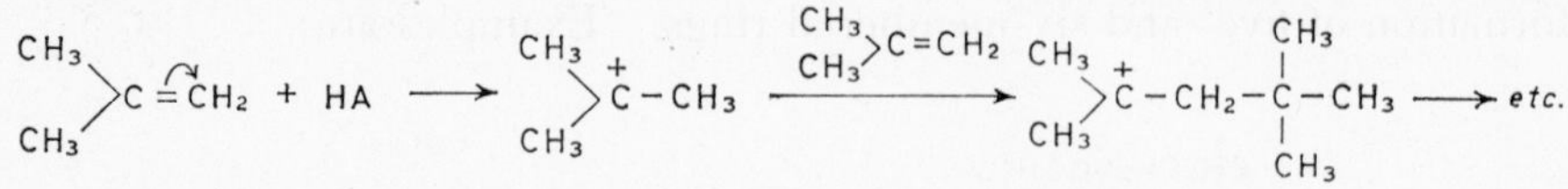

If two double-bonds in an open chain molecule are suitably separated, reaction may occur *intra-* rather than *inter-*molecularly, e.g.

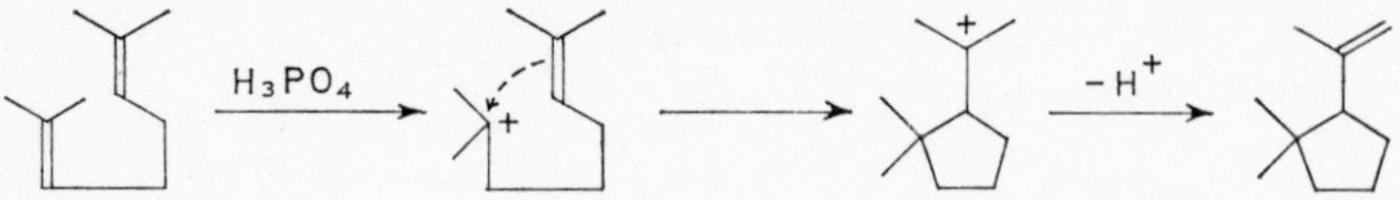

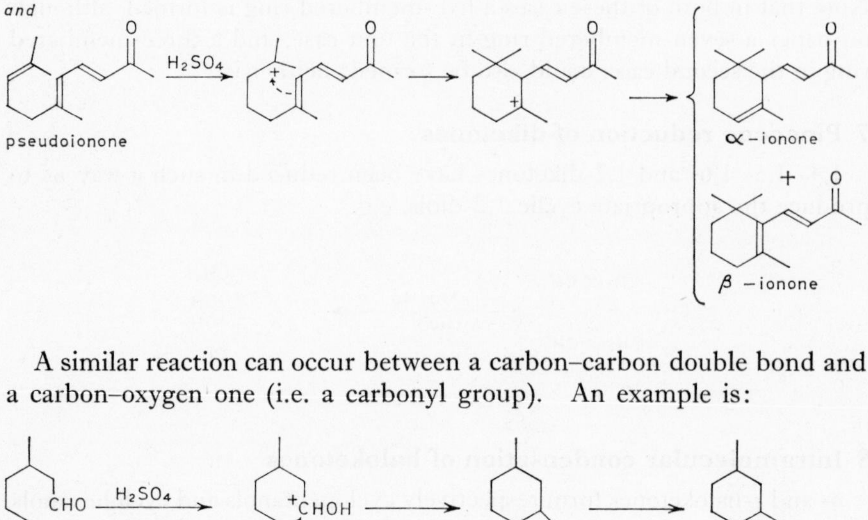

and

pseudoionone

α –ionone

β –ionone

A similar reaction can occur between a carbon–carbon double bond and a carbon–oxygen one (i.e. a carbonyl group). An example is:

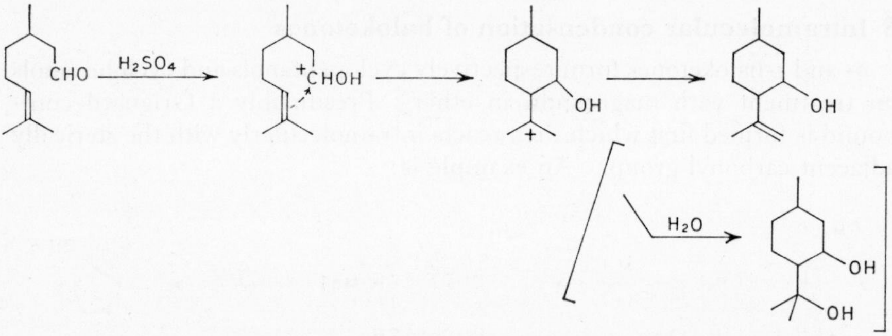

Reactions of this kind have been used widely to form five- and six-membered rings.

V. The Formation of Cyclic Ketones with Fused Benzene Rings

10 Ring-closure of aryl substituted carboxylic acids and acid chlorides

β-, γ-, and δ-phenyl-substituted aliphatic acid chlorides may be converted into cyclic ketones with fused benzene rings by means of intramolecular Friedel-Crafts reactions, giving, respectively, five-, six-, and seven-membered rings:

COCl   AlCl₃ →   O

COCl   AlCl₃ →   O

Six-membered rings are formed most readily. *Ortho-* and *para*-directing groups in the benzene ring tend to facilitate ring-closure, *meta*-directing groups tend to hinder it.

Cyclization has also been carried out by the action of hydrofluoric acid, sulphuric acid and especially polyphosphoric acid on phenyl-substituted carboxylic acids.

The reaction has also been investigated as a way of preparing larger rings. From a series of ω-phenylaliphatic acids, $Ph(CH_2)_nCO_2H$, it proved possible to obtain cyclic ketones by carrying out the reaction in high dilution in carbon disulphide. When, in the above formula, $n = 5$ or 6, cyclic ketones analogous to the ones already mentioned were obtained, the eight-membered ring being obtained in good yield but the nine-membered ring in poor yield. When $n = 7$, no cyclic ketone could be obtained, and when $n \geqslant 8$, the ring closure took place at the p-position rather than at the o-position, or, if the p-position was already substituted, at the m-position.

$\dfrac{AlCl_3}{CS_2}$ →   —CO / —(CH₂)ₙ

(CH₂)ₙCOCl

($n \geqslant 8$)

CH₃ $\dfrac{AlCl_3}{CS_2}$ →   CH₃ —CO / —(CH₂)ₙ

(CH₂)ₙCOCl

The method has also been extended to ω-naphthylaliphatic acids.

VI. Methods available for the Synthesis of Larger Rings

The methods already discussed are, for most practical purposes, restricted to the preparation of compounds with seven or less carbon atoms in the ring, although a series of larger ring compounds have been prepared by intramolecular Friedel-Crafts acylation as discussed in 10 above. In recent work 13-, 14- and 15-membered rings have also been prepared by means of the Dieckmann reaction (method 4 above) carried out in high dilution. It proved impossible to obtain 9- to 12-membered rings in this way. It is possible that larger rings might be prepared by method 7 above, whilst it should also be noted that Franke and Hanken (1910) claimed to have prepared ethyl cycloundecane-1,1-carboxylate by the condensation of sodio-malonic ester with 1,10-dibromodecane (method 2).

The methods of ring-closure to be discussed now are those which have been applied especially, and with success, to the preparation of larger rings. The success of some of these methods is well shown on the accompanying graph. It is interesting to note the relative difficulty of obtaining 8- to 12-membered ring compounds, the so-called 'medium-sized' ring compounds, whose physical and chemical properties are also somewhat anomalous, as will be discussed in a later chapter (Chapter VII).

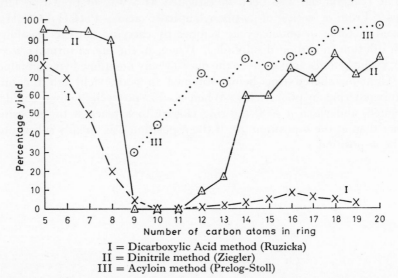

I = Dicarboxylic Acid method (Ruzicka)
II = Dinitrile method (Ziegler)
III = Acyloin method (Prelog-Stoll)

In all ring-closure reactions there is competition between the intramolecular reaction leading to ring formation and an intermolecular reaction leading to open-chain di- or poly-meric products. A molecule having two groups —X which must react together to bring about ring formation can react as follows:

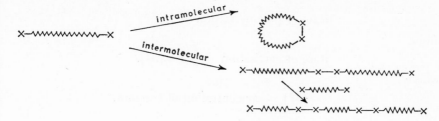

A factor of considerable importance in deciding which of these courses predominates in any reaction is the relative ease with which one reactive group —X can approach and interact with the other group —X in the molecule. If this is readily achieved intramolecular reaction and cyclisation predominate. If, on the other hand, there is greater likelihood that any group —X will come into proximity with another group —X in a different molecule rather than with the other group —X in its own molecule, then intermolecular reaction and polymerisation will predominate.

It has already been mentioned (p. 31) that in the case of five- and six-membered ring formation the distances separating the groups which must react together is specially favourable, but that intermolecular reaction is favoured when very long chains separate the reacting groups, as must be the case in attempting to form large rings.

Hence special techniques are used which make use of factors tending to bring the two reacting ends of a molecule together. One method (11, below), involving pyrolysis of the salts of dibasic acids, depends on the association of the two carboxylate ions with one metal ion to bring the two reacting groups together:

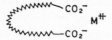

In another method (13, below, acyloin condensation) the two groups are similarly brought near to each other by adsorption on the surface of a metal, thus promoting their interaction over the competing intermolecular reaction:

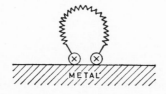

In other methods (12, 14, 15, below) the reactions are carried out at very high dilution.   From the law of mass action it follows that:

$$\text{Rate of polymerisation} = k_p[M]^2$$

and

$$\text{Rate of cyclisation} \quad = k_c[M],$$

where

$$[M] = \text{concentration of reactant.}$$

Hence,
$$\frac{\text{Rate of cyclisation}}{\text{Rate of polymerisation}} = \frac{k_c}{k_p[M]}$$

Thus it follows that with increasing dilution the cyclisation reaction is increasingly favoured with respect to polymerisation.

Some of these reactions are now discussed in more detail.

11 Pyrolysis of the salts of dibasic acids

Distillation of the calcium or barium salts of adipic or pimelic acids give good yields of cyclopentanone and cyclohexanone respectively; a fair yield of cycloheptanone may also be obtained by the dry distillation of calcium suberate, e.g.

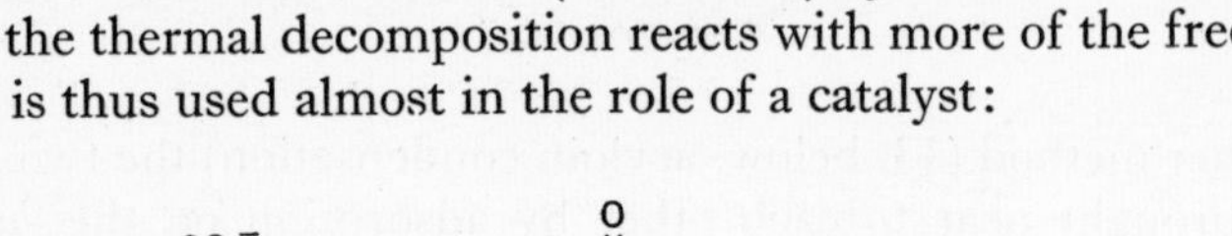

Rather than using simply the metal salts a better method is to use the free acids together with a little barium (or calcium) hydroxide.   The carbonate formed in the thermal decomposition reacts with more of the free acid; the hydroxide is thus used almost in the role of a catalyst:

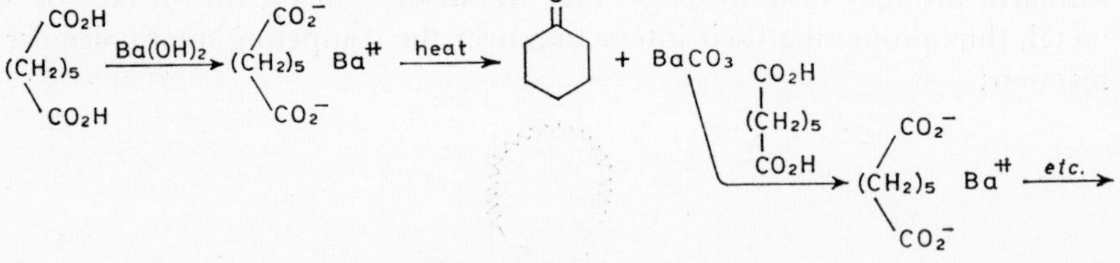

Calcium glutarate and succinate do not form three- and four-membered rings under these conditions. From calcium succinate cyclohexane-1,4-dione is obtained;

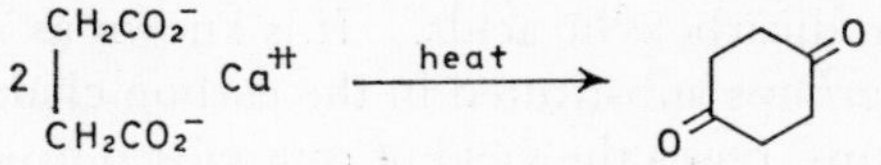

Calcium glutarate gives no cyclic ketone.

Ruzicka (1928) adapted this method to the synthesis of larger rings by using the thorium, cerium or yttrium salts of dicarboxylic acids rather than the salts of the alkaline-earth metals. It is interesting to compare the yields obtained by using different salts:

Acid	Ring-size Produced	Yield From Ca salt	From Th salt
Glutaric acid	4	0	0
Adipic acid	5	45	15
Pimelic acid	6	40–50	70
Suberic acid	7	35	50
Azelaic acid	8	5	20
Sebacic acid	9	<1	1·5

The differences have been ascribed to the different degrees of association of the different salts. The closer the association of the two $-CO_2^-$ groups with the cation, then the closer the $-CO_2^-$ groups will be held to each other, thus increasing the chance of their reacting together intramolecularly.

As the graph above shows, the yields of cyclic ketone produced stay very low (<1%) for C_9—C_{12} rings, but rise somewhat (up to 5%) for larger rings (C_{13}—).

A modification of this method, applicable only to the formation of five- and six-membered rings, is to distil a mixture of the appropriate dibasic acid with acetic anhydride at atmospheric pressure:

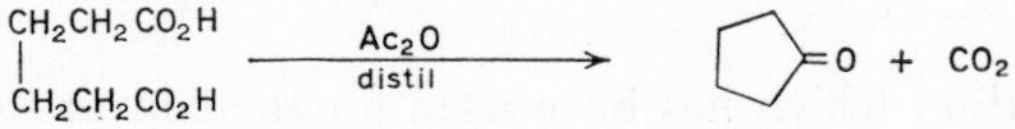

Under identical conditions, glutaric and succinic acids and their derivatives form cyclic intramolecular anhydrides:

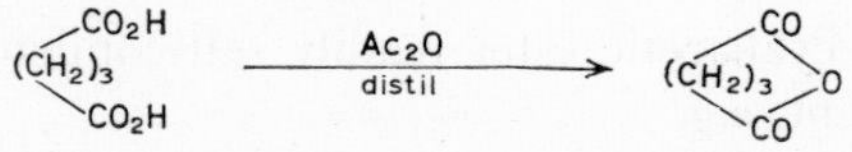

This distinction in behaviour between, on the one hand, 1,4- and 1,5-dicarboxylic acids, and, on the other hand, 1,6- and 1,7-dicarboxylic acids has been used as a diagnostic test to determine the relative locations of the carboxyl groups in dicarboxylic acids. It is known as *Blanc's Rule*. The presence of alkyl groups substituted in the carbon chain, and especially of *gem*-dimethyl groups, raises the yield of ring-closed product obtained.

Blanc's rule may be summarised as:

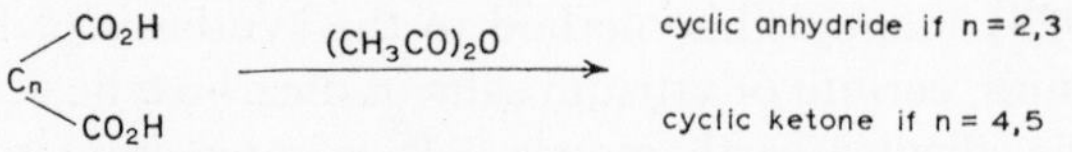

It has been very useful in alicyclic chemistry for determining the ring-size of cyclic ketones. The ketones are oxidised to dibasic acids, and the reaction of the latter with acetic anhydride investigated. If the product is another ketone, the sequence of reactions is repeated until a cyclic anhydride is produced. The number of oxidations and subsequent cyclisations required to produce the cyclic anhydride indicates the size of the ring in the original ketone. Thus for cyclohexanone:

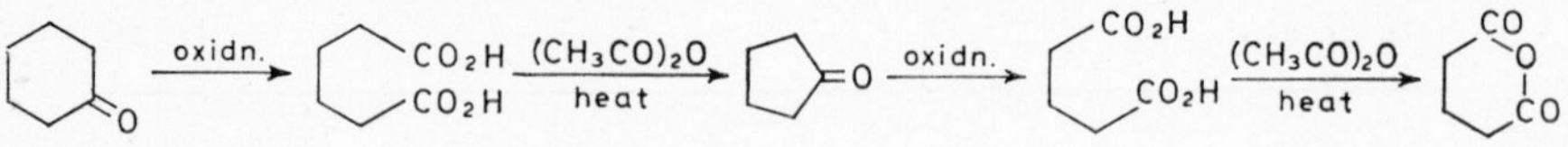

i.e. six-membered ring ketones $\xrightarrow[\text{(ii) }(CH_3CO)_2O]{\text{(i) oxidn.}}$ ketone $\xrightarrow[\text{(ii) }(CH_3CO)_2O]{\text{(i) oxidn.}}$ anhydride

Similarly

cyclopentanones $\xrightarrow[\text{(ii) }(CH_3CO)_2O]{\text{(i) oxidn.}}$ anhydride,

and cycloheptanones $\xrightarrow[\text{(ii) }(CH_3CO)_2O]{\text{(i) oxidn.}}$ ketone

$\xrightarrow[\text{(ii) }(CH_3CO)_2O]{\text{(i) oxidn.}}$ ketone $\xrightarrow[\text{(ii) }(CH_3CO)_2O]{\text{(i) oxidn.}}$ anhydride.

It would thus, for example, be possible to decide whether a cyclic ketone, $C_7H_{12}O$, was cycloheptanone or an alkylated cyclohexanone or cyclopentanone.

Another method which has been used for the conversion of adipic acid to cyclopentanone is by distillation with potassium fluoride.

12 Thorpe reaction

Nitriles such as cyanacetic ester readily self-condense in the presence of an alkaline reagent, e.g.

$$EtOOC{-}CH_2CN + CNCH_2COOEt \xrightarrow{NaOEt} EtOOC{-}\underset{\displaystyle CN}{\underset{|}{CH}}{-}\underset{\displaystyle NH}{\underset{\|}{C}}{-}CH_2COOEt$$

This reaction can take place intramolecularly with suitable dinitriles, e.g.

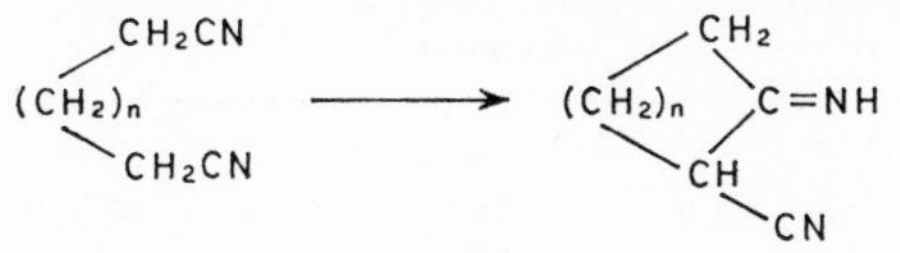

The product can readily be converted into a keto-acid or ketone:

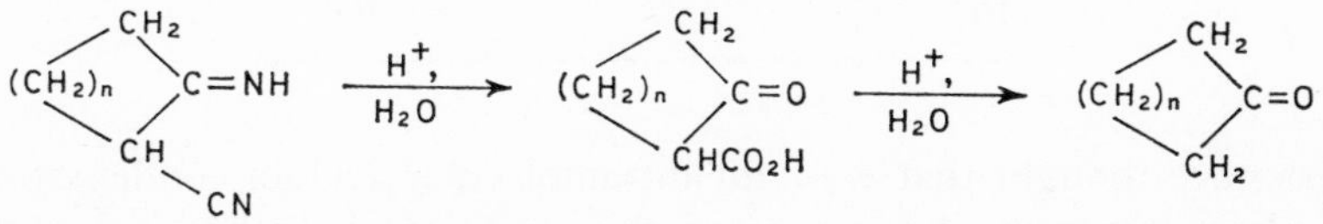

There is of course competition with intermolecular reaction; intramolecular reaction can be favoured at the expense of the former by working at high dilution.

Ziegler (1933) applied such a high-dilution technique to the Thorpe reaction, using powerful condensing agents such as the ether-soluble lithium ethylanilide (LiNEtPh), and obtained excellent yields of large-ring ketones, as shown in the earlier graph. Highly sterically hindered bases are desirable as catalysts because they favour the necessary proton abstraction reaction in preference to the alternative possibility of addition of the base to the nitrile group. The C_{15} ring ketone is important in perfumery and this technique is used to obtain it.

13 Acyloin condensation

Ester molecules condense together in the presence of sodium and in an inert solvent and atmosphere, to form 2-hydroxyketones, known as *acyloins*.

$$2\,RCOOR' \xrightarrow[Et_2O,\ N_2]{Na,} \begin{array}{l} R{-}C{=}O \\ \quad\ \ | \\ R{-}CHOH \end{array}$$

This condensation has been applied most usefully to the formation of large rings by intramolecular condensation of dicarboxylic esters:

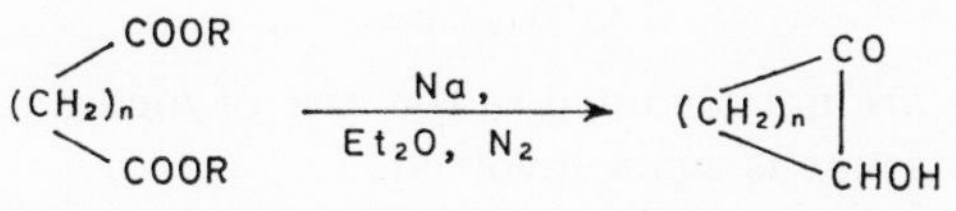

No special high-dilution technique is required, but very efficient stirring is necessary. Excellent yields are obtained, as shown in the following table:

Ester n =	Size of ring formed	Yield (%)
7	9	9
8	10	45
10	12	76
12	14	79
14	16	84
16	18	96

It was once thought that $n \geqslant 7$ for intramolecular acyloin condensation to take place, but in more recent years the conditions have been adapted for smaller rings (four- to seven-membered), although yields are not as high.

Two synthetic routes (14) (15) which have been developed in recent years for the synthesis of large-ring compounds are of interest although they have not been applied so generally as the ones just considered.

14 Self-condensation of diketens

Blomquist has adapted the known ready polymerisation of ketens to give a useful method of ring-closure applicable to the formation of large-ring compounds,

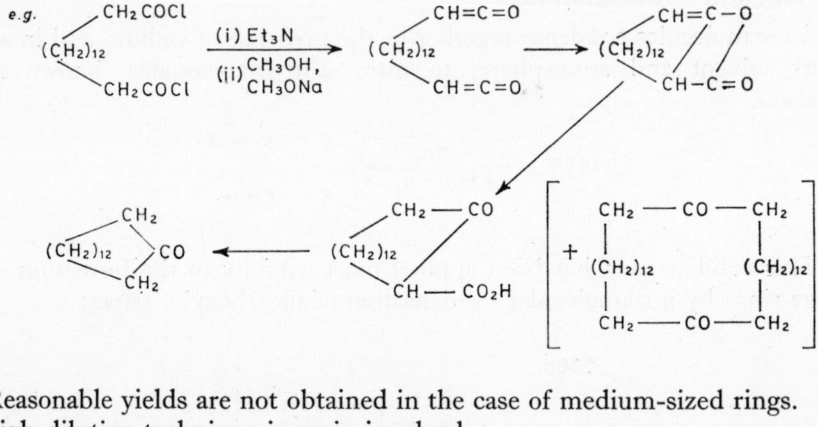

Reasonable yields are not obtained in the case of medium-sized rings. A high-dilution technique is again involved.

15 Intramolecular condensation of an ω-iodo-β-ketoester

Hunsdiecker has prepared ω-iodo-β-ketoesters and cyclised them as shown in the following chart:

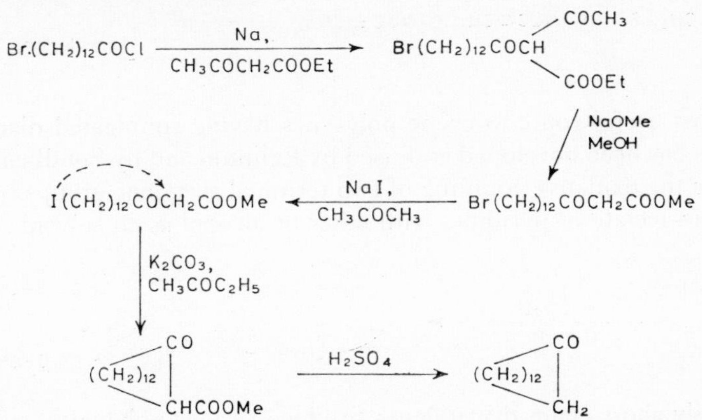

This method, which also requires high-dilution techniques, gives useful yields of large-ring ketones, but does not give reasonable yields of the medium-sized rings.

A fundamentally similar reaction has been used to prepare three-membered rings, since γ-halo- and γ-p-tosyloxy-ketones can be converted into cyclopropane derivatives by the action of bases. By this method dicyclopropylketone has been prepared from 1,7-dichloroheptan-4-one, and bicyclo[3,1,0]hexan-2-one from the p-tosyl derivative of 4-hydroxy-cyclohexanone:

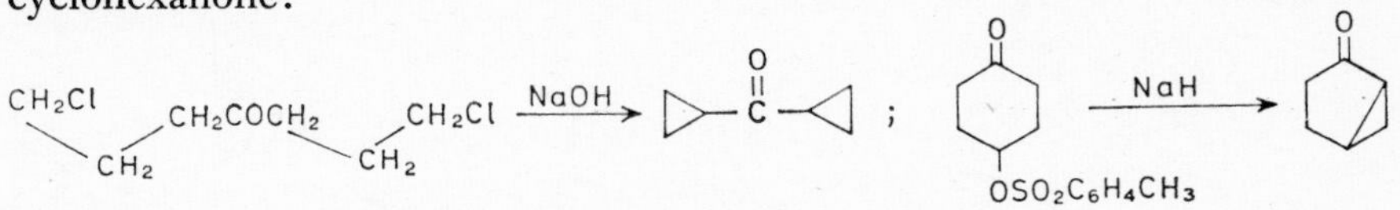

(The latter product has also been obtained by the action of strong alkali on the methiodide of p-dimethylaminocyclohexanone.) γ-Halonitriles may take the place of γ-haloketones, e.g.

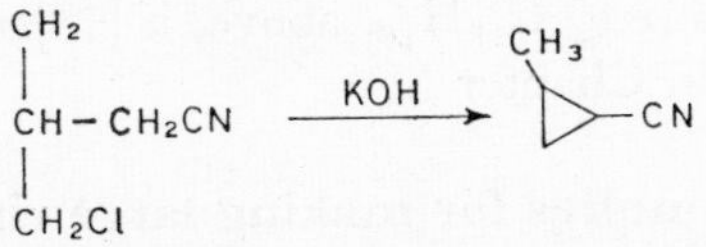

16 Use of acetylenes in the formation of large rings

Non-conjugated cyclic poly-ynes can readily be obtained by interaction of suitable dibromo-compounds with a mixture of mono- and di-sodium acetylides:

$$Br(CH_2)_n Br \; + \; NaC\equiv CH \; + \; NaC\equiv CNa \; \longrightarrow \; \left[\begin{array}{c} C\equiv C-(CH_2)_n \\ | \qquad\quad \diagdown \\ (CH_2)_n-C\equiv C \end{array} \right]_x$$

A most useful route to cyclic poly-ynes having conjugated diacetylenic linkages has been developed and used by Eglinton and by Sondheimer. It involves the oxidative coupling of two terminal acetylene groups by means of cupric acetate in pyridine, with ether or alcohol as co-solvent, e.g.

Relatively short-chain diacetylenes produce various polymers:

$$HC\equiv C-X-C\equiv CH \xrightarrow{(CH_3CO_2)_2Cu, \; C_5H_5N} \left[\begin{array}{c} C\equiv C-X-C\equiv C \\ | \qquad\qquad | \\ C\equiv C-X-C\equiv C \end{array} \right]_n \quad n=1-5.$$

Prototropic rearrangement of suitable cyclic polyalkynes followed by partial hydrogenation of the remaining triple bonds has provided a route to large-ring completely conjugated polyolefins, e.g.

cyclooctadecanonaene
or [18] annulene

These completely conjugated polyolefins are known as *annulenes*; individual examples are further designated as [X]annulene, where [X] is the number of ring atoms (e.g. $C_{18}H_{18}$, above, is [18]annulene). Annulenes are discussed further in Chapter X.

17 Use of rigid assemblies for making large rings

If molecules are sufficiently rigid in structure, then the ways in which they can inter-react are greatly limited. It is possible to make such structures so that they 'fit' together to form macrocyclic compounds. A number of examples of such an approach to the preparation of large rings are available. One is the intermolecular condensation of *m*-xylylene dibromide (Baker, 1951):

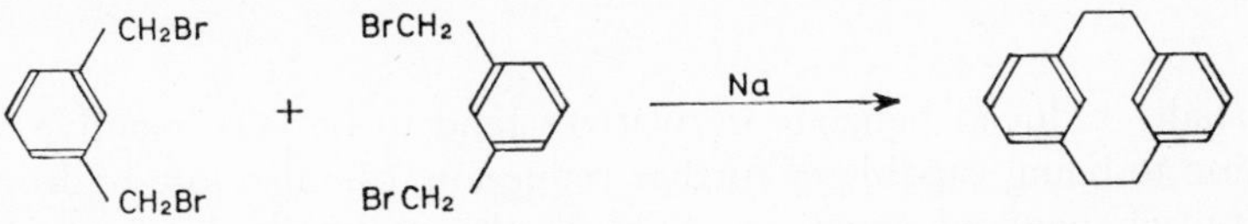

In this example, once two bromomethyl groups, one from each molecule, have reacted together, the two remaining bromomethyl groups are so arranged that they readily come into close proximity with each other and thus interact to complete ring-closure. Similarly *o*-xylylene dibromide gives rise to dibenzocyclooctadiene and tribenzocyclododecatriene:

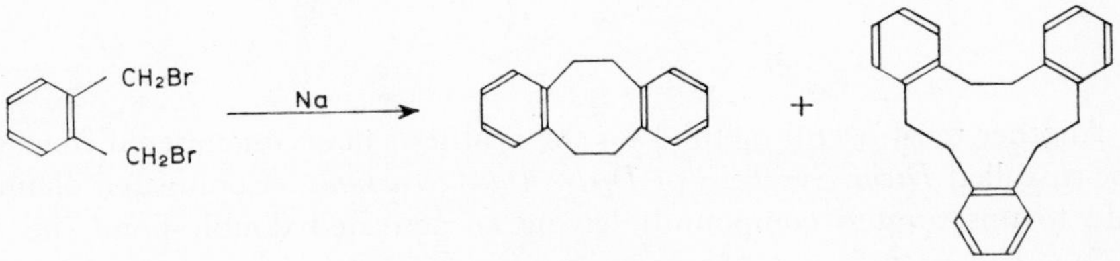

VII. Special Methods for the Preparation of certain Specific-sized Rings

(a) Cyclohexane derivatives

An obvious way of obtaining cyclohexane derivatives is by the reduction of benzenoid compounds. The ease with which this may be accomplished depends on the substituents in the benzene ring. Thus whereas toluic acids may be reduced with sodium and alcohol to give the corresponding methylcyclohexanecarboxylic acids, to reduce benzene itself catalytic hydrogenation is necessary:

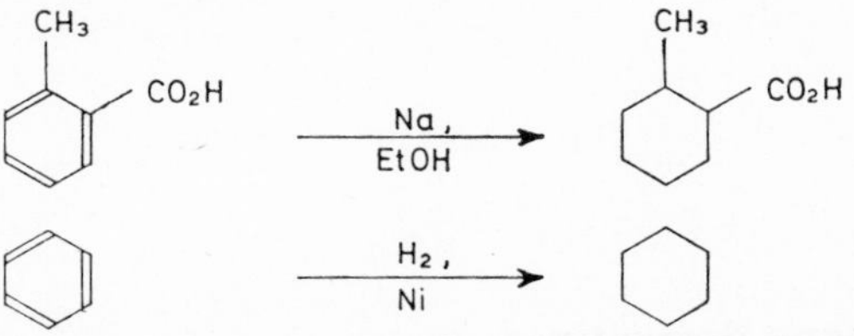

Partial reduction of benzenoid compounds can be achieved by the use of alkali metals in liquid ammonia or low-boiling amines, e.g.

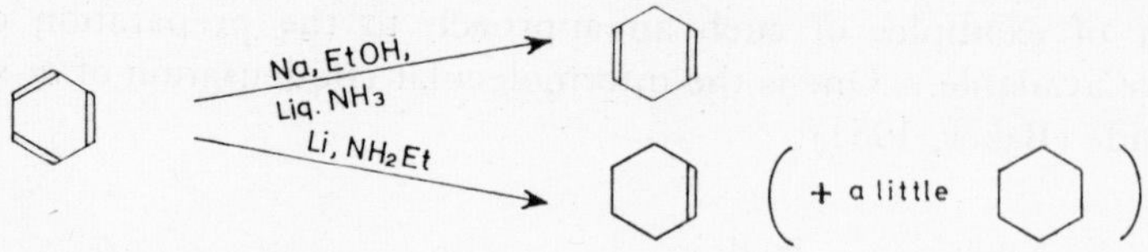

Partially reduced benzene derivatives tend to be very reactive, and, in addition to being capable of further reduction, can also lose hydrogen and revert to a benzenoid structure. Thus in the catalytic reduction of benzene care must be taken in the choice of catalyst and conditions or they may favour the reverse dehydrogenation reaction also. Because of this reactivity these partially reduced compounds have been used as mild reducing agents and as dehydrogenating agents, e.g.

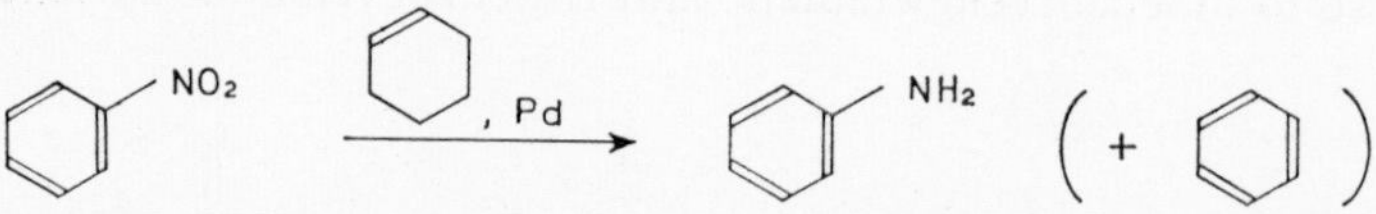

Another most useful method for the synthesis of six-membered rings is the so-called *Diene Synthesis* or *Diels–Alder Reaction*. Conjugated olefins add to unsaturated compounds having an activated double-bond (i.e. a double-bond adjacent [$\alpha\beta$] to electron-attracting groups such as $\rangle C{=}O$, —CO_2H, —COOEt, —NO_2, etc.) to form cyclohexene derivatives, e.g.

Frequently the reaction takes place with great ease, and on merely mixing the reagents heat may be evolved and the product separate, often in excellent yield. In less favourable cases heat and/or a catalyst is necessary. It should be noted that by using cyclic dienes, bridged-ring compounds are obtained:

(b) Cyclopropane derivatives

Cyclopropane derivatives can be obtained by the addition of 'methylene' (CH_2) (or 'carbene'), or derivatives thereof to olefinic bonds.

'Methylene' and its derivatives have only a transient existence and are generated in the presence of the olefin. This can be done by thermal decomposition of an aliphatic diazocompound, such as ethyl diazoacetate, in the presence of the olefin. Under these conditions ethyl diazoacetate reacts with most carbon–carbon double bonds; it even reacts with benzene:

$$\text{(benzene)} + N_2CHCOOEt \longrightarrow \text{(bicyclic)}-COOEt \xrightarrow[\text{(on acid)}]{KMnO_4} \left[\begin{array}{c} CO_2H \\ \triangleright-CO_2H \\ CO_2H \end{array} \right]$$

Considerable amounts of cycloheptatriene carboxylic acids are formed as by-products in this thermal decomposition, however. A much purer product is obtainable by photolytic decomposition of the diazoacetic ester in solution in benzene (and other benzenoid compounds).

Diazomethane is less reactive than diazoacetic ester towards double bonds, but reacts readily with activated double-bonds, as in $\alpha\beta$-unsaturated esters. The first product isolated is a pyrazoline, which on heating decomposes to a cyclopropane derivative:

$$\begin{array}{c} CHCOOEt \\ \parallel \\ CHCOOEt \end{array} + CH_2N_2 \longrightarrow \begin{array}{c} COOEt \\ | \\ CH-CH_2 \\ | \quad \ \ NH \\ C \\ | \ \ \diagdown N \\ COOEt \end{array} \xrightarrow{heat} \begin{array}{c} COOEt \\ \triangleright \\ COOEt \end{array}$$

Pyrazolines, and hence cyclopropane derivatives, can also be obtained by the action of hydrazine on $\alpha\beta$-unsaturated ketones:

$$\begin{array}{c} CH_3 \\ \diagdown \\ \quad \ \ C=CHCOCH_3 \\ \diagup \\ CH_3 \end{array} \xrightarrow{NH_2NH_2} \begin{array}{c} CH_3 \quad NH-N \\ \diagdown \diagup \quad \ \parallel \\ C \qquad \quad C \\ \diagup \ \diagdown CH_2-C \diagdown \\ CH_3 \qquad \qquad CH_3 \end{array} \xrightarrow{heat} \begin{array}{c} CH_3 \\ \diagdown \\ \quad \ \triangle \\ \diagup \quad \ \ \diagdown \\ CH_3 \qquad CH_3 \end{array}$$

In addition to decomposing with formation of a cyclopropane derivative, pyrazolines can also decompose on heating to give an olefin, and only when carbethoxy, acyl or aroyl substituents are present, does the formation of a cyclopropane ring normally predominate. The decomposition of pyrazolines has recently been brought about by the action of light as well as thermally.

'Methylene' (or derivatives thereof) can also be produced by the action of strong bases on various compounds having two or more halogen atoms attached to one carbon atom. Thus in 1954 Doering and Hoffman reacted cyclohexene with chloroform and potassium tert.-butoxide:

$$\text{cyclohexene} + CHCl_3 \xrightarrow{Bu^tOK} \text{(bicyclic product with } Cl, Cl)$$

Other more recent examples of formation of cyclopropane derivatives by this method include:

Wagner (1959)

$$\text{cyclohexene} + CCl_3CO_2Na \xrightarrow[CH_3OCH_2CH_2OCH_3]{\text{heat in}} \text{(bicyclic product with } Cl, Cl)$$

Closs (1959)

$$(CH_3)_2C=C(CH_3)_2 + CH_2Cl_2 \xrightarrow{LiBu^n} \underset{CH_3 \quad CH_3}{\overset{Cl \quad H}{CH_3 \triangle CH_3}}$$

Vol'pin et al. (1959)

$$\text{cyclohexadiene} + CH_2Cl_2 \xrightarrow{Bu^tOK} \text{(bicyclic product)}-Cl$$

Mousseron et al. (1959) ; McCoy (1958)

$$RCH=C\overset{R'}{\underset{X}{}} \xrightarrow[RONa]{R''CHClCOOEt} \underset{H \quad X}{\overset{R'' \quad COOEt}{R \triangle R'}}$$

(X = COOEt, CHO, CN, COCH$_3$)

An apparently similar method by Simmons and Smith (1959) consists of the reaction of an olefin with methylene iodide in the presence of a copper/zinc couple:

Simmons & Smith (1959)

$$\text{cyclohexene} + CH_2I_2 \xrightarrow{Cu/Zn} \text{(bicyclic product)}$$

$$C_6H_{13}CH=CH_2 \xrightarrow[Cu/Zn]{CH_2I_2,} C_6H_{13}-\triangle$$

It has been suggested, however, that this reaction does not involve 'methylene' as an intermediate, but that rather a complex, ICH_2ZnI, is formed, which reacts directly with the olefinic bond.

(c) Cyclobutane derivatives

Certain ethylenic compounds, notably ketens, allenes, fluoro- and fluorochloroolefins having a double-bond substituted with a *gem*-difluoro-group, and compounds having activated double-bonds, dimerise, especially under the influence of light, to give cyclobutane derivatives. This is rarely of any preparative value, however. A common example is the dimerisation of cinnamic acid; this reaction may be reversed by heat.

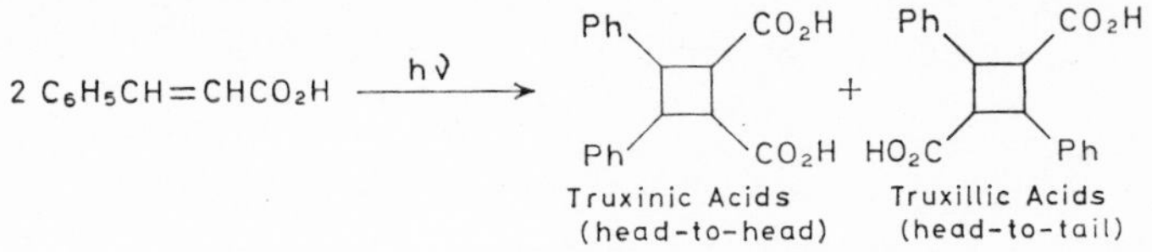

$$2\ C_6H_5CH{=}CHCO_2H \xrightarrow{h\nu}$$

Truxinic Acids (head-to-head)   +   Truxillic Acids (head-to-tail)

Truxillic acids occur along with cocaine in coca leaves.

The stereochemistry of such dimers is complex, for in addition to the head-to-head and head-to-tail arrangements possible, different *cis*- and *trans*-arrangements of the substituent groups must be taken into consideration. A further example of such a dimerisation, showing the stereochemistry of the products is:

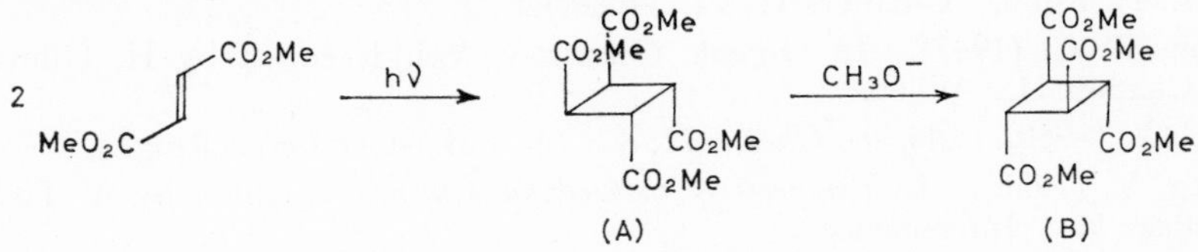

(A)   (B)

(The isomer (A) first formed is less thermodynamically stable, owing to the proximity of the adjacent *cis*-carbomethoxy groups, than isomer (B) and is converted into the latter by alkali.) Fumaronitrile and maleic anhydride also dimerise in the same way.

Dimethyl-acetylene has been made to dimerise to a cyclobutene derivative by the action of sulphuryl chloride:

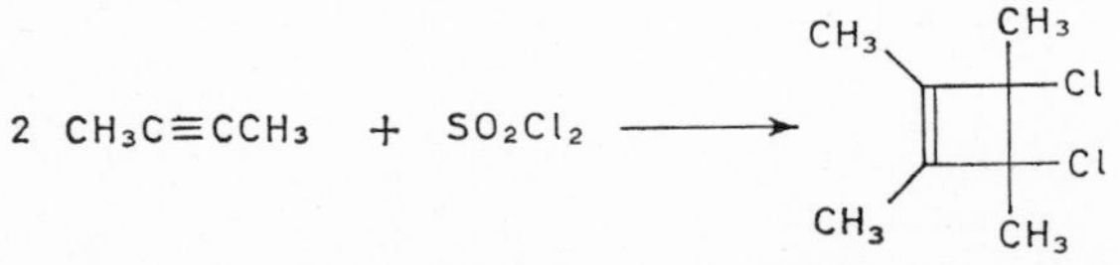

$$2\ CH_3C{\equiv}CCH_3\ +\ SO_2Cl_2 \longrightarrow$$

(This dimer was an intermediate in the preparation of a tetramethylcyclobutadiene complex; see also p. 95.)

Cycloadditions involving two different olefins or an olefin and an acetylene have also been used in the preparation of cyclobutanes and cyclobutenes, e.g.

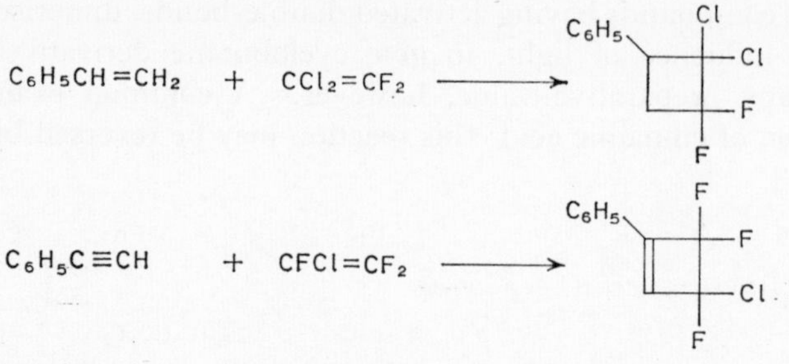

$$C_6H_5CH=CH_2 \quad + \quad CCl_2=CF_2 \quad \longrightarrow$$

$$C_6H_5C\equiv CH \quad + \quad CFCl=CF_2 \quad \longrightarrow$$

In all cases one of the reactants is either an allene, a keten, or a fluoro- or fluorochloro-alkene having a *gem*-difluoro-substituted double bond. The other reactant is normally a compound with an activated olefinic or acetylenic bond.

FOR FURTHER READING

Raphael, R. A. (1953). In *Chemistry of Carbon Compounds*, Vol. IIA, edited by E. H. Rodd. Chapters II–VI. Elsevier.

Fuson, R. C. (1942). In *Organic Chemistry*, Vol. I, edited by H. Gilman. Chapter II. Wiley.

Vogel, E. (1960). *Angew. Chem.*, **72**, 4. (3- and 4-membered Rings.)

Prelog, V. (1956). In *Perspectives in Organic Chemistry*, edited by A. Todd. Page 96. Interscience.

Eliel, E. L. (1956). In *Steric Effects in Organic Chemistry*, edited by M. S. Newman. Page 114 ff.

Also some individual reactions are discussed in:

Organic Reactions, edited by R. Adams. Vol. 1 (1942)—Dieckmann Reaction; Vol. 2 (1944)—Intramolecular Acylation; Vol. 4 (1948)—Acyloin Condensation; Vols. 4 (1948) and 5 (1949)—Diels–Alder Reaction.

IV

SOME REACTIONS OF ALICYCLIC COMPOUNDS

THE reactions of alicyclic compounds in general resemble those of their aliphatic analogues, and there is therefore no need to discuss them specifically.

In consequence only three topics will be considered

(i) Variation of reactivity with ring-size, which is dealt with in a following chapter.

(ii) Reactions leading to opening of the alicyclic ring.

(iii) Rearrangement reactions involving changes in the size of the ring.

Ring-opening reactions

The rings in saturated alicyclic compounds with ring-size of five and greater are not normally capable of being opened, except under very vigorous conditions. The situation is in almost every way parallel to that involved in the breaking of aliphatic chains of carbon atoms, which is only readily accomplished if some substituent group (or groups) in the chain provides a point of attack. Thus aliphatic or alicyclic 1,2-diols can readily be cleaved:

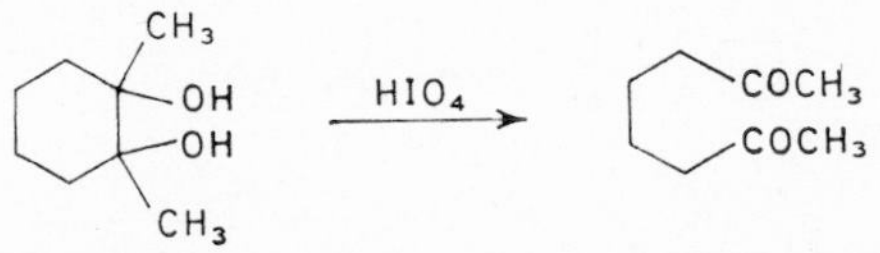

Similarly alicyclic ketones are oxidised by nitric acid either to dibasic acids or to ketoacids, e.g.

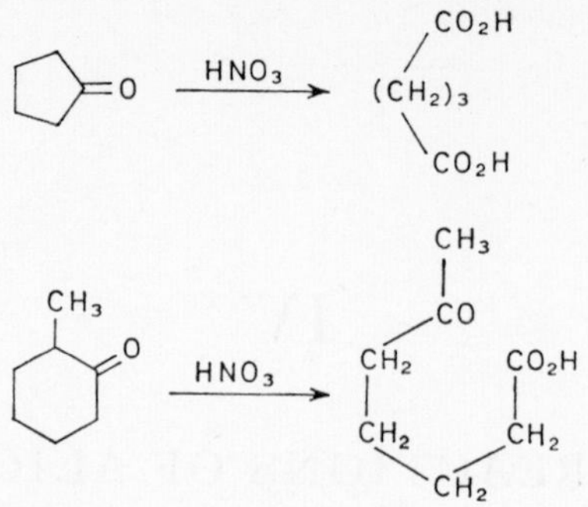

This reaction has proved very useful for the opening of alicyclic rings.

Another rather ingenious method of ring-opening which is applicable to cyclic ketones is due to Wallach. It consists of conversion of the ketone to its oxime followed by a Beckmann transformation on the oxime. The final product is a lactam, which may in turn be hydrolysed to an amino-acid hydrochloride:

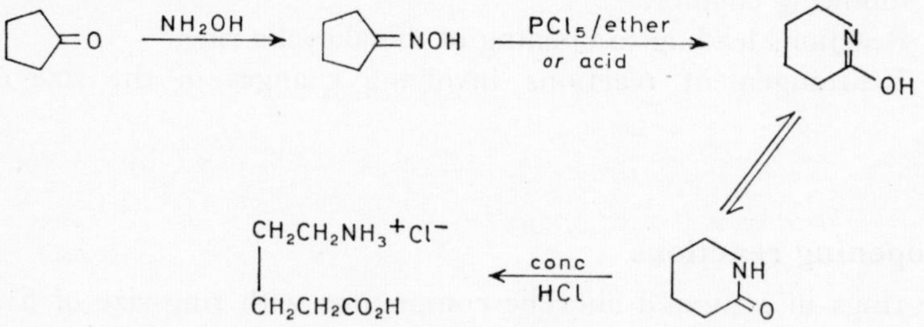

Cyclopropane and cyclobutane rings can be opened by reduction with hydrogen in the presence of a nickel catalyst:

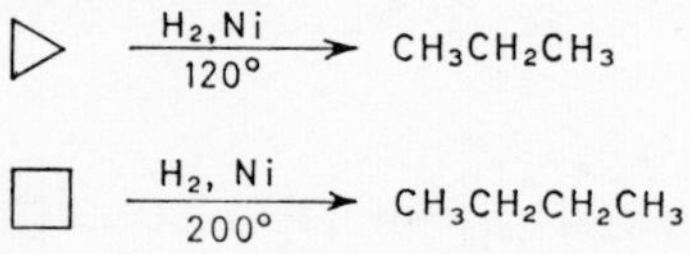

Increase in ring-size demands increasingly more drastic conditions as the above examples indicate; to reduce five-membered or larger rings a powerful catalyst and a very high temperature ($> 300°$) is required.

As mentioned in Chapter I cyclopropane derivatives behave in some ways like olefinic compounds.   Thus they react additively with bromine, hydrogen bromide, sulphuric acid, etc., to form open-chain compounds:

In contrast, chlorine reacts with cyclopropane by a substitution reaction. The presence of substituent alkyl groups, and especially of *gem*-dialkyl groups, seems to increase the ease of ring-opening of the cyclopropane ring, whilst carboxyl groups seem to decrease it.

A rather interesting reaction, comparable to that of an olefinic compound and resulting in ring-fission, occurs when a cyclopropane carboxylic ester reacts with the sodio-derivative of malonic ester.   This reaction is analogous to the Michael Reaction.   An example is:

Other examples are known of the ring-opening of cyclopropane esters and carbonyl compounds being brought about by nucleophilic reagents.

Rearrangement reactions leading to change in ring-size

Numerous examples are known in which reactions of alicyclic compounds result in a change of ring-size, either by contraction or expansion of the ring.   These reactions have their counterparts in similar rearrangement reactions of corresponding aliphatic compounds.

It was thought at one time that in such rearrangements the change in ring-size always involved transition to a less-strained ring system, thus providing support for Baeyer's Strain Theory.   This is now known not to be the case and little correlation of this nature can be found.   Satisfactory explanations are usually available in terms of modern organic chemical theory.

Some examples of these reactions are now given.

(a) Rearrangements of cyclic hydrocarbons over heated catalysts

Many hydrocarbons, aliphatic as much as alicyclic, undergo profound changes in their structure when heated in the presence of aluminium chloride. An interesting point is the relatively mild conditions under which some of these changes can occur in the case of alicyclic compounds. Examples are:

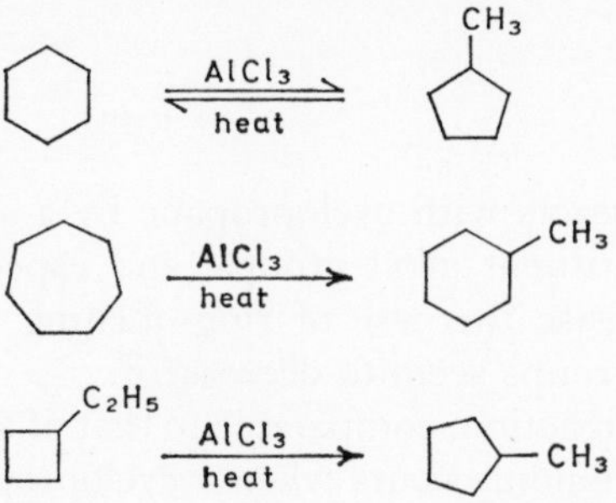

Other acid catalysts will also bring about such changes; frequently mixtures of compounds are obtained. Carbonium ions are presumably involved as intermediates.

(b) Rearrangements involving α-haloketones

α-Haloketones frequently undergo ring-contraction, producing a carboxylic acid, when they are treated with strong alkali, e.g.

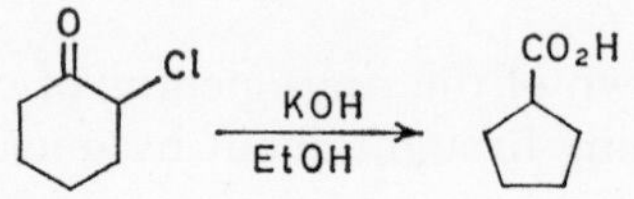

The mechanism is thought to involve formation of a carbanion on a carbon atom α to the carbonyl group:

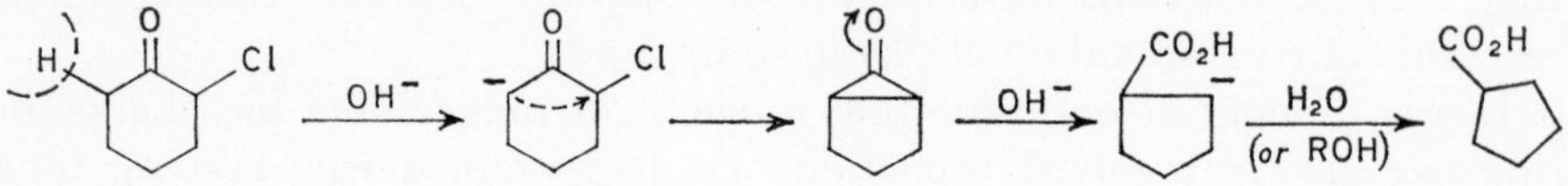

If an alkoxide is used as base, the product is an ester of the carboxylic acid. This is sometimes called the Favorskii rearrangement. Some αα'-dihaloketones can similarly rearrange to 1-hydroxycarboxylic acids:

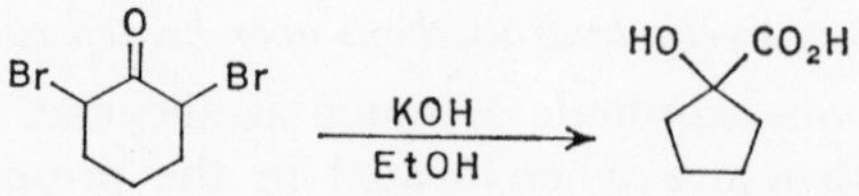

Other $\alpha\alpha'$-dihaloketones have been found to rearrange to unsaturated acids, e.g 2,8-dibromo- and 2,8-dichloro-cyclooctanone are converted into cycloheptene-1-carboxylic acid in high yield.

(c) Demjanov rearrangements

The action of nitrous acid on primary non-aromatic amines can frequently cause rearrangements of the carbon skeleton. Examples involving both ring-contraction and ring-expansion can be found among alicyclic primary amines.

Cyclopropylamine and cyclobutylamine on treatment with nitrous acid at room temperature both give rise to ring-contracted products. In the case of cyclobutylamine some cyclobutanol is also formed.

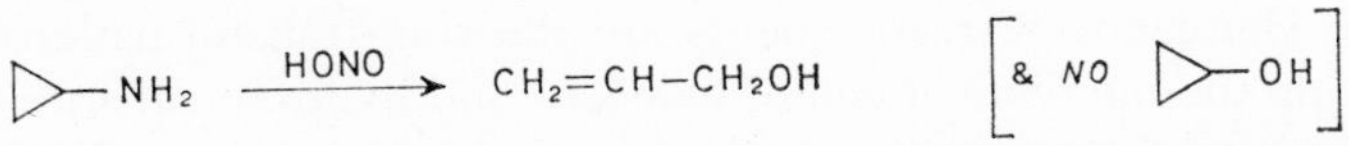

Larger ring amines do not give rise to such rearranged products.

Alicyclic primary amines with the amine group attached to an exocyclic carbon atom which is itself attached directly to the alicyclic ring react with nitrous acid to give a mixture of products, including ring-enlarged ones, as shown in the following example:

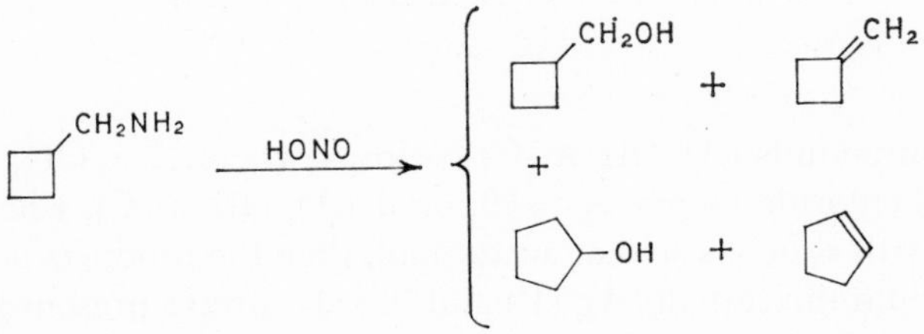

All ring sizes from three- to eight-membered rings have been shown to undergo ring expansion in this reaction, although it is most successful for the preparation of five-, six-, and seven-membered rings. Demjanov rearrangements proceed through an intermediate carbonium ion, formed from the amine and nitrous acid. This carbonium ion may react further by formation of an alcohol, formation of an olefin, or by first of all rearranging to a different carbon skeleton followed by alcohol or olefin formation. Thus for the example cited above of the action of nitrous acid on cyclobutylmethylamine we have:

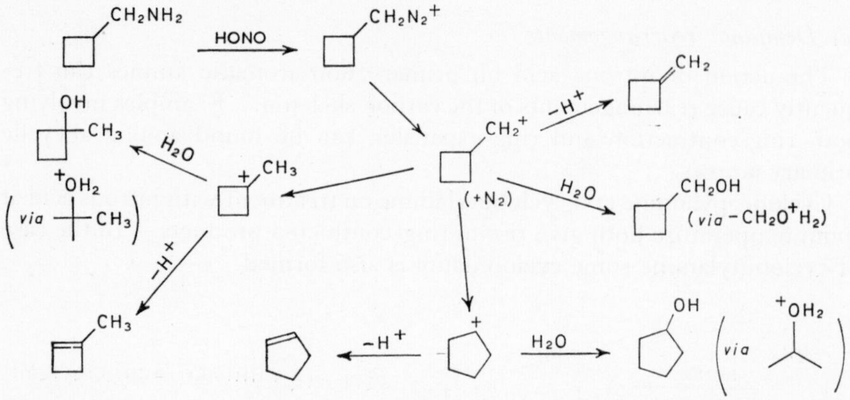

Related to the Demjanov rearrangements are the ring-transformations which occur during the interconversion of halogen- and hydroxy-substituted alicyclic compounds; intermediate carbonium ions are again involved. Examples are the action of hydrogen bromide with cyclopropyl- and cyclobutyl-carbinols which give, respectively, quantities of bromocyclobutane and bromocyclopentane:

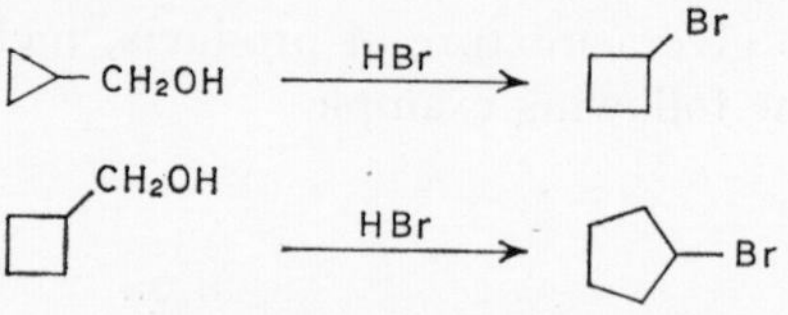

If the compounds (A), (B) or (C) (below), where $X = OH$, are treated with thionyl chloride to give $X = Cl$, or if (A), (B) or (C), where $X = Cl$, are treated with aqueous acid or acetic acid, then the products in the resulting equilibrium mixture of (A), (B) and (C) are always present in the same ratio.

It was at one time suggested that the equilibria between cyclobutyl, cyclopropylmethyl and allyl compounds had as intermediate a common symmetrical non-classical carbonium ion, $C_4H_7^+$, derived from all three species, but it is now thought that a limited interconversion between three different non-classical ions (each $C_4H_7{}^+$) is involved.

(d) Ring-expansion of cyclic ketones by the action of diazomethane

Cyclic ketones on treatment with one molar equivalent of diazomethane undergo ring-enlargement, the principal product usually being the cyclic ketone with one more carbon atom in the ring. The rates of reaction and yields are both dependent on ring-size. Amounts of still higher members of the series are also formed, e.g.

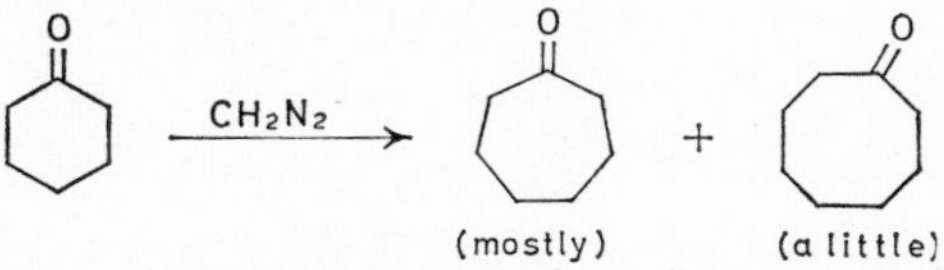

(mostly)   (a little)

The ratio of the products depends on the relative reactivities of the starting ketone and the homologue formed from it. Thus starting from cyclopentanone the principal product is in fact cycloheptanone, since the cyclohexanone first formed reacts with diazomethane faster than cyclopentanone does.

The suggested mechanism for this reaction is as follows:

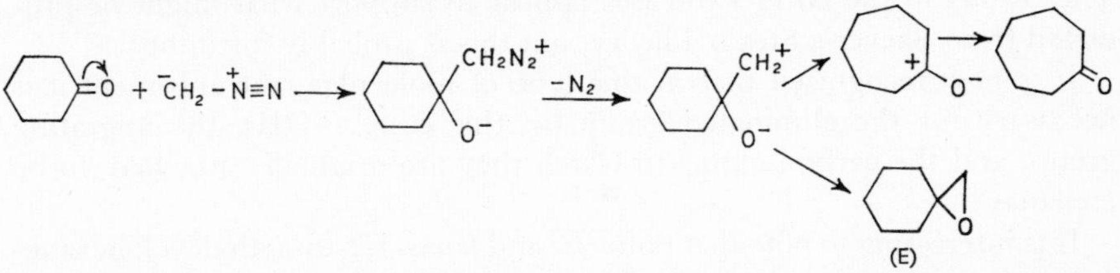

(E)

The isolation of some of the epoxide (E) is strong evidence in favour of this mechanism.

In attempts to prepare the as yet unknown cyclopropanone, diazomethane has been reacted with keten, but the main product of the reaction proved to be cyclobutanone.

(e) Pinacol–pinacolone rearrangement

The pinacol–pinacolone rearrangement of ditertiary glycols also proceeds by a carbonium ion mechanism:

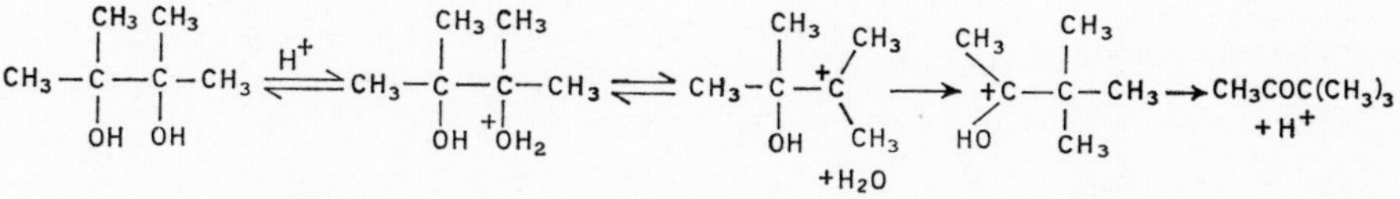

Similar rearrangements of ditertiary or of tertiary-secondary glycols take place in the alicyclic series. Both of the hydroxyl groups may be directly attached to the alicyclic ring, or one of the hydroxyl groups to the ring and one to an exocyclic carbon atom; ring-expansion occurs in the latter case, and ring-contraction in the former. Examples are:

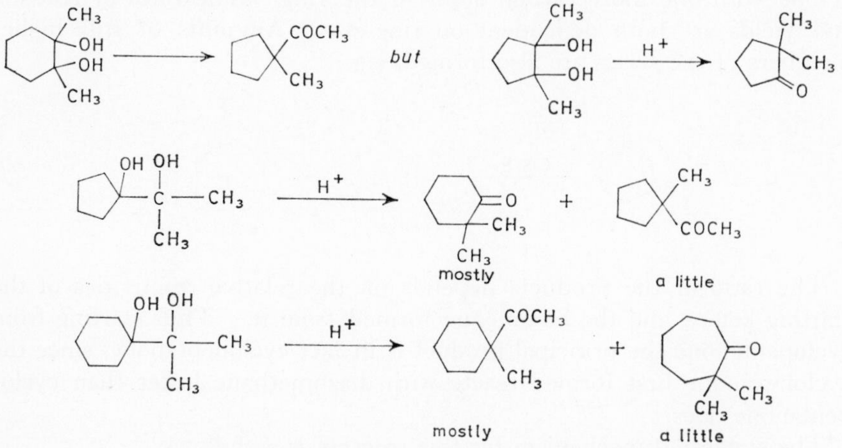

The results in the latter two cases appear to support what might be predicted from Baeyer's Strain Theory, but this is probably fortuitous.

It is now recognised that in this type of molecular rearrangement it is necessary for the eliminated group (in this case, —OH), the migrating group, and the carbon atoms to which they are originally attached, to be coplanar.

It is interesting to note that both *cis*- and *trans*-1,2-dimethylcyclohexane-1,2-diols are converted to a cyclopentane derivative in this reaction (see example above.) In both cases an equatorial hydroxyl group is coplanar with an adjacent ring bond, which migrates giving rise to ring contraction:

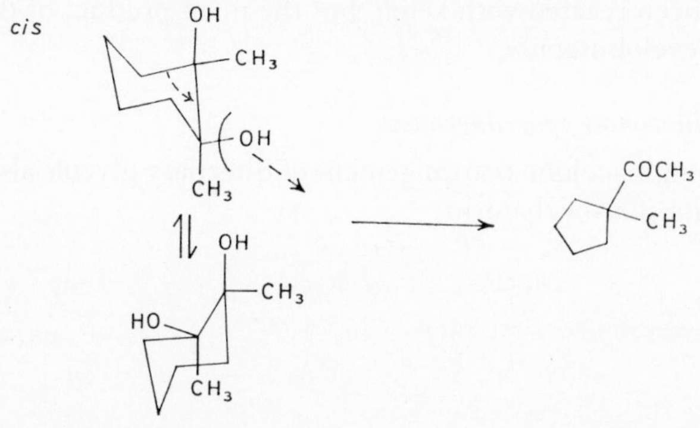

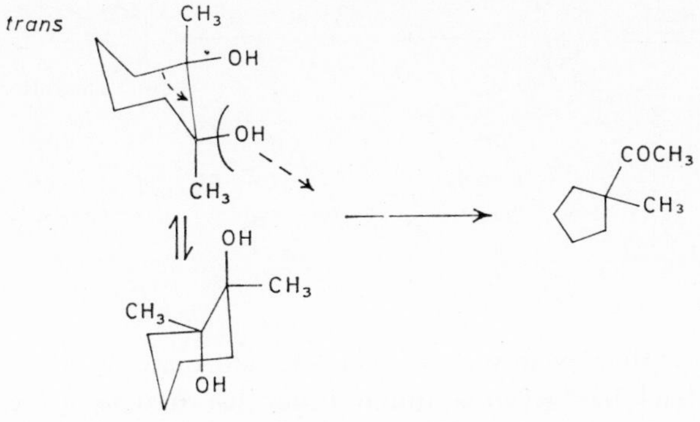

In the case of the *cis*-isomer it is also possible for a hydroxyl group and a methyl group to be coplanar (both axial), but elimination of a hydroxyl group with migration of a methyl group does not seem to take place, since the resultant product of such a reaction (2,2-dimethylcyclohexanone) is not formed. In the case of the *trans*-isomer, it is not possible for a methyl group and a hydroxyl group to be coplanar.

(f) Wagner–Meerwein rearrangement

In the dehydration of β-substituted alcohols, and in their reaction with acidic reagents such as hydrogen chloride, thionyl chloride or phosphorus pentachloride, rearrangement of the carbon skeleton frequently occurs. Skeletal rearrangements can also take place during the addition reactions of hydrogen chloride to bridged-ring olefins and in exchange reactions of β-substituted halogen compounds. This type of rearrangement has loomed large in terpene chemistry, complicating the determination of the structure of many terpene compounds. The rearrangements proceed once again through carbonium ion intermediates. Typical examples are:

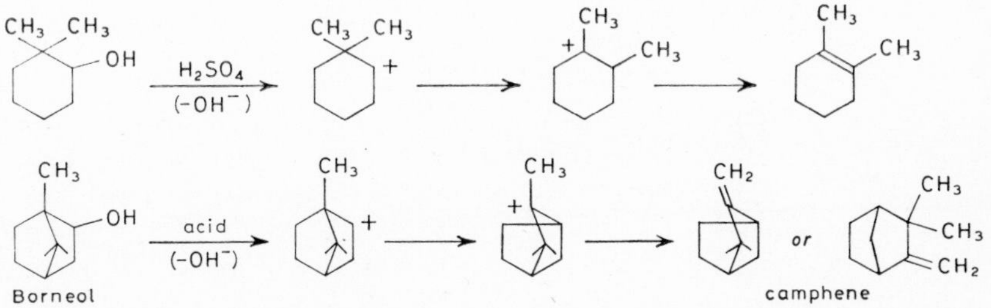

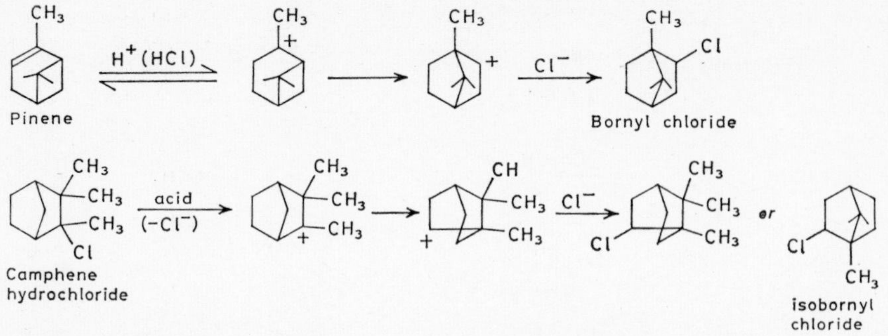

CH₃ H⁺(HCl) CH₃⁺ → CH₃ + Cl⁻ → CH₃ Cl

Pinene

Bornyl chloride

CH₃ CH₃ Cl — acid (−Cl⁻) → — CH₃ + CH₃ → CH + CH₃ + CH₃ Cl⁻ → CH₃ + CH₃ + CH₃ Cl or Cl CH₃

Camphene hydrochloride

isobornyl chloride

Very many other examples of ring-transformations are known; for example Raphael has given a much fuller list in *Chemistry of Carbon Compounds* (1953), Vol. IIA, edited by E. H. Rodd, pp. 11–22. Elsevier.

FOR FURTHER READING

Raphael, R. A. (1953). In *Chemistry of Carbon Compounds*, Vol. IIA, edited by E. H. Rodd. Chapter I. Elsevier.

Fuson, R. C. (1942). In *Organic Chemistry*, Vol. I, edited by H. Gilman. Chapter II. Wiley.

MECHANISMS OF REARRANGEMENT REACTIONS ARE DISCUSSED IN:

Gould, E. S. (1959). *Mechanism and Structure in Organic Chemistry*. Especially Chapter XIV. Holt, Rinehart and Winston.

Sykes, P. (1961). *A Guidebook to Mechanism in Organic Chemistry*. Longmans.

Tucker, S. H. (1959). *An Electronic Outline of Organic Chemistry*. Univ. London Press.

Individual reactions are discussed in:

(1960). *Organic Reactions*, Vol. XI, Edited by A. C. Cope.—Demjanov and Favorskii rearrangements. Wiley.

V

SOME SATURATED ALICYCLIC COMPOUNDS

(a) Cycloalkanes

Cyclopropane occurs in natural gas; cyclopentane, cyclohexane, and cycloheptane, and alkyl derivatives of these hydrocarbons occur in crude petroleum. Cyclohexane is important as a solvent, both industrially and in laboratory work. Cyclopropane is widely used as an anaesthetic.

Most cycloalkanes are prepared via the corresponding ketones or diketones (prepared as described in Chapter IV) which are then reduced to the desired hydrocarbon. Cyclopropane is normally prepared by the action of zinc on 1,3-dibromopropane. An interesting synthesis of cyclodecane from decalin was carried out by Hückel (1933):

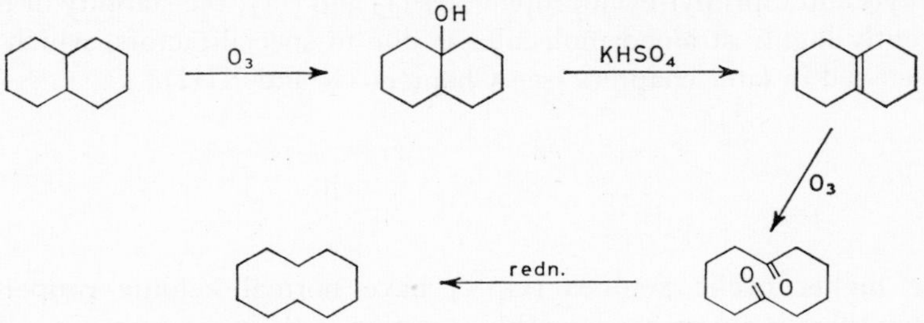

Commercially cyclohexane is made by catalytic reduction of benzene, and cyclopropane from n-propane obtained from the petroleum industry:

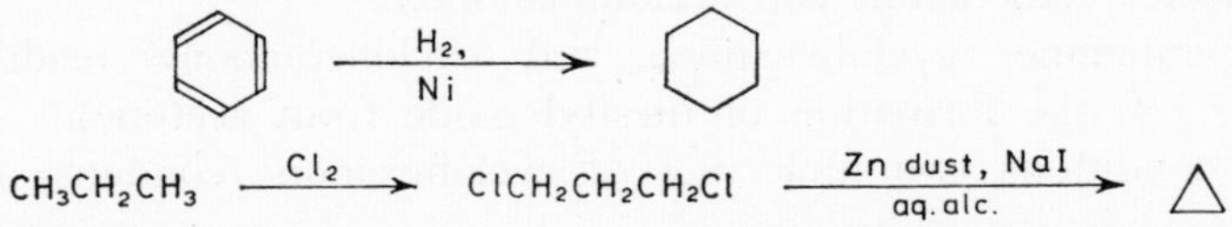

$$CH_3CH_2CH_3 \xrightarrow{Cl_2} ClCH_2CH_2CH_2Cl \xrightarrow[aq.\,alc.]{Zn\ dust,\ NaI} \triangle$$

(b) Cycloalkanones

Cyclic ketones are readily prepared by methods discussed in Chapter IV. They are the most commonly available alicyclic compounds.

Cyclopropanone has not yet been prepared and is apparently too reactive to have a stable existence. This idea is further supported by the formation of cyclobutanone in the reaction between diazomethane and keten, as discussed in the previous chapter. It may be noted that by use of excess keten some acetals have been isolated, e.g. in the presence of methanol a methyl hemiacetal, and in the presence of water a solid hydrate. The latter isomerises to propionic acid. Additionally an enol form of 2-carbethoxycyclopropanone has been prepared by the action of diazoacetic ester on keten:

$$CH_2=C=O \quad + \quad N_2CHCOOEt \quad \longrightarrow \quad \triangleright\!\!-\!OH$$
$$COOEt$$

Reactions between diazoacetic ester and dimethylketen and diphenylketen have failed to produce any cyclopropanone derivatives, however. Earlier attempts to prepare cyclopropanone by the action of sodium amalgam on α,α'-dibromoacetone gave cyclohexane-1,4-dione:

$$2 \ CO \overset{CH_2Br}{\underset{CH_2Br}{<}} \quad \xrightarrow{Na/Hg} \quad O\!\!=\!\!\bigcirc\!\!=\!\!O$$

The only stable cyclopropanone derivatives as yet prepared are the diphenyl- and dipropyl-cyclopropenones (I) and (II); the stability of these apparently highly strained molecules is due to special factors, which will be discussed in later chapters [see Chapters IX and XIII].

$$Ph\!-\!\!\!\overset{\triangledown}{\underset{O}{}}\!\!\!-\!Ph \qquad Pr\!-\!\!\!\overset{\triangledown}{\underset{O}{}}\!\!\!-\!Pr$$
$$(I) \quad O \qquad\qquad (II) \quad O$$

The higher cyclic ketones (C_4—) have normal ketonic properties, although there is a very considerable variation in their reactivity, as will be discussed in the following chapter. For example, cyclic ketones of ring-size up to eight form bisulphite compounds in the same way as methyl ketones do, but cyclononanone does not. This has been used to separate mixtures of cyclooctanone and cyclononanone.

Cyclopentanone, cyclohexanone and cycloheptanone readily self-condense (cf. the formation of mesityl oxide from acetone). Thus in alkaline conditions two molecules of cyclohexanone condense to form 2-cyclohexylidene-cyclohexanone:

$$2 \ \bigcirc\!\!\!\overset{O}{} \quad \xrightarrow{alk.} \quad$$

This self-condensation is due to the activation of the 2-methylene group by the adjacent carbonyl group; these ketones also condense readily with esters. Thus the 2-carbethoxycycloalkanones, valuable as synthetic intermediates, are made by condensation of the ketone with ethyl oxalate, followed by decarbonylation of the resulting 2-oxalyl derivative. The latter reaction can be brought about simply by distillation of the ketooxalyl ester at reduced pressure, but is assisted by the presence of a catalyst such as boric acid or even powdered glass.

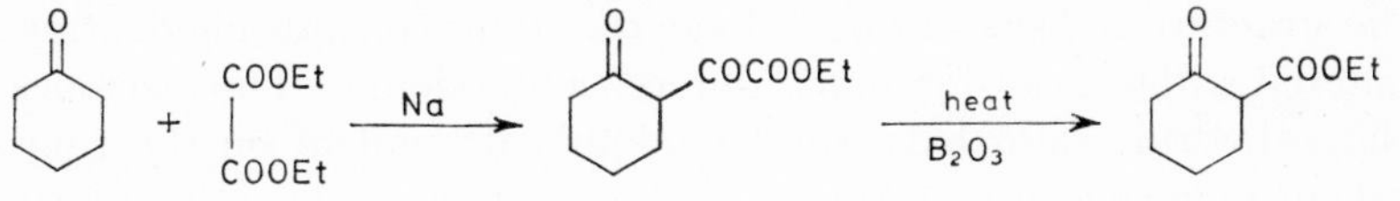

These 2-carbethoxycycloalkanones are β-ketoesters having a reactive hydrogen atom at the α-position which can readily be replaced by other groups.

Many cyclohexanone derivatives occur naturally in essential oils, e.g.

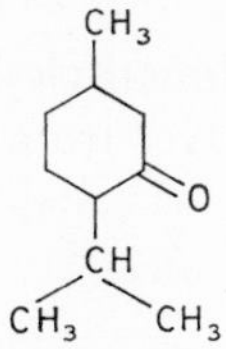

Menthone
(peppermint oils etc.)

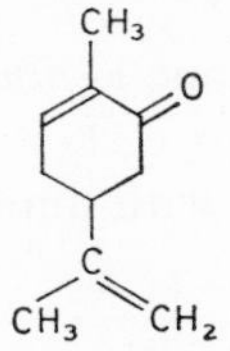

Carvone
(dill, caraway oils, etc.)

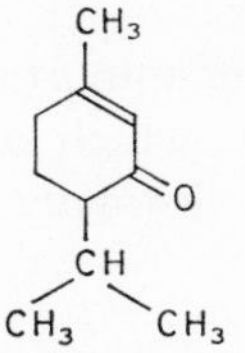

Piperitone
(eucalyptus oils, etc.)

The cyclopentenone derivative, jasmone (III) (from *jasminium grandiflorum*) is used in perfumery, as are some of the larger-ring ketones, such as muscone (IV) and civetone (V), the odiferous principles of the muskdeer and civet cat respectively.

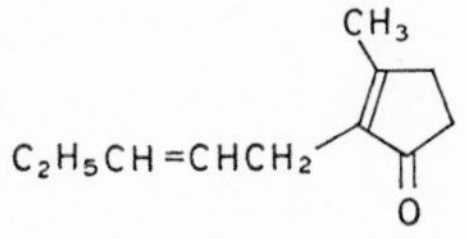

(III) 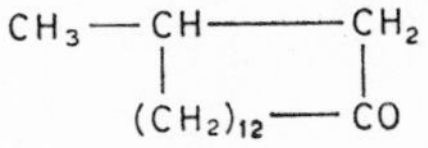   (IV) 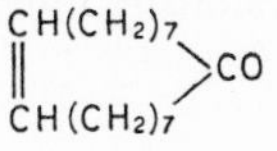   (V) 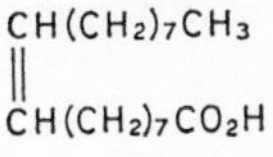   Oleic Acid

The structural similarity between civetone and oleic acid may be noticed.

All cyclic ketones have characteristic odours which appear to be dependent on the ring-size. The odours have been described as follows:

Ring-size of   5   Bitter almonds
           6   Mint
       7–9   Transition to camphor-like
   10–12   Camphor-like
      13   Cedar
   14–18   Musk-like

The most pronounced odour is associated with the 15-membered ring. This ketone is made synthetically and has been introduced into perfumery under the name of 'exaltone'. The smell appears to depend only on the cyclic structure and size of ring. Even the atoms constituting the ring may be altered without causing much difference in odour. Thus lactones and cyclic anhydrides also have similar odours, dependent on the ring-size, although an oxygen atom takes the place of carbon as one of the ring atoms. Lactones may be prepared by the action of organic peracids on cyclic ketones:

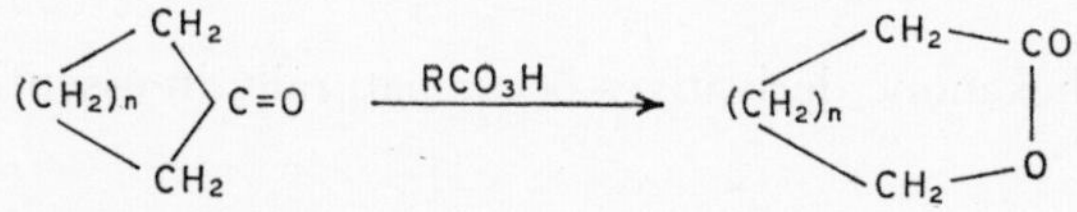

Another important cyclic ketone is *dimedone*, 5,5-dimethylcyclohexane-1,3-dione, which is used to prepare crystalline derivatives from aldehydes. (Ketones normally do not react with dimedone.)

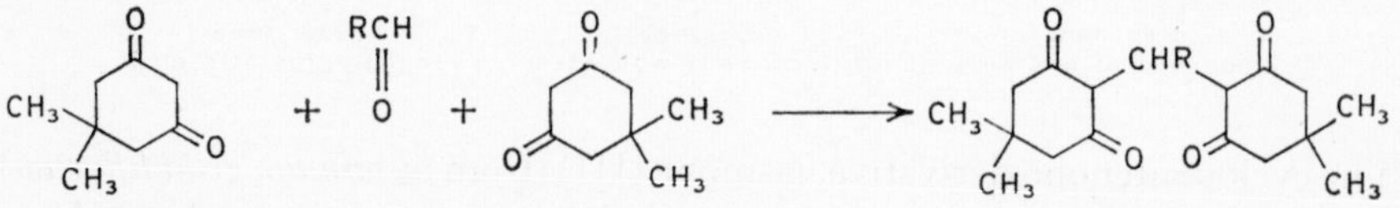

On treatment with acetic anhydride, acetic acid or absolute ethanol, these dimedone derivatives are converted into 'anhydrides', which may be used as further confirmatory derivatives.

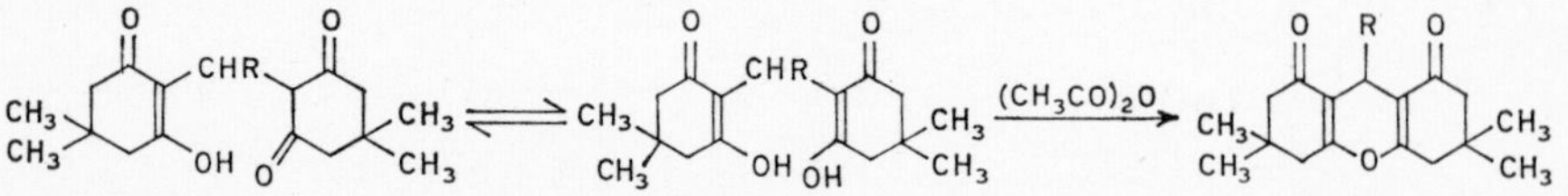

A particular use of dimedone has been for the quantitative estimation of formaldehyde.

Derivatives of cycloheptatrienone (tropone) (VII) and 2-hydroxycyclo-heptatrienone (tropolone) (VIII) have been shown in recent years to occur naturally and have received considerable attention owing to their interesting chemical properties. They will be dealt with more fully in Chapter XII.

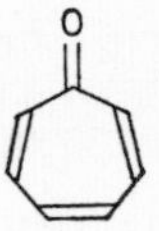

(VII) 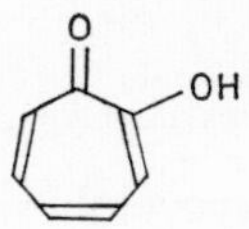   (VIII)

(c) Cycloalkanols

Cyclic alcohols with the hydroxyl group directly attached to the alicyclic ring behave as typical secondary alcohols. They may be oxidised to cyclic ketones which, on stronger oxidation, give dibasic acids by opening of the ring.

Cyclopropanol was unknown until 1951. It had been suspected of being unstable, like cyclopropanone, and of rearranging on formation to allyl alcohol, since all attempts to prepare it, e.g. by the action of nitrous acid on cyclopropylamine, had led to the formation of allyl alcohol.

It has now been prepared, however, by two different methods:

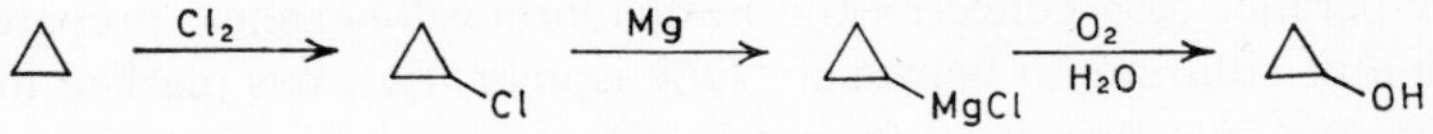

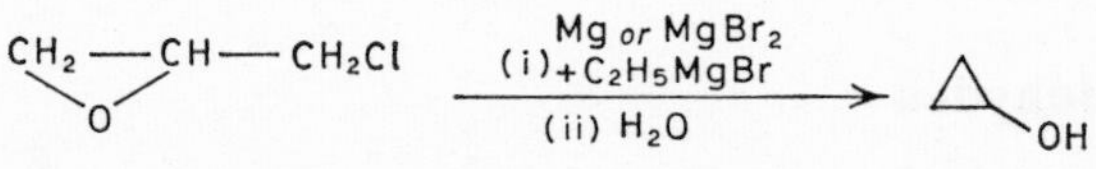

Cyclopropanol rearranges readily to propionaldehyde, but its esters are stable, and are difficult to hydrolyse.

A more recent method of preparation of 1-substituted cyclopropanols (De Puy et al., 1962) is as follows:

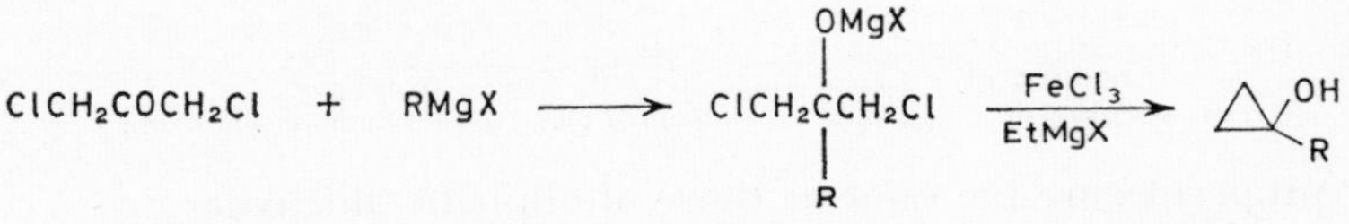

A large number of cyclohexanol derivatives occur naturally; examples are:

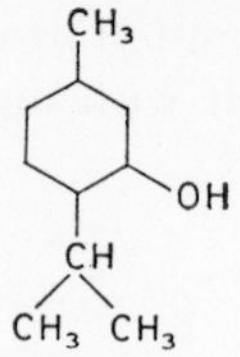

Menthol
(from peppermint oils,etc.)

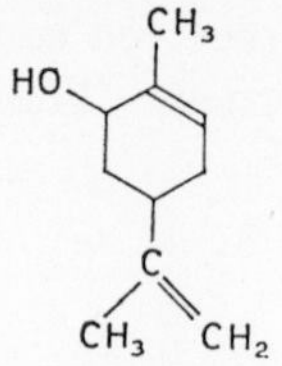

Carveol
(from oil of caraway, etc.)

Many polyhydroxycyclohexanes also occur naturally, e.g. *quercitols*, $[C_6H_7(OH)_5]$ (of various stereochemical conformations), from oak and other plants, and *inositols*, $[C_6H_6(OH)_6]$. *Meso*-inositol (IX) is widely distributed in plants and animals, and is of biological importance as a component of the Vitamin B complex.

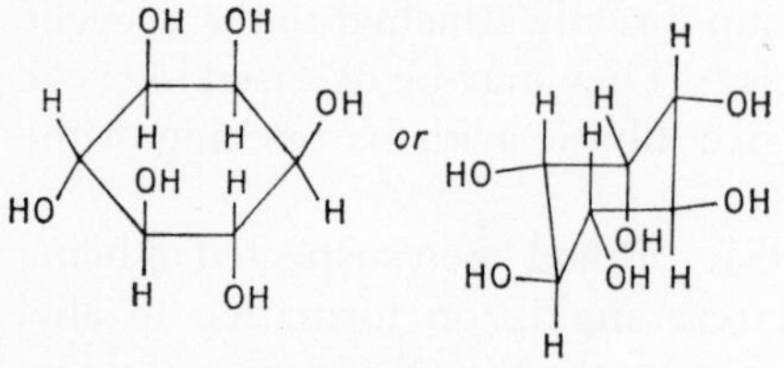

(IX) 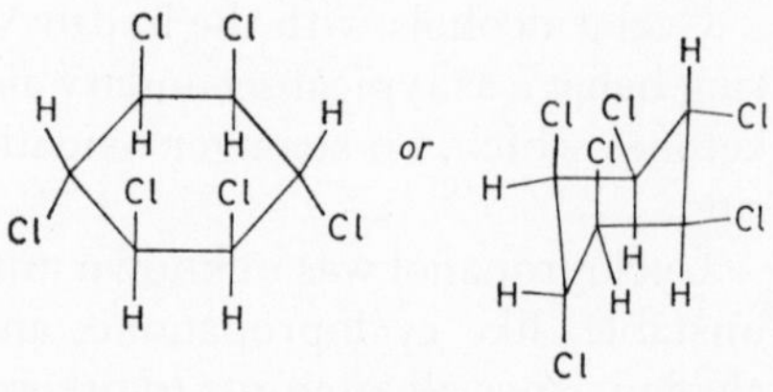   (X)

Numerous stereoisomers of *meso*-inositol are of course possible and, as is frequently the case, biological activity is associated with one particular isomer.

A parallel case concerns the hexachlorocyclohexanes, prepared by the action of chlorine on benzene. One isomer, (X), has marked insecticidal properties, not possessed to any similar degree by its stereoisomers. (X) is commonly known as 'Gammexane'.

(d) Alicyclic aldehydes

Some cyclohexane aldehydes occur naturally, e.g.

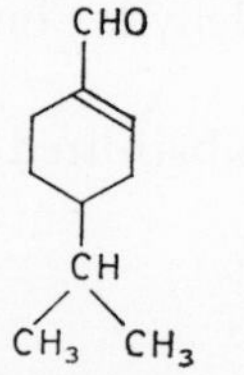

Phellandral
(from eucalyptus oils,etc.)

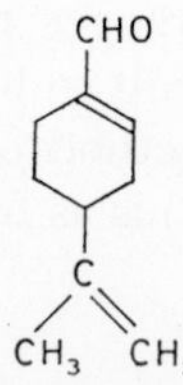

Perillaldehyde
(from oil of false camphor wood, etc.)

Their properties are the same as those of aliphatic aldehydes.

(e) Alicyclic acids

Methods of preparing alicyclic acids have been mentioned in Chapter IV. Some of these acids are useful as synthetic intermediates in alicyclic chemistry.

In the case of 3- to 5-membered rings only *cis*-1,2-dicarboxylic acids can form intramolecular anhydrides, for steric reasons:

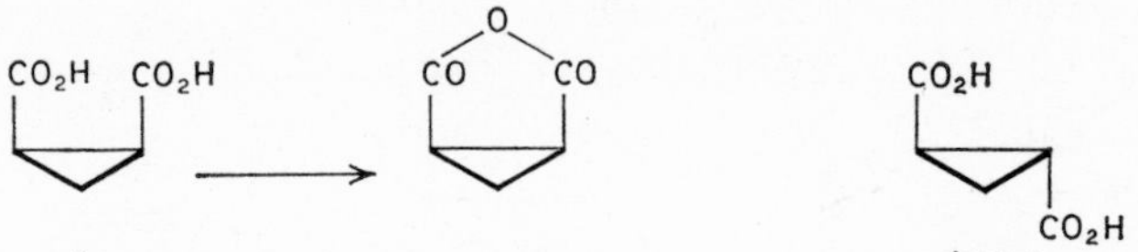

This sometimes presents a means of separating a mixture of the *cis*- and *trans*-isomers. For example, on treatment of a mixture of *cis*- and *trans*-cyclopropane-1,2-dicarboxylic acids with acetic anhydride, only the *cis*-isomer forms an anhydride, which may be extracted with toluene, in which the unchanged *trans*-acid is insoluble.

In the case of cyclohexane-1,2-dicarboxylic acids, however, both *cis*- and *trans*-acids can form anhydrides, owing to the shape of the ring. In the case of 2-carboxycyclohexaneacetic acid the *trans*-anhydride (XI) is actually more stable than the *cis*-anhydride (XII).

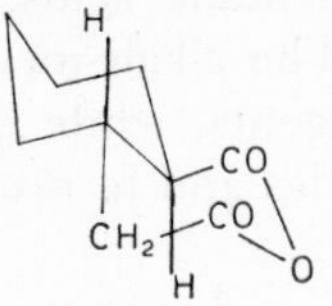

It is worth noting that in the case of *endo*ethylenehexahydrophthalic acid (bicyclo-[2,2,2]-octane-2,3-dicarboxylic acid), (XIII), the bridged ring prevents the flexibility necessary for formation of a *trans*-anhydride, and only the *cis*-isomer forms one.

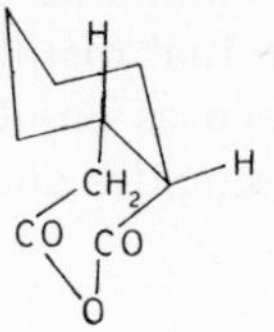

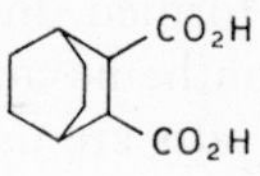

Many alicyclic acids occur naturally. Examples are:

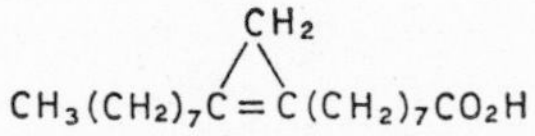

$$CH_3(CH_2)_7C = C(CH_2)_7CO_2H$$

Sterculic Acid
(Kernel oil of *Stercula foetida*)

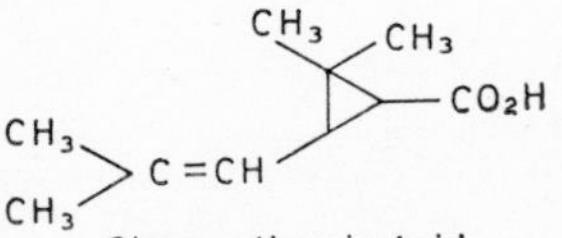

Chrysanthemic Acid
(Flower heads of pyrethrum)

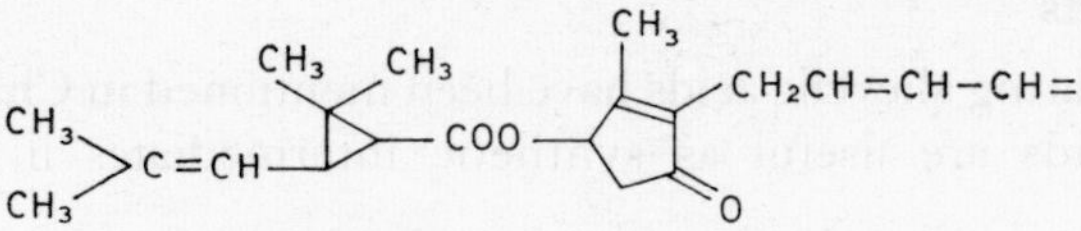

Pyrethrin (I)(an ester of chrysanthemic acid, above)
(Flower heads of pyrethrum)

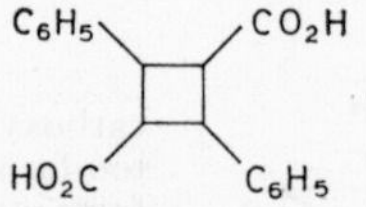

Truxillic Acid
(Coca leaf)

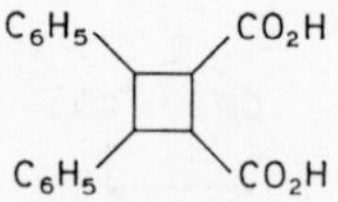

Truxinic Acid
(Coca leaf)

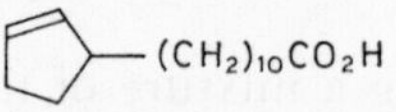

Hydnocarpic Acid
(Chaulmoogra oil)

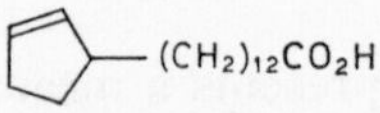

Chaulmoogric Acid
(Chaulmoogra oil)

Pyrethrin I is used as an insecticide; pyrethrum is cultivated commercially for this purpose. Hydnocarpic and chaulmoogric acids have long been used as native remedies for leprosy and tuberculosis.

In addition the naphthenic acids found among the distillation products from crude oil contain large amounts of cyclopentane acids, probably artefacts formed during the actual distillation. The alkali metal salts of these naphthenic acids are used as emulsifying agents, while the copper and zinc salts are used as insecticides and fungicides and to protect wood against dry rot and mildew.

FOR FURTHER READING

Raphael, R. A. (1953). In *Chemistry of Carbon Compounds*, Vol. IIA, edited by E. H. Rodd. Chapters II–VI. Elsevier.

Fuson, R. C. (1942). In *Organic Chemistry*, Vol. I, edited by H. Gilman. Chapter II. Wiley.

Vogel, E. (1960). *Angew. Chem.*, **72**, 4. (3- and 4-membered rings.)

VI

RATES OF REACTION
OF ALICYCLIC COMPOUNDS AND RING-SIZE

MENTION has frequently been made in the foregoing chapters of the variation in reactivity of organic compounds with ring-size. This will now be discussed in more detail.

Ring compounds have been classified into groups as follows:

3–4 membered rings	'Small'
5–7	„	„	'Common'
8–11	„	„	'Medium'
⩾ 12	„	„	'Large'

Sachse and Mohr's original ideas on puckered rings indicated that rings made up of six or more atoms would all tend to be similar in properties. This has since been shown to be untrue.

In particular the medium-ring compounds are anomalous in both their physical and chemical properties. Thus, whereas in the aliphatic series physical properties tend to vary steadily as a homologous series is ascended, this is not the case with alicyclic compounds. When plotted against ring-size many physical properties tend to come to a maximum or a minimum for the medium-rings, among them melting-points, density, atomic refractions, spectra, etc. As an example a list of the ultra-violet spectra of a series of alicyclic 1,3-dienes is given showing the wavelength and intensity of the maxima in each case:

Diene	λ max.	ε max.
cyclopenta-1,3-diene	238·5	3400
cyclohexa-1,3-diene	256·5	8000
cyclohepta-1,3-diene	248	7500
cycloocta-1,3-diene	228	5600
cyclonona-1,3-diene	219·5	2500
cyclodeca-1,3-diene	223	5000
cycloundeca-1,3-diene	225	6000
cyclotrideca-1,3-diene	232	

In Chapter I the effect of strain caused by a compression of the valency angles—and hence now called *angle strain*—on the heats of combustion per methylene group of small-ring compounds was discussed. It is nowadays realised that there are also small but significant increases in the heats of combustion per methylene group of the medium-sized rings, as shown in the following table.

No. of carbon atoms in ring	6	7	8	9	10	11
Mol.ht. of combustion per CH_2 group (kcal.)	157·4	158·3	158·6	158·8	158·6	158·4
No. of carbon atoms in ring	12	13	14	15	16	17
Mol.ht. of combustion per CH_2 group (kcal.)	157·7	157·8	157·4	157·5	157·5	157·2

(Cf. Mol.ht. of combustion per CH_2 group for an alkane = 157·4 kcal.)

The anomalous behaviour of the medium-rings has been explained by the 'crowded' environment of the atoms in these rings resulting in much non-bonded intramolecular interaction between the atoms, including interactions between atoms which formally may be regarded as being on opposite sides of the rings. This intramolecular interaction between atoms attached to different parts of the ring in alicyclic compounds is described as *trans-annular* interaction. It gives rise to *transannular strain* in these molecules.

Some other examples of anomalous properties of medium-rings are listed by Prelog [*J. Chem. Soc.*, 1950, p. 422].

In rings of fifteen or more carbon atoms this 'crowding' with its associated transannular strain disappears. In these molecules the ring atoms arrange themselves into two roughly parallel chains and thus resemble more nearly aliphatic compounds:

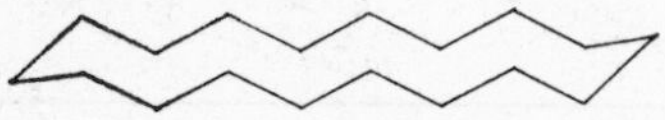

The difficulty of preparing medium-sized rings, as illustrated in the graph on p. 40, is also believed to be due to the strain in these rings. In this connexion it has been found that in the formation of medium-sized rings, replacement of a methylene group in the carbon chain by a carbonyl group or an oxygen atom increases both the ease of ring-closure and the yield of the cyclic product. This may be due both to the lower co-ordination numbers and the different bond angles associated with the latter groups, both of which would lower the 'crowding' in the resultant ring-compounds.

Variations in chemical reactivities with ring-size present a similar picture to the variations in physical properties. Figs. I, II, III and IV show respectively:

(I) the rate of solvolysis of cyclic halides;
(II) the rate of decomposition of cyclic azo-compounds;
(III) the equilibrium for the dissociation of the cycloalkanone cyan-hydrins;
(IV) the rate of reaction of cycloalkanones with sodium borohydride.

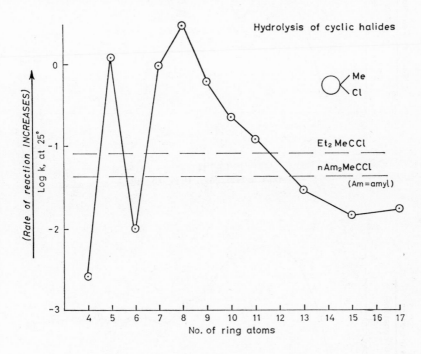

Fig. I
(*J. Amer. Chem. Soc.*, 1952, **74**, 1898)

Many similar diagrams could be shown giving the same overall picture. The trend in all of them is similar, with again a maximum or minimum for the medium-rings. The values for large rings approximate to those for aliphatic compounds.

Other general points to be noted are as follows:

(i) When the values for small rings are *less* than those for large rings (or aliphatic compounds) then the values for medium rings are *greater* than those for the large rings (and vice versa).

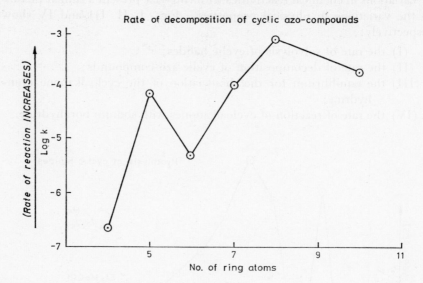

Fig. II
(*J. Amer. Chem. Soc.*, 1953, **75**, 2082)

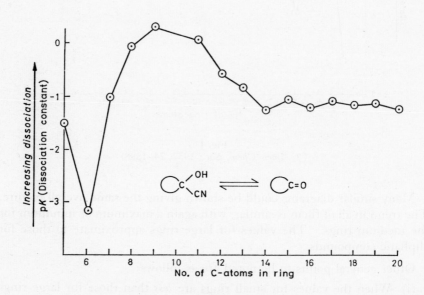

Fig. III
(*J. Chem. Soc.*, 1950, 423)

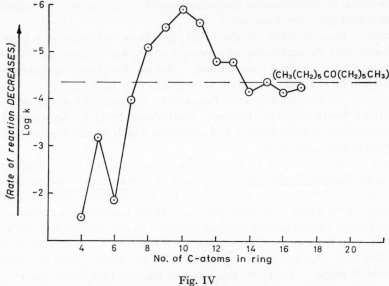

Fig. IV
(*Tetrahedron*, 1957, **1**, 226)

(ii) The values for five-membered and six-membered rings are 'irregular' and do not fall on the same smooth curve as the values for the other rings.

It is thought that a number of factors are involved in these differences of reactivity. Three of these factors are:

(a) an angle-strain factor, which is of most importance for the rings where angle-strain is large, i.e. the three- and four-membered rings;

(b) transannular strain due to the crowded structure of medium rings.

(c) a conformational strain factor, which is of most importance in the case of five- and six-membered rings, where factors (a) and (b) are of small importance.

Let us first consider the hydrolysis reactions (Fig. I). The hydrolysis of cyclopropyl and cyclobutyl halides is slower than the hydrolysis of aliphatic halides, whereas the medium rings react faster. Similar evidence is provided by the rates of hydrolysis of cyclic p-toluenesulphonates. Fig. II follows a similar pattern.

With cyclic ketones the order of the rates of reaction is reversed. (See Figs. III and IV.) Fig. IV shows this directly, while Fig. III illustrates the same point by demonstrating the points of equilibrium in such a series of reactions. In the case of the cycloalkanone cyanhydrins we meet two extremes for cyclohexanone cyanhydrin is almost completely undissociated, whereas cyclodecanone cyanhydrin cannot even be formed. (It may be recalled that cyclopropanone is similarly not known except as a hydrate or acetal which does not dissociate.)

Various theories have sought to explain these differences, e.g. steric hindrance and the prevention of rearward attack was said to cause the unreactivity of the medium ring ketones. But on this theory cyclohexanone should also be sterically hindered, yet it reacts very readily.

As said above a number of factors are undoubtedly involved. An important theory is that of 'I-strain', put forward by H. C. Brown in 1952, with a number of amendments and additions which he and his co-workers have suggested since then.

Brown suggested that in general the reactivity of cyclic compounds might be correlated with the strain—called *I-strain*—involved in passing from the initial state of the molecule to the intermediate state involved in the reaction in which it is participating. In S_N1 reactions a carbon atom passes from a co-ordination number of 4 to 3 in the intermediate state; in S_N2 reactions from a co-ordination state of 4 to one of 5. The intermediate in either case requires bond-angles of 120°, i.e. greater than the normal tetrahedral angle. Thus, on the basis of the classical strain theory, the intermediate in the case of a cyclopropane or a cyclobutane ring will be much more strained than the initial tetrahedral structure. This explains excellently the sluggish reactivity of cyclopropane and cyclobutane compounds in S_N1 and S_N2 type reactions. In the case of medium rings it is thought that the change from a tetrahedral carbon atom to a trigonal carbon atom in S_N1 and S_N2 reactions may on the other hand relieve some of the angle, conformational, and especially the transannular strain in the molecule; this is consistent with the high reactivity of medium ring compounds in S_N1 reactions. Recent evidence on S_N2 type reactions of medium ring compounds, e.g. the irreversible halogen exchange reaction between cycloalkyl bromides and iodide ions, appears on the other hand to conflict with this pattern. The rates of reaction *decrease* from the seven-membered ring to the twelve-membered ring and then start to increase again. It has been suggested that yet another factor comes into play here. In an S_N2 reaction the substituting and substituted groups and the carbon atom to which they are attached normally tend to be collinear in the transition stage. In the case of medium rings this will be harder to achieve. Hence the necessity for such an alignment of the reacting groups will cause reaction to be hindered, the potential energy of the transition state increased, and the rate of reaction to be consequently lowered. It is thought that this latter effect overrides the effect due to relief of strain in the medium rings, and causes an overall lowering of their rates of reaction in S_N2 type reactions.

When the reactions of cyclic ketones are considered the situation is the reverse of that which obtains in the case of S_N1 reactions. Reactions of ketones involve a change of co-ordination number of the carbonyl carbon atom from 3 to 4. Hence reaction will be favoured in the case of three- and four-membered rings (because angle strain is relieved in the reaction), but not favoured in the case of medium rings (because the presence of a trigonal carbon atom relieves both conformational and transannular strain in these molecules, since less crowding of atoms is then involved). This is in agreement with the observed reactivities.

The question of five- and six-membered ring compounds remains to be clarified. For these ring sizes the changes in angle strain involved in reactions are not so great and are certainly insufficient to explain the great differences in reactivity between cyclopentane and cyclohexane derivatives. It is now thought that an important factor here may be the differences in conformational strain between the initial molecule taking part in a reaction and the intermediate state in that reaction.

A fully saturated cyclopentane ring has a completely eclipsed conformation with ten 'oppositions' between adjacent hydrogen atoms:

It thus has a maximum of unfavourable conformations. On the other hand cyclopentanone or other five-membered ring compounds having one carbon atom with a co-ordination number of 3, has only 6 'oppositions':

Thus an intermediate in an S_N1 or S_N2 reaction of a cyclopentane derivative has much less conformational strain than the original compound and reactions proceeding through such an intermediate will be favoured and proceed rapidly. In contrast, addition reactions of cyclopentanone, involving the exchange of a trigonal carbon atom for a tetrahedral one will not be favoured and hence proceed only slowly.

In the case of six-membered rings fully saturated cyclohexane derivatives have no oppositions and are made up entirely from favourable 'skew' conformations. But cyclohexanone or trigonal S_N1 or S_N2 intermediates derived from cyclohexane compounds have a less favourable conformation. Thus in this case substitution reactions of saturated compounds will be energetically hindered and addition reactions of trigonal atoms, as in cyclohexanone, favoured. Yet a further factor in the case of cyclohexane derivatives may be that, whereas in the case of fully saturated compounds the bond angles are almost precisely the most favoured ones, in the case of a ring containing a trigonal carbon atom this is no longer the case.

It may seem somewhat wrong to apply one set of tenets to explain the reactivities of some sizes of ring and other tenets for other ring sizes. In fact all the factors discussed must be involved in all cases, but it seems reasonable to expect that transannular factors will only be important where the ring has a crowded structure, i.e. in the case of medium rings; that angle strain will be the predominant factor in cases where it is known to be an important factor in the behaviour of the molecule, i.e. in small rings; and that conformational strain will be predominant in the cases where neither angle strain nor transannular interaction are important factors in the chemistry of the molecules concerned, i.e. in the case of five- and six-membered rings.

Transannular reactions

Not only do physical properties and rates of reaction become 'abnormal' for medium ring compounds, but certain abnormal reactions occur in the case of C_8—C_{11} ring compounds, involving at the same time two ring atoms apparently well separated from each other in the ring. An example of such a reaction is the hydrolysis of 1,2-epoxycyclodecane; instead of obtaining a 1,2-dihydroxycyclodecane in fact 1,6-dihydroxycyclodecane and a bicyclodecanol are obtained:

In these medium rings, apparently separated atoms, as in the example above, are in fact brought near to each other by the crowded steric configuration of the ring and can thus interact with each other. For instance, if the epoxycyclodecane is represented as:

it is easy to see how the resulting products could be formed.

Other examples of *transannular reactions*, similar to the one we have just considered, include the following:

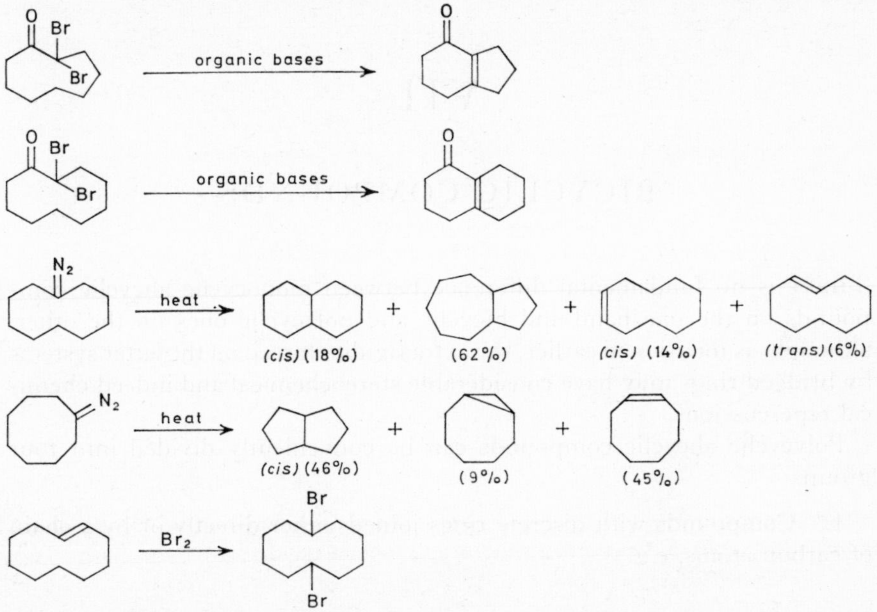

organic bases

organic bases

heat

(cis) (18%)   +   (62%)   +   (cis) (14%)   +   (trans) (6%)

heat

(cis) (46%)   +   (9%)   +   (45%)

Br₂

These transannular reactions must involve transannular electronic interactions in the transition state.   Direct evidence of electronic interaction in an unreacting molecule is provided by the U.V. spectrum of a molecule such as cyclodec-5-en-1-one, which differs from the spectrum obtained by a simple addition of the spectra of cyclodecene and cyclodecanone.

FOR FURTHER READING

Eliel, E. L. (1962). *Stereochemistry of Carbon Compounds*. Pages 265–9. McGraw-Hill.

Eliel, E. L. (1956). In *Steric Effects in Organic Chemistry*, edited by M. S. Newman. Pages 121 ff. Wiley.

MEDIUM RING COMPOUNDS

Prelog, V. (1950). *J. Chem. Soc.*, 422.

Prelog, V. (1956). In *Perspectives in Organic Chemistry*, edited by A. Todd. Page 96. Interscience.

Sicher, J. (1962). In *Progress in Stereochemistry*, Vol. III, edited by P. B. D. de la Mare and W. Klyne. Pages 202 ff. Butterworth.

Fieser, L. F. and Fieser, M. (1957). *Introduction to Organic Chemistry*. Pages 520 ff. Heath.

VII

BICYCLIC COMPOUNDS

THERE is no fundamental difference between monocyclic alicyclic compounds on the one hand and bicyclic and polycyclic ones on the other, although, as mentioned earlier, the extra rigidity forced on the latter systems by bridged rings may have considerable stereochemical and indeed chemical repercussions.

Polycyclic alicyclic compounds can be conveniently divided into four groups:

1. Compounds with discrete rings joined either directly or by a chain of carbon atoms, e.g.

2. *Spirans* in which *one* carbon atom is common to two rings, e.g.

3. *Condensed-ring* systems in which *two* carbon atoms are common to two rings, e.g.

4. *Bridged-ring* compounds in which two rings share three or more carbon atoms, e.g.

Compounds with discrete rings

In this type of bicyclic compound the different rings are isolated from each other and are thus effectively monocyclic. They are prepared by orthodox methods; for example the two compounds shown above are prepared as follows:

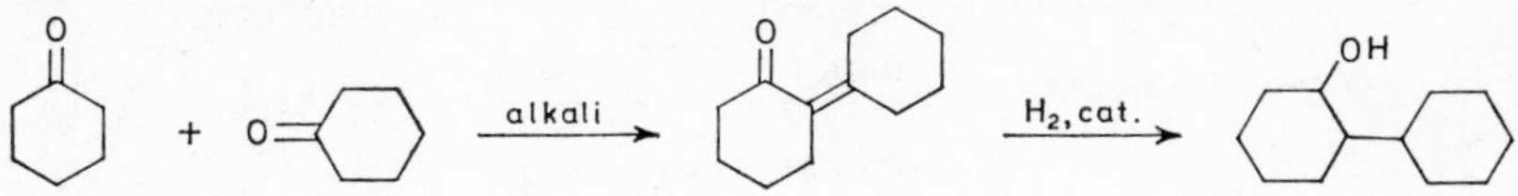

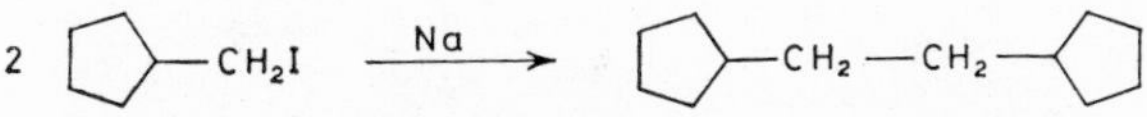

Spirans

Because of the tetrahedral arrangement of the valencies of carbon the two rings in a spiran must be at right angles to each other. Substitution in both rings of a spiran can thus lead to a lack of a centre or plane of symmetry in the molecule. In consequence stereoisomers are possible analogous to those possible in the allene series. For example spiro[3,3]heptane-2,5-dicarboxylic acid (I) has been resolved into d and l forms. This acid was prepared as shown in the following chart.

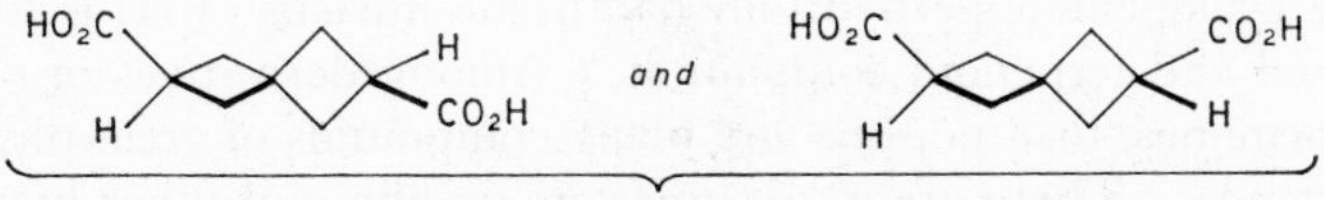

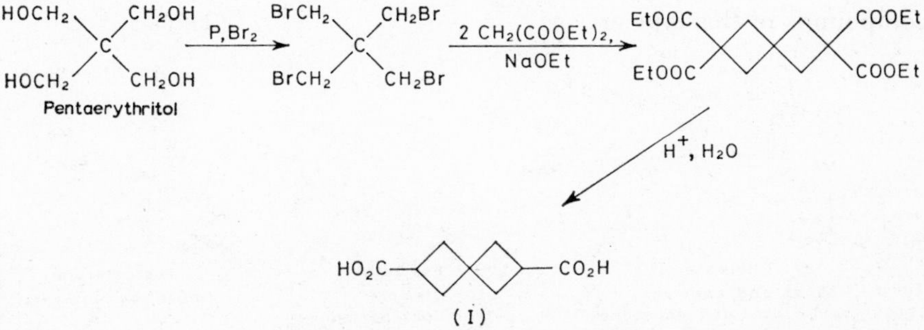

In general spirans are prepared by applying the usual methods of cyclisation to 1,1-disubstituted monocyclic compounds, e.g.

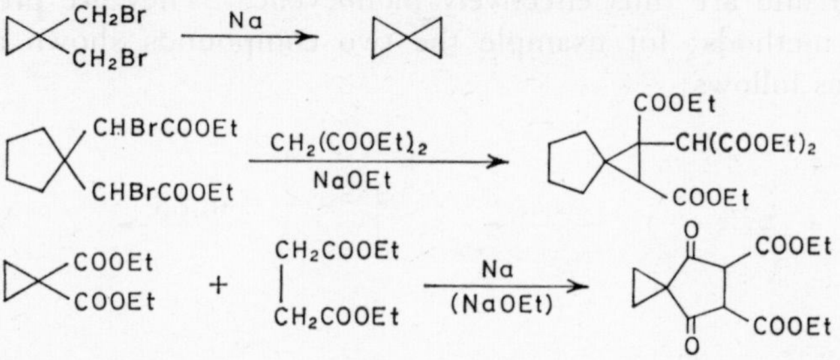

Condensed-ring systems

The commonest bicyclic alicyclic compound is probably the condensed-ring compound decalin (II), which is used as a solvent and is prepared by the catalytic reduction of naphthalene. Less complete reduction of naphthalene results in the formation of tetralin (III), an example of a mixed alicyclic–benzenoid compound. Other compounds having fused benzene and alicyclic rings are indane (IV), indene (V) and fluorene (VI).

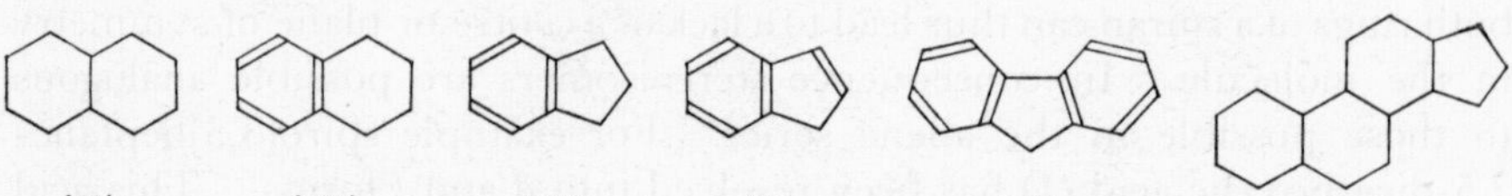

Condensed-ring compounds occur frequently in natural products; in particular the cyclopentanoperhydrophenanthrene nucleus (VII) is found in many steroid and terpenoid compounds. Among derivatives of (VII) are the sex hormones, toad poisons and many compounds of great physiological importance. There are also numerous decalin and other bicyclic derivatives which occur naturally. Examples of naturally occurring compounds of this type are

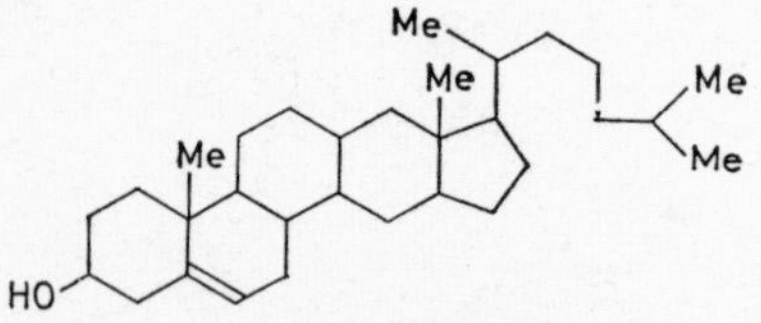

Cholesterol
(in all tissues and especially
brain, spinal cord and gallstones)

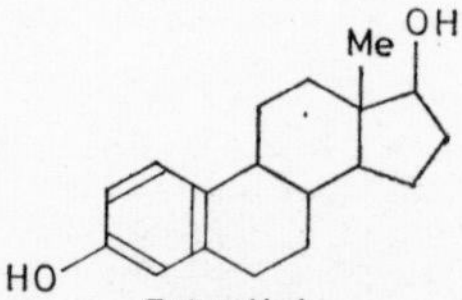

Estradiol
(female
sex hormone)

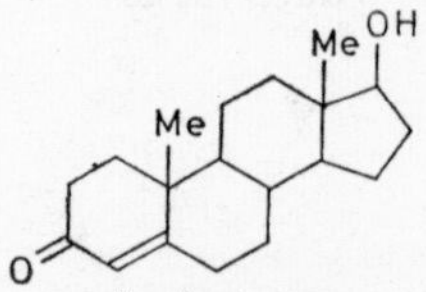

Testosterone
(male sex hormone)

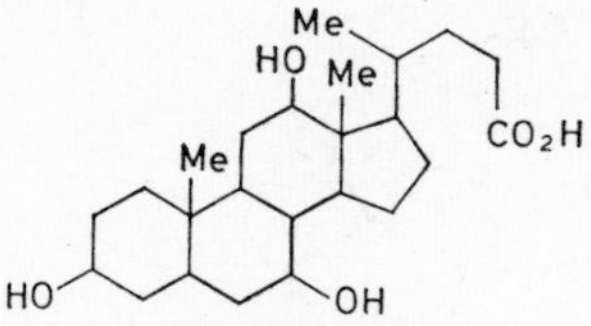

Cholic Acid
(a bile acid)

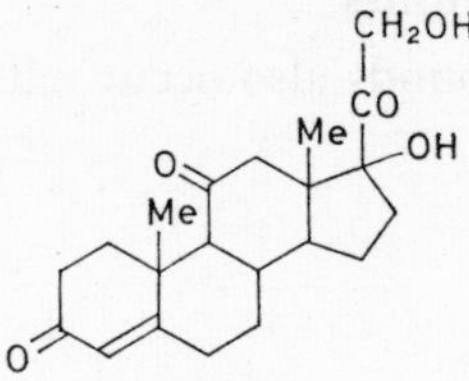

Cortisone
(from adrenal cortex)

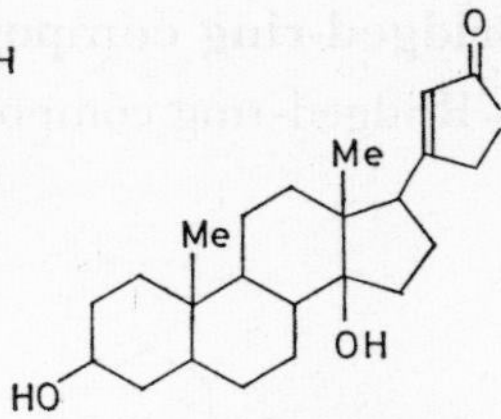

Digitoxigenin
(from foxgloves)

Compounds having condensed rings are prepared by normal ring-closure methods, starting from 1,2-disubstituted alicyclic compounds or by hydrogenation of benzenoid compounds, e.g.

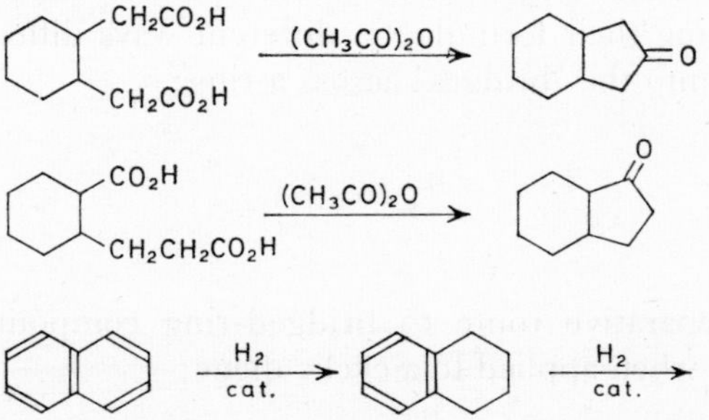

The stereochemistry of decalin has already been discussed in Chapter II. Hexahydroindane (bicyclo[4,3,0]nonane) (VIII) can also exist in *cis* and *trans* forms. In the case of both decalin and hexahydroindane the *cis*-isomer has the slightly higher heat of combustion of the two isomers, which is in accord with the theoretical calculations of strain present in these molecules (due to extra intramolecular interactions in the case of the *cis*-isomers).

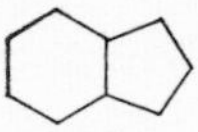

(VIII)

Decalin:

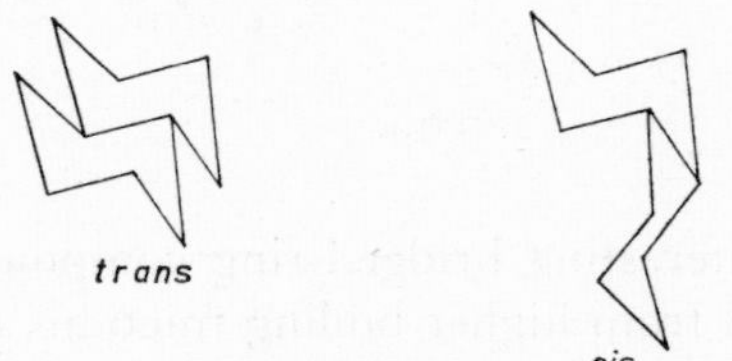

trans

cis

Hexahydroindane

trans

cis

Bridged-ring compounds

Bridged-ring compounds also occur naturally, e.g.

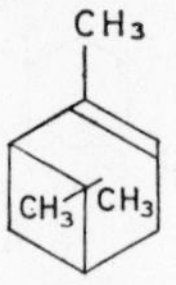

∝-Pinene 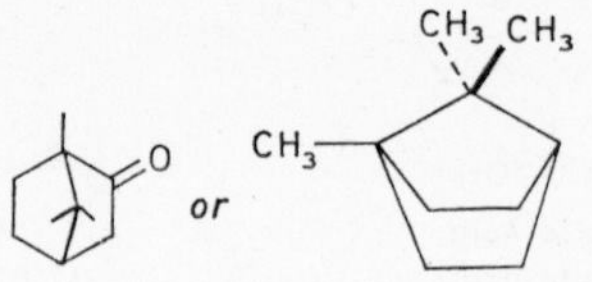   Camphor

Note that in these compounds no one particular chain of carbon atoms is a 'bridge' any more than any other chain. To emphasise this point it may be seen that by drawing their formulae in different ways different chains can in turn be made into the 'bridges' across a ring;

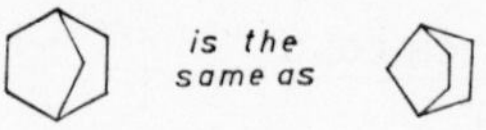

is the same as

A most useful preparative route to bridged-ring compounds is the Diels–Alder reaction, when applied to a cyclic diene:

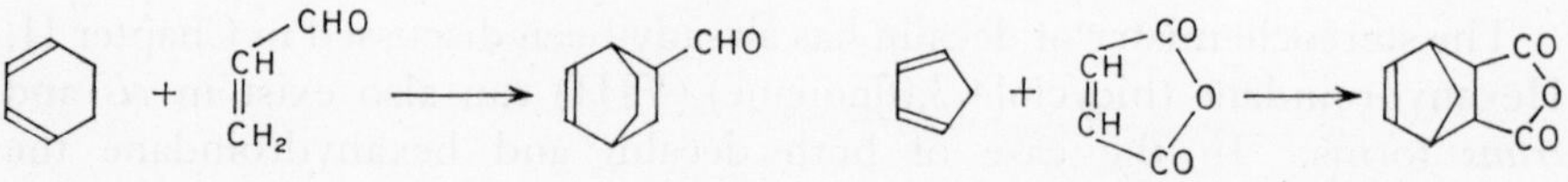

Bridged-ring compounds may also be made by the cyclisation of suitable disubstituted alicyclic compounds (i.e. not 1,1- or 1,2-disubstituted), for example:

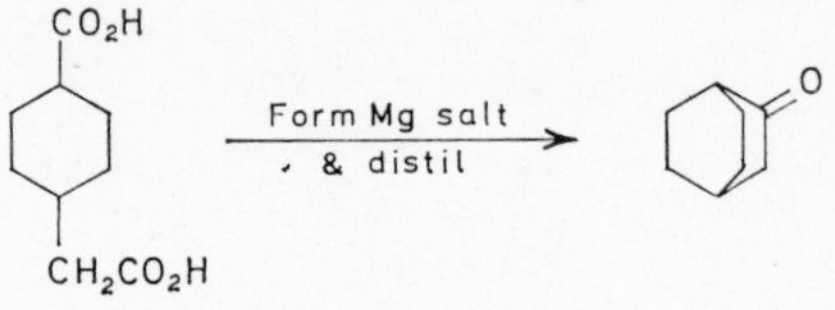

Form Mg salt & distil

A most interesting bridged-ring compound is adamantane, which has been isolated from higher boiling fractions in the distillation of crude oil.

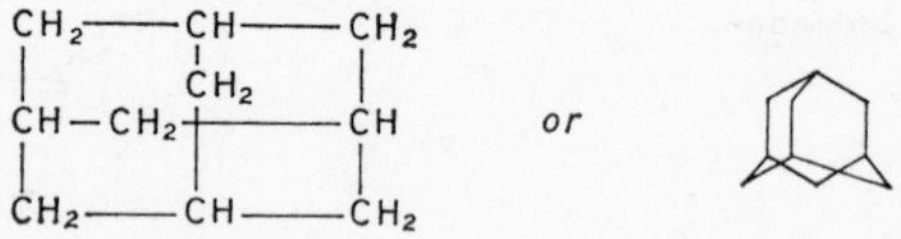

or

The second formula drawn for adamantane gives some idea of its actual structure and of its beautiful symmetry.   The spatial arrangement of the carbon atoms is identical with that in diamond.   Adamantane is an extremely stable hydrocarbon and is very inert chemically, being unaffected by hot nitric acid, chromic acid and potassium permanganate.   It can be prepared from dicyclopentadiene (see p. 91), or from cyclopentene and cyclopentadiene, as follows:

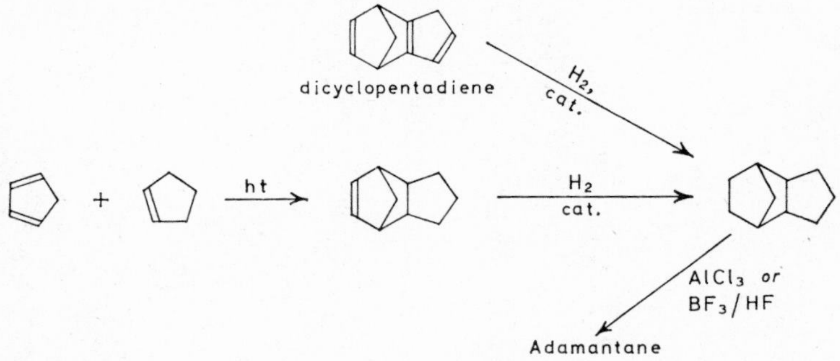

The last stage is another example of the isomerisation of a cycloalkane brought about by acid catalysis.   (See pp. 57–58.)

Catenanes

In 1960 the first example of a new type of bicyclic compound, with interlocked rings, was prepared by acyloin cyclisation of the diester $EtO_2C(CH_2)_{32}CO_2Et$ in the presence of a large excess of a cycloalkane, $C_{34}H_{63}D_5$, which had been 'labelled' by deuteration.   About 1% of a product which investigation clearly proved to have interlocked rings was identified.

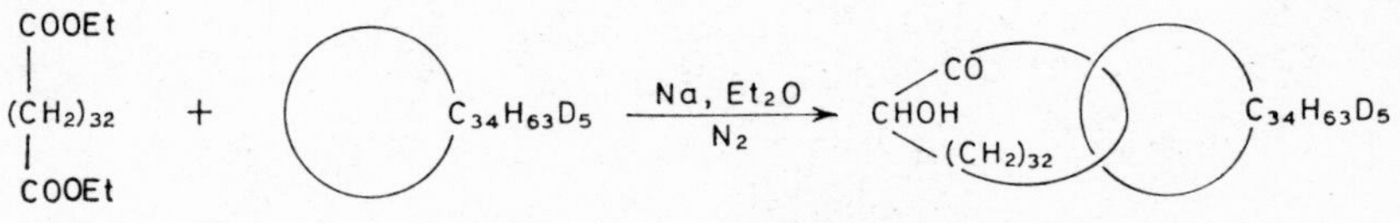

Proof derived from the facts that the acyloin produced was shown (by I.R. spectrum) to contain molecules having C—D bonds, and that oxidation of the acyloin liberated isolable amounts of the original deuterated cycloalkane.   The name *catenane* has been proposed for compounds having interlocked rings.

7—A.C.

FOR FURTHER READING

Raphael, R. A. (1953).   In *Chemistry of Carbon Compounds*, Vol. IIA, edited by
E. H. Rodd.   Chapters VII–IX.   Elsevier.

STEREOCHEMISTRY

Eliel, E. L. (1962).   *Stereochemistry of Carbon Compounds*.   Chapter X.
McGraw-Hill.

VIII

SOME UNSATURATED
ALICYCLIC COMPOUNDS, INCLUDING
CYCLOPENTADIENE, CYCLOBUTADIENE
AND CYCLOOCTATETRAENE

Monoalkenes and alkynes

In the normal way cycloalkenes are prepared by the methods used for acyclic olefines, e.g. by removal of the elements of water from alcohols or of hydrogen halide from halogen containing compounds:

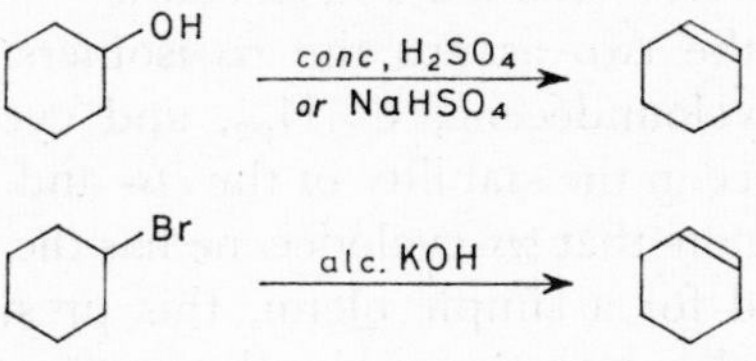

$$\text{(cyclohexanol)} \xrightarrow[\text{or NaHSO}_4]{conc, \text{H}_2\text{SO}_4} \text{(cyclohexene)}$$

$$\text{(bromocyclohexane)} \xrightarrow{\text{alc. KOH}} \text{(cyclohexene)}$$

Owing to the lower stability of cyclopropene and cyclobutene rings these methods are not always applicable and more gentle methods are then used such as the decomposition of quaternary ammonium bases, or the removal of bromine from a 1,2-dibromocompound by means of potassium iodide:

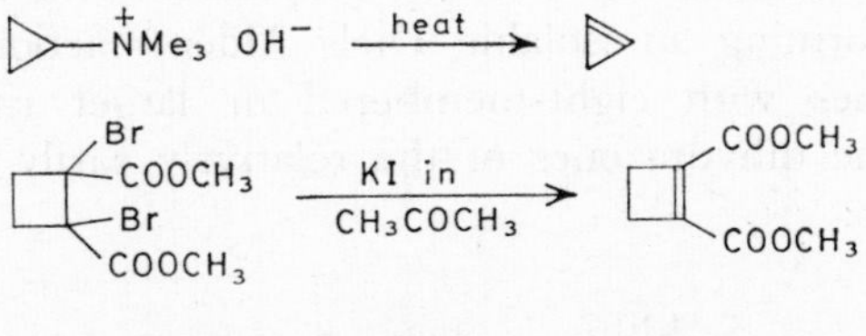

$$\triangleright\!\!-\overset{+}{\text{N}}\text{Me}_3 \ \ \text{OH}^- \xrightarrow{\text{heat}} \triangleright$$

$$\square \xrightarrow[\text{CH}_3\text{COCH}_3]{\text{KI in}} \square$$

Cyclopropene is not stable and rapidly polymerises.   It is interesting to note that none the less a cyclopropene derivative, sterculic acid has been found in nature in the seeds of a plant.

$$CH_3(CH_2)_7C \overset{\overset{\displaystyle CH_2}{\diagup\!\diagdown}}{=\!\!=} C(CH_2)_7CO_2H$$

Sterculic Acid

Another interesting unsaturated cyclopropane derivative is Feist's Acid (I), which was thought for many years to have the alternative structure (II). This acid is completely stable.

$$CH_2 =\!\!\!<\!\!\!\begin{array}{l} -CO_2H \\ -CO_2H \end{array} \qquad CH_3 -\!\!\!<\!\!\!\begin{array}{l} -CO_2H \\ -CO_2H \end{array} \qquad CH_2 =\!\!\!<\!\!\!\begin{array}{l} -CH_2-CH\!\!\begin{array}{l} \diagup NH_2 \\ \diagdown CO_2H \end{array} \end{array}$$

    (I)   (II)   (III)

The methylenecyclopropane derivative (III), hypoglicin A, has been identified as a naturally occurring plant product.

In general cycloalkenes show the normal properties associated with olefinic compounds, such as addition of hydrogen, bromine, halogen halides, etc., to the double-bond. Very many terpenoid compounds are cyclohexene derivatives. For three- to seven-membered rings only a *cis*-compound is known; steric considerations prohibit a *trans*-isomer. In the case of cyclooctene, however, both a *cis*- and a *trans*-isomer are known, although the latter is very strained and unstable. The *cis*-isomer is thus the more stable of the two as are the *cis*-isomers of cyclononene and cyclodecene. For cycloundecene, $C_{11}H_{20}$, and cyclododecene, $C_{12}H_{22}$, there is little difference in the stability of the *cis*- and *trans*-isomers.

It is interesting to note that *cis*-cyclodecene has the lowest heat of hydrogenation yet reported for a simple olefin, this presumably being due to the relief of transannular strain caused by the presence of the double-bond.

Cycloalkynes appear to be obtainable only when the ring-size is eight or greater, presumably because of the strain which would result from the introduction of a triple bond into any smaller sized ring. It may be noted, however, that there is evidence that smaller ring alkynes may exist as transitory reaction intermediates. For example, in the reaction of magnesium on 1,2-dibromocyclopentene, small amounts of cyclopentyne have been 'trapped' by having a reactive diene present with which the cyclopentyne reacts forming an isolable Diels–Alder reaction adduct. The stable cycloalkynes with eight-membered or larger rings are readily obtained from the dihydrazones of the relatively easily available cycloalkane-1,2-diones:

$$(CH_2)_n \overset{\diagup}{\underset{\diagdown}{}}\begin{array}{l} C=\!NNH_2 \\ | \\ C=\!NNH_2 \end{array} \quad\overset{\text{HgO,}}{\underset{\text{KOH}}{\longrightarrow}}\quad (CH_2)_n \overset{\diagup}{\underset{\diagdown}{}}\begin{array}{l} C \\ ||| \\ C \end{array}$$

Of greater interest than the simple cycloalkenes are a number of alicyclic compounds having two or more double-bonds.   Some of these compounds, which are of particular interest, are now discussed in separate sections.

Cyclopentadiene, indene and fluorene; fulvenes

Cyclopentadiene (IV) is obtained from coal-tar.   It has some commercial use in the manufacture of resins.   Hexachlorocyclopentadiene

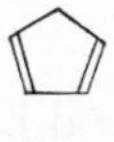

(IV)

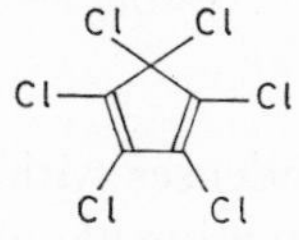

(V)

(V) is an important intermediate in the manufacture of pesticides.

Cyclopentadiene dimerises readily by a Diels–Alder type of reaction:

This dimer, dicyclopentadiene, is stable, and cyclopentadiene is usually kept in this form.   The dimer may readily be decomposed again to cyclopentadiene by distillation, especially when distilled through a platinum gauze.

Cyclopentadiene reacts as a normal conjugated diene, taking part in 1,4-addition reactions, e.g.

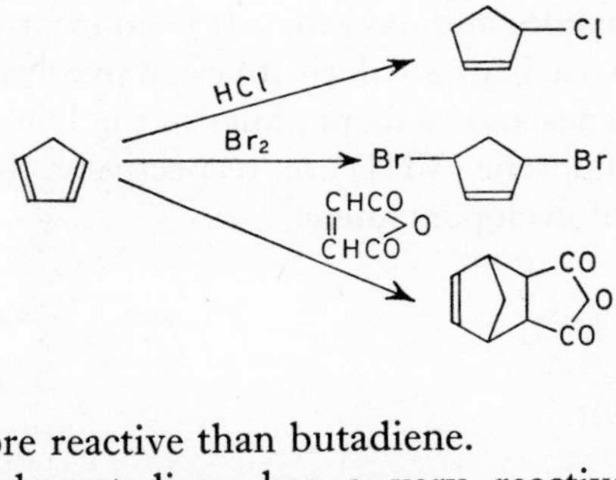

It is in fact far more reactive than butadiene.

Additionally cyclopentadiene has a very reactive methylene group, comparable in reactivity to that in compounds of the type $RCOCH_2COR$. This reactivity will be discussed again in later chapters; at present some of the reactions which are due to this labile hydrogen atom will merely be listed.

With sodium, potassium or lithium, cyclopentadiene forms a metal salt such as $K^+(C_5H_5)^-$. These salts are very reactive and will inflame in moist air. It also reacts with Grignard reagents to form a cyclopentadienyl magnesium halide, and with oxalic ester to give an oxalyl derivative:

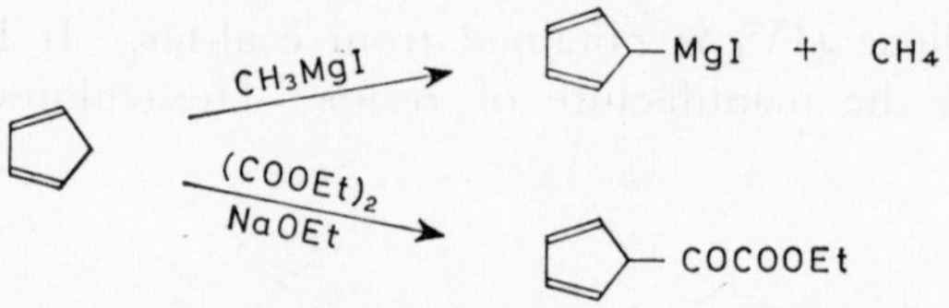

Cyclopentadiene condenses with aldehydes and ketones in the presence of bases such as sodium ethoxide to form yellow or red compounds known as *fulvenes*:

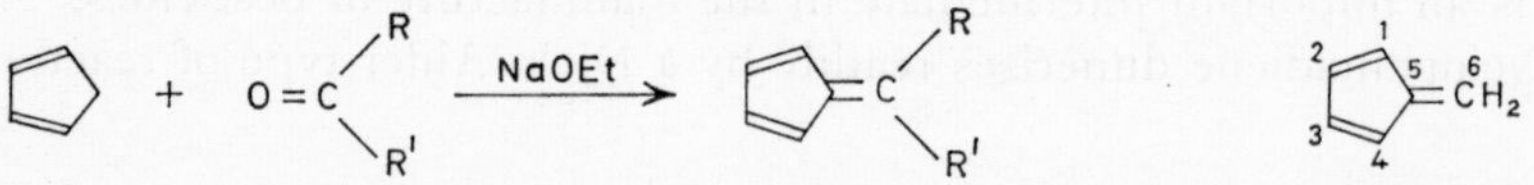

The parent compound of this series, fulvene, (VI), prepared from cyclopentadiene and formaldehyde, is unstable and in a few minutes polymerises and/or oxidises to a black oil. All the fulvenes derived from simple aliphatic aldehydes are unstable, being very sensitive to atmospheric oxygen. Increasing substitution of the 6-carbon atom [see (VI)] and especially substitution by phenyl groups, results in increased stability; it also causes deepening of the colour. Thus whereas fulvene is a yellow oil, 6-phenylfulvene is a red solid.

The fulvenes react more or less readily with hydrogen, chlorine, bromine, hydrogen halides and oxygen. It is noteworthy that they do not rearrange to the isomeric benzene derivatives on pyrolysis. Fulvenes have been used both as dienes and as dienophiles in the Diels–Alder reaction.

Indene (VII) and fluorene (VIII) are, respectively, the monobenzo- and dibenzo-derivatives of cyclopentadiene.

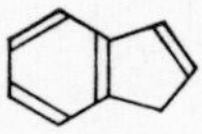

(VII)

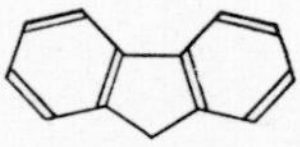

(VIII)

Indene, like cyclopentadiene, polymerises fairly readily, but fluorene is reasonably stable—not surprisingly since both double-bonds form part of benzene rings. Both compounds have reactive methylene groups and can form metal salts and Grignard complexes and can react with carbonyl compounds. The methylene group of fluorene can be oxidised to a carbonyl group by means of chromic acid:

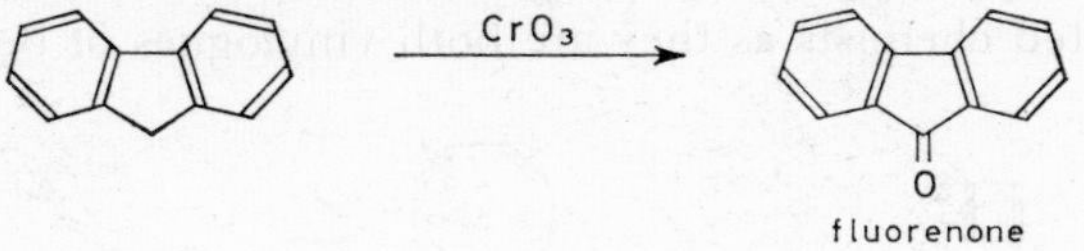

fluorenone

Cycloheptatriene

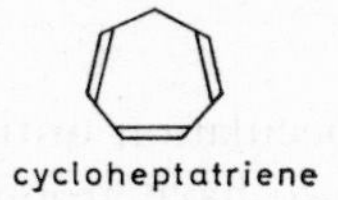

cycloheptatriene

Cycloheptatriene, or tropilidene, C_7H_8, has assumed importance in recent years because of the interest in aromatic seven-membered ring compounds (see Chapter XII). It was formerly obtained by bromination and dehydrobromination of cyclohepta-1,3-diene. More recent methods of preparation start, respectively, from benzene, benzoic acid and cyclopentadiene.

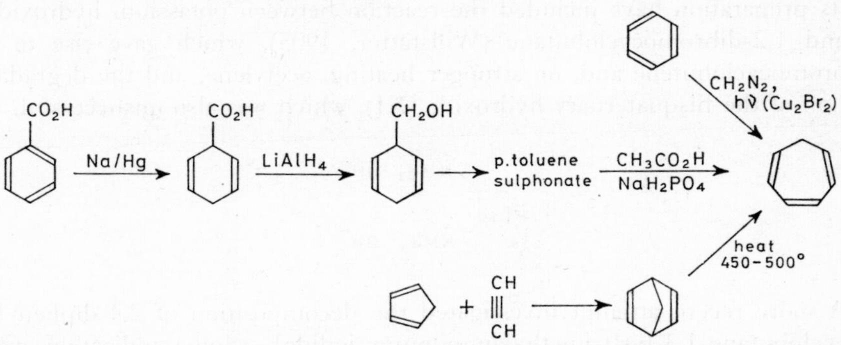

Cycloheptatriene can be reduced catalytically to cycloheptane, and to cycloheptadiene or cycloheptene by means of sodium in liquid ammonia. It readily undergoes Diels–Alder reactions with maleic anhydride, etc. Unlike cyclopentadiene it will not condense with aldehydes or form a Grignard reagent. It readily loses a hydride anion from the methylene group to form a stable carbonium ion known as the tropylium ion. This can be achieved by oxidation or by bromination and dehydrobromination.

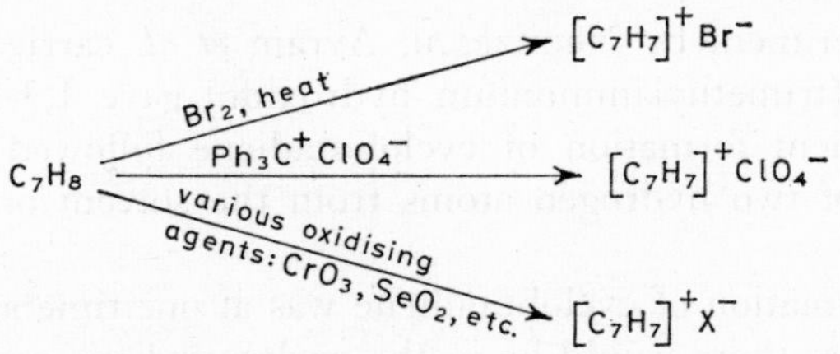

Tropylium ions are discussed in detail in Chapter XII.

Cyclobutadiene and derivatives; biphenylene

The molecules of cyclobutadiene (IX) and cyclooctatetraene (X) have always interested chemists as they are both vinylogues of benzene.

(IX)   (X)

There was considerable speculation until the late 1930s as to whether these molecules would prove to have aromatic character in the same way as benzene. It is now realised that this could not be the case; this will be discussed in the next chapter.

Cyclobutadiene has never yet been prepared, and it is now considered unlikely to be stable enough to be isolable, although there is strong evidence that it has been generated as a transient intermediate. Attempts at its preparation have included the reaction between potassium hydroxide and 1,2-dibromocyclobutane (Willstätter, 1905), which gave rise to a bromocyclobutene and, on stronger heating, acetylene, and the degradation of the bisquaternary hydroxide (XI), which was also unsuccessful.

A more recent attempt investigated the decomposition of 2,4-diphenyl-cyclobutane-1,3-bis[trimethylammonium iodide]. Some indication was obtained that a diphenylcyclobutadiene was formed as an intermediate, as a dimer of the latter was a product of the reaction.

A similar experiment by Nenitzescu, Avram et al. carried out on cyclo-butane-1,3-bis[trimethylammonium hydroxide] gave 1,3-butadiene, possibly by transient formation of cyclobutadiene followed by abstraction by the latter of two hydrogen atoms from the solvent or other adjacent molecules.

The non-formation of cyclobutadiene was at one time attributed to the angle-strain that there would be in the cyclobutadiene molecule, but this cannot be the overriding factor as the compounds (XII), (XIII) and others have been prepared, yet they must have as much angle-strain in their molecules as cyclobutadiene would have.

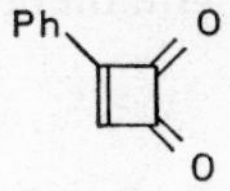

(XII) 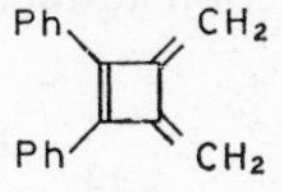   (XIII)

Longuet-Higgins and Orgel suggested in 1956 that complexes between cyclobutadiene and certain transition metals might be stable, and in 1959 two such complexes were prepared, independently, the complex (XIV) by Criegee *et al.*, and (XV) by Nenitzescu, Avram *et al.* (But see below.) The tetraphenylcyclobutadiene complex (XVI) has also been prepared.

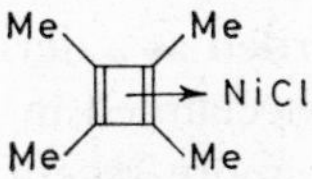

(XIV) 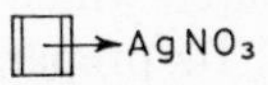   (XV) 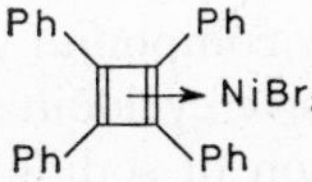   (XVI)

Compound (XIV) was prepared from dimethylacetylene as follows:

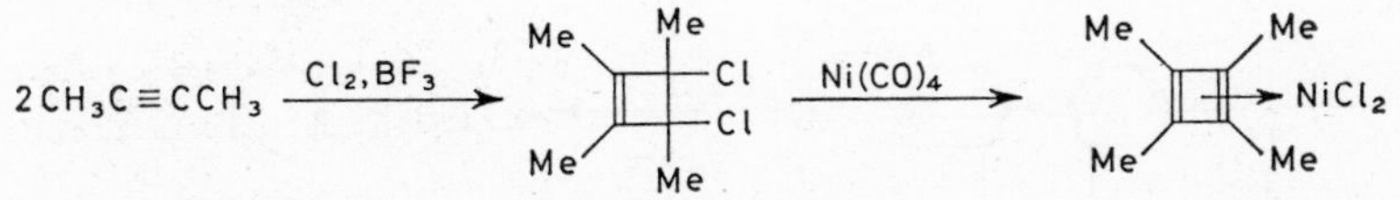

It forms reddish-violet crystals soluble in water and chloroform giving, respectively, red and violet solutions. It decomposes on heating under reduced pressure, but only at 250°, forming a dimer of tetramethylcyclobutadiene.

Compound (XV) was prepared as follows from 1,2,3,4-tetrabromo-cyclobutane; it has since been shown to be a complex of a dimer of cyclobutadiene. The dimer itself is obtained on addition of water to the complex.

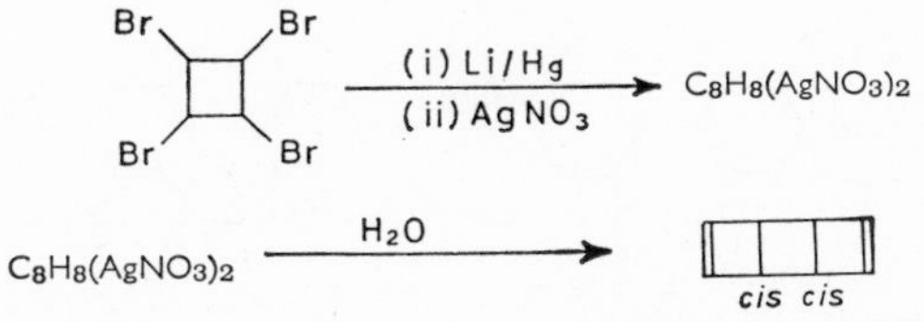

Attempts have also been made to isolate the benzocyclobutadiene (XVII), but again without avail. For example the action of zinc on the dibromo-cyclobutene (XVIII) produces, according to the reaction conditions, either a dimer (XIX), or a polymer of benzocyclobutadiene, the monomer presumably being a transient intermediate in the reaction sequence. Nenitzescu, Avram and Dinu have proved the latter supposition to be correct by treating the dibromocompound (XVIII) with zinc in the presence of cyclopentadiene and obtaining compound (XX), which is a Diels–Alder reaction adduct derived from cyclopentadiene and benzocyclobutadiene.

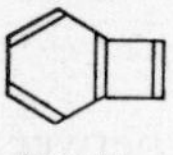

(XVII) 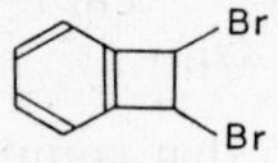   (XVIII) 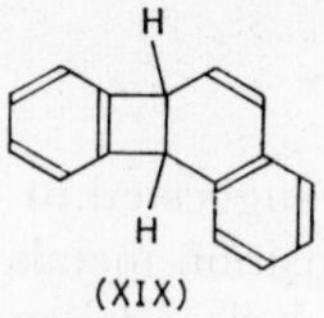   (XIX) 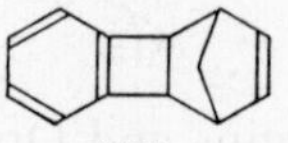   (XX) 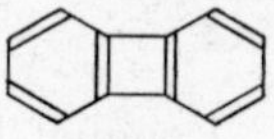   (XXI)

Biphenylene

Biphenylene (XXI) is the dibenzo-derivative of cyclobutadiene and is, apart from its own derivatives and the metal complexes described above, the only compound yet prepared which may be regarded as a derivative of the elusive cyclobutadiene. Its preparation was first claimed in 1911, by the action of sodium on 2,2'-dibromodiphenyl, but more recent workers could not repeat this reaction. It was prepared unambiguously by Lothrop in 1941 by reaction between 2,2'-diiododiphenyl and cuprous oxide:

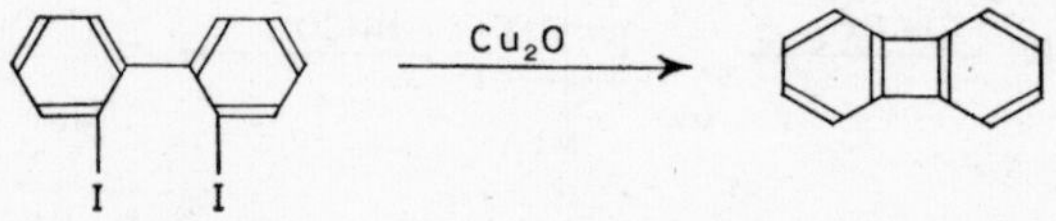

Various minor modifications of this method have since been made, especially by Baker, McOmie, and their collaborators. Alternative routes to biphenylene include the following:

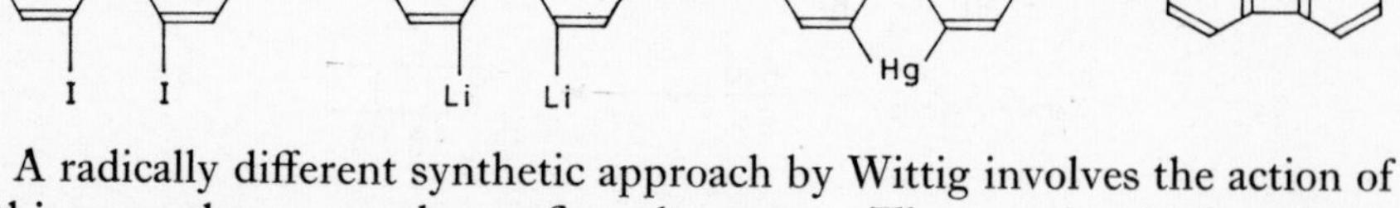

and

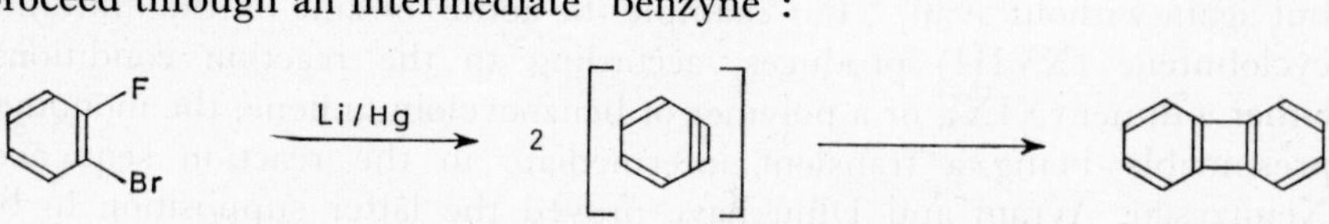

A radically different synthetic approach by Wittig involves the action of lithium amalgam on o-bromofluorobenzene. The reaction is thought to proceed through an intermediate 'benzyne':

Biphenylene might be expected to be strained and unstable but in fact it is a very stable compound. Its structure has been proved by X-ray analysis.

The only reaction yet known which involves splitting of the four-membered ring is catalytic hydrogenation, which produces biphenyl. Otherwise biphenylene undergoes substitution reactions with retention of the four-membered ring, and is a typical aromatic compound.

Substitution takes place in the 2-position, which is in accordance with wave-mechanical calculations; thus acetylation under Friedel-Crafts conditions gives 2-acetylbiphenylene:

Nitration and halogenation similarly take place at the 2-position.

Great interest centred round the reactions of 2-substituted biphenylenes as they provided a rare case where resonance theory and molecular orbital theory predicted opposing answers. Longuet-Higgins suggested, from molecular orbital calculations, that coupling of 2-hydroxybiphenylene with diazo-compounds should take place in the 3-position, whereas resonance theory suggested that the 1-position would be preferentially attacked.

Very recently McOmie et al. have shown that 2-hydroxybiphenylene does indeed couple at the 3-position, confirming the molecular orbital predictions. A parallel reaction has also been studied by Baker and McOmie, namely the bromination of 2-acetamidobiphenylene, which is readily obtained as follows:

They showed that bromination takes place at the 3-position, again confirming the molecular orbital predictions.

The lengths of the two bonds joining the benzene rings in biphenylene are 1·52 Å, which is markedly longer than the length of a carbon–carbon bond in benzene (1·40 Å). This suggests lack of aromatic character in the cyclobutadiene ring. On the other hand, biphenylene absorbs U.V. light at much longer wavelengths than biphenyl, showing that there must be interaction between the two benzene rings. The colour of its picrate confirms this, as does the position of entry of the second acetyl group (in the 6-position) on acetylation of 2-acetylbiphenylene.

Cyclooctatetraene

Cyclooctatetraene has been known since 1911 and has been prepared by a number of methods.

Its first reported preparation was in 1911 and 1913 by Willstätter, starting from the alkaloid ψ-pelletierine, obtained from pomegranate bark:

$$
\begin{array}{c}
CH_2-CH-CH_2 \\
| \quad\quad | \\
CH_2 \ NCH_3 \ CO \\
| \quad\quad | \\
CH_2-CH-CH_2
\end{array}
\xrightarrow[EtOH]{Na,}
\begin{array}{c}
CH_2-CH-CH_2 \\
| \quad\quad | \\
CH_2 \ NCH_3 \ CHOH \\
| \quad\quad | \\
CH_2-CH-CH_2
\end{array}
\xrightarrow[CH_3CO_2H]{conc.\,H_2SO_4}
\begin{array}{c}
CH_2-CH-CH \\
| \quad\quad \| \\
CH_2 \ NCH_3 \ CH \\
| \quad\quad | \\
CH_2-CH-CH_2
\end{array}
$$

$$\xrightarrow{CH_3I,\,Ag_2O}$$

$$
\begin{array}{c}
CH_2-CH----CH \\
| \quad\quad\quad \| \\
CH_2 \ N(CH_3)_2 \ CH \\
| \quad\quad\quad | \\
CH_2----CH=CH
\end{array}
\xleftarrow[in\ vacuo]{distilln.}
\begin{array}{c}
CH_2----CH----CH \\
| \quad\quad\quad\quad \| \\
CH_2 \ HO^-\{N^+(CH_3)_2 \ CH \\
| \quad\quad\quad\quad | \\
CH_2----CH----CH_2
\end{array}
$$

$$\xrightarrow{CH_3I,\,Ag_2O}$$

$$
(CH_3)_3N^+\}OH^- \\
| \\
\begin{array}{c}
CH_2-CH-CH \\
| \quad\quad \| \\
CH_2 \quad CH \\
| \quad\quad | \\
CH_2-CH=CH
\end{array}
\xrightarrow[in\ vacuo]{distilln.}
\begin{array}{c}
CH=CH-CH \\
| \quad\quad \| \\
CH_2 \quad CH \\
| \quad\quad | \\
CH_2-CH=CH
\end{array}
\xrightarrow{Br_2}
\begin{array}{c}
CHBr-CH=CH \\
| \quad\quad\quad | \\
CH_2 \quad CH \\
| \quad\quad\quad \| \\
CH_2-CHBr-CH
\end{array}
$$

$$\xrightarrow[\substack{CH_3I,\\Ag_2O}]{NH(CH_3)_2,}$$

$$
(CH_3)_3N^+\}OH^- \\
| \\
\begin{array}{c}
CH-CH \\
/ \quad\quad \backslash \\
CH_2 \quad\quad CH \\
| \quad\quad\quad \| \\
CH_2 \quad\quad CH \\
\backslash \quad\quad / \\
CH-CH \\
| \\
(CH_3)_3N^+\}OH^-
\end{array}
$$

cyclooctatetraene $\xleftarrow[in\ vacuo]{distilln.}$

The product was reported to be olefinic and not benzenoid in character. On standing it polymerised and resinified.

This work was questioned and even disputed up to 1945. Most objections were based on the apparent close similarity between the properties of Willstätter's product and those of styrene. But in 1945 it was found that during the Second World War Reppe, in Germany, had devised a simple method of synthesis of cyclooctatetraene, and that it had in fact been produced on a plant scale. Reppe's synthesis, together with other syntheses devised by Cope, have completely justified Willstätter's original claims and showed that his product was indeed cyclooctatetraene. Cope and Overberger (1947) also repeated Willstätter's original preparation from ψ-pelletierine and found it to be correct in all particulars.

Reppe polymerised acetylene in furan as solvent, and in the presence of a nickel salt as catalyst, to obtain his cyclooctatetraene:

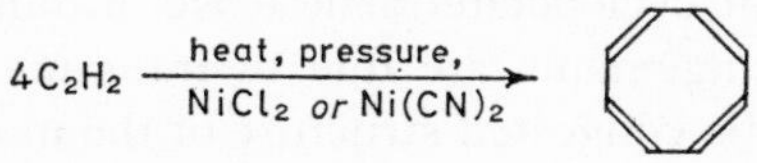

$$4C_2H_2 \xrightarrow[\text{NiCl}_2 \text{ or Ni(CN)}_2]{\text{heat, pressure,}}$$

Cope's syntheses (1950) are as follows:

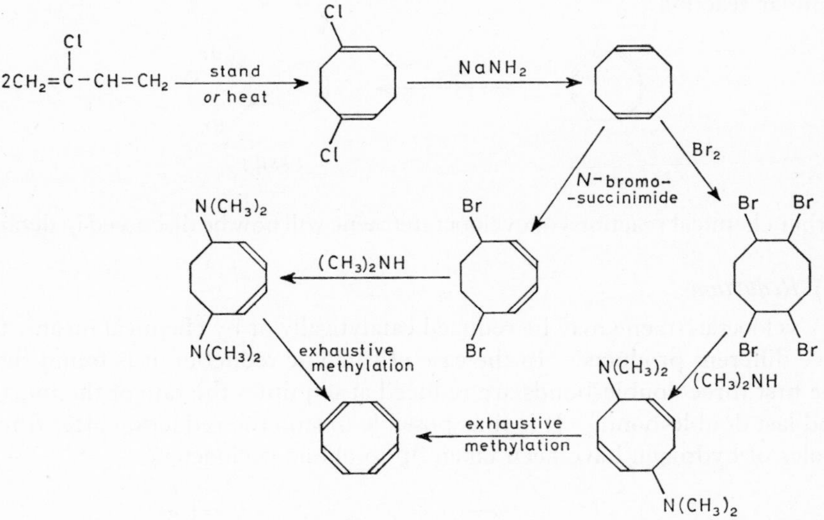

Physical measurements indicate that cyclooctatetraene has a low resonance energy and that there is little conjugation between the double bonds in the molecule. This must be due to the buckled shape of the molecule. For interaction by conjugation the groups concerned must all be coplanar, but a planar conformation would result in much extra steric strain in the molecule which would not be compensated for by the gain in resonance energy.

The chemical properties of cyclooctatetraene are those of an olefinic compound. In fact it is more reactive than simple olefins as indicated by its reduction potential. It is easily oxidised and reduced, readily adds on halogens, and undergoes the Diels–Alder reaction.

It is remarkable, however, for the number of molecular rearrangements which frequently accompany its chemical reactions. These were initially explained on the basis of cyclooctatetraene reacting in three forms, (A), (B) and (C):

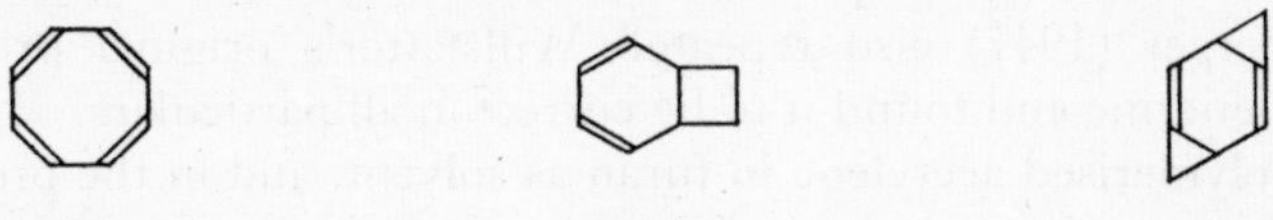

(A)   (B)   (C)

It is now realised that cyclooctatetraene exists in but one form [(A)] and that the many rearrangements are due to transannular interactions and reactions caused by the congested structure of the molecule.

Thus, addition of bromine to cyclooctatetraene gives the bicyclic dibromide (XXII) whose formation is explained in terms of such a transannular reaction:

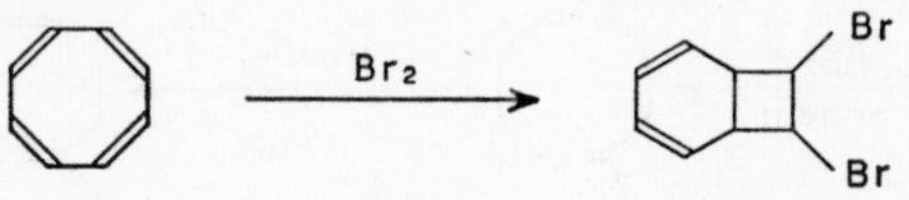

(XXII)

Other chemical reactions of cyclooctatetraene will now be discussed in detail.

(a) Reduction

Cyclooctatetraene may be reduced catalytically or by chemical means, to give different products. In the case of catalytic reduction it is found that the first three double-bonds are reduced at ten times the rate of the fourth and last double-bond. It is thus possible to stop the reduction after three moles of hydrogen have been taken up to obtain cyclooctene.

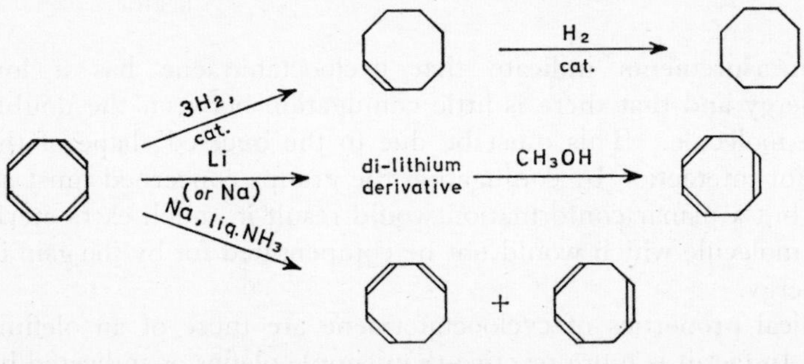

By treating the di-lithium derivative of cyclooctatetraene with carbon dioxide a cyclooctatrienedicarboxylic acid is obtained.

(b) Oxidation

Various products are again obtained, dependent on what oxidising agent is used. The final products are in each case benzene derivatives.

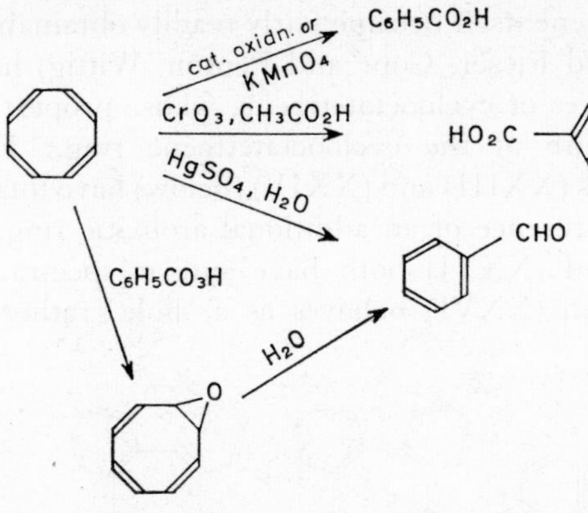

(Permanganate oxidation can also give rise to a seven-membered ring product; this is discussed in Chapter XII.)

(c) Addition reactions

Cyclooctatetraene reacts readily with the reagents which normally react additively with olefins. The products usually have a rearranged carbon skeleton and belong to the bicyclo[4,2,0]-ring system. Because of such a rearrangement only a hexabromo-compound can be obtained, and not an octabromide. Two examples of addition reactions are now given. Some reactions of dichlorocyclooctatetraene are also shown, some of which were utilised to prove its structure.

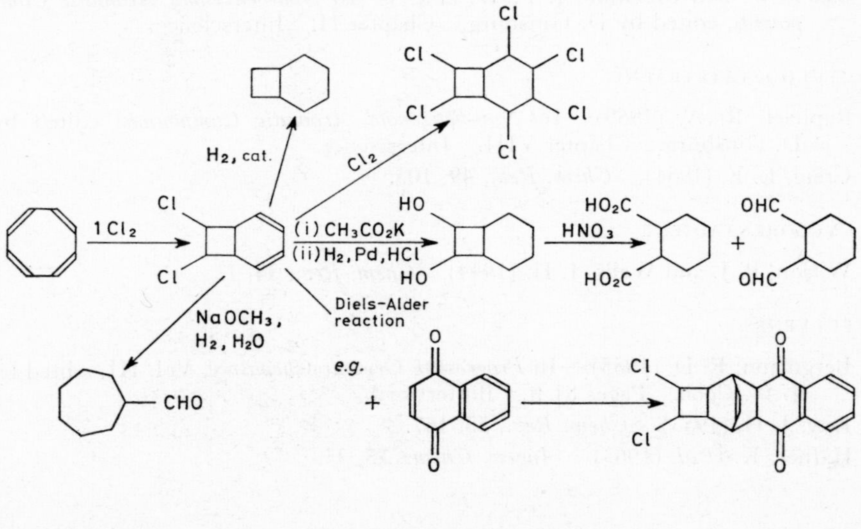

Before cyclooctatetraene itself became fairly readily obtainable a number of workers (Rapson and Fieser, Cope and Fenton, Wittig) had prepared various benzo-derivatives of cyclooctatetraene, whose properties illustrate the non-aromatic nature of the cyclooctatetraene ring. For instance whereas the compounds (XXIII) and (XXIV) (below) have totally different spectra owing to the presence of an additional aromatic ring in (XXIV), compounds (XXV) and (XXVI) both have similar spectra. Thus the eight-membered ring in (XXVI) behaves as a 'hole' rather than as an aromatic ring.

(XXIII)   (XXIV)   (XXV)   (XXVI)   (XXVII)

Similarly in compound (XXVII) the double bonds at x and y behave as typical ethylenic bonds and show no trace of aromatic behaviour.

FOR FURTHER READING

CYCLOBUTADIENE

Baker, W. and McOmie, J. F. W. (1958).   *Chem. Soc. Special Publications*, **12**, 49.

Baker, W. and McOmie, J. F. W. (1959).   In *Non-benzenoid Aromatic Compounds*, edited by D. Ginsburg.   Chapter II.   Interscience.

CYCLOOCTATETRAENE

Raphael, R. A. (1959).   In *Non-benzenoid Aromatic Compounds*, edited by D. Ginsburg.   Chapter VIII.   Interscience.

Craig, L. E. (1951).   *Chem. Rev.*, **49**, 103.

CYCLOPENTADIENE

Wilson, P. J. and Wells, J. H. (1944).   *Chem. Rev.*, **34**, 1.

FULVENES

Bergmann, E. D. (1955).   In *Progress in Organic Chemistry*, Vol. III, edited by J. W. Cook.   Pages 81 ff.   Butterworth.

Day, J. H. (1953).   *Chem. Rev.*, **53**, 167.

Hafner, K. *et al.* (1963).   *Angew. Chem.*, **75**, 35.

IX

NON-BENZENOID AROMATIC COMPOUNDS

Aromatic compounds and aromatic character

The term 'aromatic' was first applied, over a hundred years ago, to certain naturally occurring organic compounds obtained from vanilla, wintergreen, meadowsweet, etc., all of which had a striking aroma.

It was soon recognised that most of these compounds were derivatives of the hydrocarbon benzene, and the term 'aromatic' came to indicate a benzene derivative, in contrast to *aliphatic* compounds which could all be classified as derivatives of methane. This is the definition of an aromatic compound which is most commonly met with in text-books of organic chemistry, and it is indeed arguable that this is the most convenient definition of an aromatic compound.*

It was soon recognised that benzene and related compounds had a special 'stability' and that, in particular, the benzene ring had a remarkable tendency to remain intact through a wide variety of chemical reactions. This stability was correlated with the particular molecular structure of benzene. The type of 'stability' and the particular reactions associated with the benzene ring came to be regarded as 'aromatic character', and the term 'aromatic' began to mean 'having properties like those of benzene' in addition to the purely structural definition.

At this stage it will be useful to consider what these aromatic properties are. The original properties considered were chemical ones and included the following:

1. The 'stability' of aromatic systems and, in particular, the manner in which the benzene ring of carbon atoms remains intact through a wide variety of chemical reactions.
2. The relative difficulty of effecting addition reactions at the double bonds.
3. The relative ease of replacement of a hydrogen atom by what are now known as electrophilic reagents (e.g. nitration, sulphonation, halogenation).

* It is more satisfactory, however, to use the term 'benzenoid compounds', for this is unequivocal.

4. The characteristic properties of certain substituent groups when directly attached to the benzene ring, e.g. the acidity of the phenolic hydroxyl group, the unreactivity of halogen atoms.

5. The fact that not only does the benzene ring affect the properties of substituent groups, but that all these groups have, in their turn, a marked effect on the reactivity of the benzene ring to which they are attached.

In more recent times various physical properties have also been regarded as typical of aromatic compounds, for example:

1. The carbon–carbon bonds in the ring are all of length intermediate between those of a carbon–carbon single bond and a carbon–carbon double bond.
2. The ring of carbon atoms is planar (or almost so).
3. Aromatic compounds have a high resonance energy.
4. Aromatic compounds absorb light at comparatively long wavelengths.
5. Aromatic compounds are readily polarised.

It is important to stress the fact that these 'aromatic' properties are not uniform for all aromatic compounds, even when only benzene derivatives are considered. For example the extent to which olefinic properties are lacking varies markedly between different indisputably 'aromatic' compounds. Some benzene derivatives are reduced much more readily than benzene itself, whilst other benzene derivatives, unlike benzene itself, are susceptible to oxidation by permanganate. Indeed it needs to be emphasised that the chemical differences between 'olefinic' and 'aromatic' compounds are differences of degree rather than of kind. This was pointed out as long ago as 1925 by Robinson and Armit who commented, for instance, that olefinic character increased as one went from benzene to naphthalene to anthracene, yet all are regarded as aromatic compounds.

Nor are the physical properties any more constant. For example the carbon–carbon bond lengths in aromatic compounds are not all the same, nor are they necessarily all equal even within one compound, as is the case in benzene. In fact they may vary appreciably within one molecule, e.g. in naphthalene they vary from $1 \cdot 36$ Å to $1 \cdot 42$ Å (cf. aliphatic single bonds *ca.* $1 \cdot 54$ Å, olefinic bonds *ca.* $1 \cdot 34$ Å, and bonds in benzene, $1 \cdot 39$ Å). Thus again we find that the differences between aromatic and olefinic compounds are differences of degree rather than of kind.

Aromatic compounds other than benzene

Pyridine has obvious chemical similarities to benzene and, on the interpretation of aromatic character just considered, was classified as an 'aromatic' compound. Replacement of a carbon atom of the benzene ring by a suitable hetero-atom therefore need not affect the aromatic character.

At an early date in the study of aromatic compounds it was realised that there were various compounds with rings other than six-membered whose properties resembled those of an aromatic compound, thiophen being a striking example. Thus aromatic character is not connected exclusively with six-membered rings or with carbocyclic compounds. However, there are considerable (and conflicting) variations in the aromatic character of many of these compounds compared to that of benzene, e.g. pyrrole and furan on the one hand undergo electrophilic substitution reactions more readily than benzene, but on the other hand also form addition products more readily.

It is convenient to classify aromatic compounds as benzenoid and non-benzenoid, those having a six-membered ring being benzenoid and those having a non-six-membered ring being non-benzenoid. In this text we are particularly concerned with carbocyclic non-benzenoid aromatic compounds.

Theories of aromatic character and properties

Following Kekulé's hypothesis (1865) of a structure for benzene made up from alternate double and single bonds, and especially his later suggestion (1872) that the two possible forms (I) were in a state of rapid interconversion,

(I)

the special aromatic character of benzene was felt to be associated with this closed system of alternating double and single bonds.

If this were indeed the case, then it would seem reasonable to expect that cyclobutadiene (II) and cyclooctatetraene (III) would also prove to be

[] ⬡

(II)   (III)

aromatic in character. Willstätter's preparation of cyclooctatetraene (1911), which showed it to be entirely olefinic in character, and his failure to obtain cyclobutadiene even in traces, dealt a serious blow to these ideas.

As far back as 1890, Bamberger connected the aromatic character of benzene with its six 'residual valencies'. The first explicit formulation of the idea that the aromaticity of benzene was connected with a sextet of electrons was made in 1925 by Robinson and Armit, who wrote 'six electrons are able to form a group which resists disruption and may be called the aromatic sextet'. They suggested that in benzene each carbon atom contributed one electron (the other three being utilised in linking the adjacent hydrogen and carbon atoms) and that the resultant six electrons interacted together and thereby stabilised the molecule. Such a sextet of electrons represented a particularly stable arrangement. They also introduced the symbol (IV) for benzene, writing 'the circle in the ring symbolises the view that six electrons in the benzene molecule produce a

(IV)

stable association which is responsible for the *aromatic* character of the substance'.

Robinson and Armit went on to explain the aromatic character of hexagonal and pentagonal heterocyclic compounds using the same concept of the aromatic sextet, and pointed out that the stability of the cyclopentadienide ion (V) was also explained. It would have the electronic structure (VA),

(V)   (VA)   (VB)

which has a sextet of electrons, two from each double bond and two from the methylene group which has lost a proton. This ion is usually represented nowadays as in (VB). The inscribed circle indicates an aromatic sextet of electrons and the siting of the negative sign infers its delocalisation or sharing over the whole ring. The reactivity of the methylene group in cyclopentadiene is also explained, for loss of a proton leaves the stabilised cyclopentadienide anion. The fact that this ion, $[C_5H_5]^-$, is not nearly as 'stable' as benzene does not lower the validity of this theory; Robinson and Armit emphasised that all aromatic molecules would not be of equal stability. Even more to the point, the so-called lack of stability is not really this at all, but rather a greater chemical reactivity; and chemical reactivity is by no means synonymous with inherent instability in a molecule, although the terms are only too frequently used as though it were.

A mathematical basis was given to the concept of the aromatic sextet by E. Hückel in 1936. Using a molecular orbital method, he calculated that amongst fully conjugated planar monocyclic polyolefins, only those possessing $(4n+2)$ π-electrons (where n is an integer) would have aromatic character.

On this theory cyclobutadiene and cyclooctatetraene would not be expected to be aromatic in character, for they have, respectively, 4 and 8

π-electrons, neither of which 'fit' Hückel's formula.   Conversely it is also evident why the ring of cyclooctatetraene is buckled rather than planar, for there would be no gain in resonance stabilisation if the molecule adopted a planar conformation.   On the other hand, in its buckled form the molecule is less strained than it would be if planar.   Hence the buckled conformation is the preferred one.

In the same way that an aromatic anion, isoelectronic with benzene, can be derived from cyclopentadiene, so from cycloheptatriene an aromatic cation could be derived by loss of a hydrogen atom together with its bonding electrons, thus:

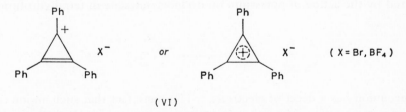

In this ion the aromatic sextet of π-electrons is equally shared between seven equivalent —CH— groups.   Such cycloheptatrienylium or *tropylium* ions have indeed been prepared.   (See pp. 145 ff.)

Peters (1960) has pointed out the important fact that the aromatic ions differ from neutral aromatic molecules in that their stable existence depends on the favourable free energy difference between a neutral form and the ion, rather than to any special low chemical reactivity of the ion.

Aromatic Compounds with other than six π-electrons

It was obviously of interest to attempt the preparation of compounds which would test the validity of Hückel's theory where $n \neq 1$.   In 1957 Breslow prepared the cyclopropenylium salts (VI).   The isolation of these and other similar cyclopropenylium salts provided striking confirmation of Hückel's theory; they have two π-electrons shared among three equivalent carbon atoms, i.e. $(4n+2)$ π-electrons, where $n=0$.

Ph   Ph

Ph   Ph   or   Ph   Ph   (X = Br, BF$_4$)

(VI)

(The dotted line is used to denote a delocalised electron system other than an aromatic sextet; for a full discussion on the use of inscribed circle formulae, etc., for aromatic compounds, see BAKER, W., *Proc. Chem. Soc.*, 1959, 75 ff.)

Some derivatives of cyclobutenedione have been prepared in recent years, which are noteworthy for being very strong acids, e.g. compounds (VII) and (VIII).   This acidity has been attributed to their structures being hybrids between (VII) and (VII A), and (VIII) and (VIII A) respectively. In (VII A) and (VIII A) there is a dipositive charge on the four-membered ring, which would strongly repel a proton from the hydroxyl group, causing the compounds to be strong acids.   Compound (VIII) is in fact as strong an acid as sulphuric acid; an additional contributing factor in this case is the high symmetry of the dianion.   In both (VII A) and (VIII A) two π-electrons are shared among the four carbon atoms of the ring.

Ph   OH   Ph   OH   HO   OH   HO   OH

   (VII)   (VII A)   (VIII)   (VIII A)

Very recently (1962) Freedman and Frantz have isolated a crystalline salt having a di-positively charged cyclobutenium cation: This salt was made from a tetraphenylcyclobutadiene nickel complex as follows:

Ph   Ph   Ph   Ph   Ph   Ph

$\xrightarrow{}$ NiBr$_2$ $\xrightarrow{[C_5H_5NH]^+ Br_3^-}$ $\xrightarrow[SnCl_4]{excess}$ SnCl$_6^{--}$

It is stable to light and dry air but reacts instantly with water and other weak nucleophiles.   It decomposes on heating at approx. 150° to stannic chloride and 1,4-dichlorotetraphenylbutadiene.

A remarkable monocyclic compound having ten π-electrons which has recently been reported is the di-potassium salt of cyclooctatetraene, prepared by the action of potassium on cyclooctatetraene in tetrahydrofuran:

$\xrightarrow{2K,}$ (10)$^{--}$ 2K$^+$

This anion has a decet of electrons.   The mere fact that such an ion can exist is most interesting and provides strong support for Hückel's theory. It is stable in solution and the potassium salt can be isolated as very pale yellow crystals which explode on drying or exposure to air.   The nuclear magnetic resonance spectrum of the ion shows that it is planar.   It is interesting to recall certain reactions of cyclooctatetraene involving the use of alkali metals in ether or liquid ammonia, e.g. its conversion to cycloocta-triene and to cyclooctatrienedicarboxylic acid. (Chapter VIII, p. 100.) These reactions must use this dianion of cyclooctatetraene as intermediate.

Macrocyclic polyolefins

Until recently no larger monocyclic polyolefins of suitable structure and planarity were known to test Hückel's theory in compounds where $n > 1$. Mislow (1952) predicted on theoretical grounds that, owing to trans-annular interactions, such large-ring polyolefins would only be planar and aromatic when in the formula C_xH_x, $x \geqslant 30$.

Bergmann (1953) prepared (IX) having a fully conjugated C_{16}-ring.

(IX)

This compound is a stable colourless crystalline solid. In accordance with Mislow's prediction the ring is buckled, but apparently unstrained.

In 1959 Sondheimer et al. prepared completely conjugated cyclic polyolefins or annulenes $C_{18}H_{18}$ and $C_{24}H_{24}$. (See p. 48.) More recently they have also prepared the vinylogues $C_{14}H_{14}$, $C_{20}H_{20}$, and $C_{30}H_{30}$. Of these compounds, those with the formulae $C_{14}H_{14}$, $C_{18}H_{18}$, and $C_{30}H_{30}$ fit the requirements for aromaticity according to Hückel's rule; only the last one also meets Mislow's requirements. In fact all but the C_{18}-compound are quite unstable. The C_{18}-compound is much more stable, but undergoes addition rather than substitution reactions. It adds bromine and maleic anhydride. In attempted nitration, sulphonation, Friedel-Crafts reactions or coupling with diazonium compounds, either starting material is recovered unchanged or decomposition occurs.* None the less preliminary X-ray measurements indicate that the compound is planar, and that all the carbon–carbon bond lengths are the same. Additionally, nuclear magnetic resonance observations indicate that the compound can sustain an induced ring current, which has been suggested as a criterion for aromaticity. (See below.) In contrast the C_{24}-compound does not sustain a ring current.

* It has since been shown that under carefully controlled conditions this annulene can be nitrated and can undergo other electrophilic substitution reactions.

Polycyclic compounds

Strictly Hückel's rule applies only to monocyclic compounds but it may be noted that the stable aromatic molecules naphthalene ($n = 2$), anthracene ($n = 3$), and phenanthrene ($n = 3$) in fact fit his formula, as does the non-benzenoid aromatic compound azulene, $C_{10}H_{10}$ (also $n = 2$; see Chapter X). Craig has suggested a modification of Hückel's rule to deal with polycyclic compounds; details can be found in the article by him which is listed in the references at the end of this chapter.

Conclusions

The term 'aromatic' has had varied meanings in organic chemistry throughout the past century. From its original straightforward meaning of 'having an aroma', it has, in turn, come to mean 'a derivative of benzene', 'a compound having chemical properties like those of benzene', and 'a compound having a particular electronic structure'. These two latter meanings are not, unfortunately, entirely interchangeable. For instance, the annulene $C_{18}H_{18}$ has physical properties (equal carbon–carbon bond lengths) and an electronic structure of an aromatic compound yet its chemical properties differ markedly from those of benzene.

There is a marked tendency at present to ignore chemical properties and use physical properties as the criterion of aromaticity. Thus Elvidge and Jackman (1961) have written: 'The essential feature is a ring of atoms so linked that π-electrons are delocalised right round the ring. We can define an aromatic compound, therefore, as a compound which will sustain an induced ring current. The magnitude of the ring current will be a function of the delocalisation of π-electrons around the ring and therefore a measure of aromaticity.' A closely related definition by Vol'pin (1960) is: 'Aromatic compounds are those unsaturated cyclic compounds in which all the ring atoms take part in the formation of a single conjugated system, and the π-electrons of this system form a closed electron shell. By a "closed electron shell" is meant a system of π-electrons such that either removal of electrons or addition of further electrons to it, increase the total energy of the system and consequently diminish its stability. The formation of the closed electron shell determines the fundamental physical and chemical properties common to all aromatic systems.'

Such straightforward definitions are obviously valuable but they may not exactly represent what organic chemists have come to regard as aromaticity. In considering the aromaticity of any compound, it is best to recognise that both the classical concept, based on chemical analogies with benzene, and the modern one based on physical factors should be taken into account; and that a compound may not satisfy both criteria equally well. Again it must be stressed that if aromaticity is linked with the possession of certain chemical properties such as a tendency to undergo substitution rather than addition reactions, this must not be confused with the reactivity or otherwise of a compound. A compound may fulfil the chemical requirements for aromaticity and yet be so reactive as to be difficult to isolate. Reactivity (so often confused with instability) depends on the difference in free energy between that of the original molecule and that of the transition state of the reaction which ensues, and not on the free energy or 'stability' of the original molecule. In any case aromaticity and π-electron delocalisation is only one factor, albeit a particularly effective one, which contributes to the overall stability of a molecule, and other contributing factors, e.g. steric factors, may in some circumstances nullify or override its effect.

Perhaps the most important point of all is the one made earlier in this discussion that the chemical differences between 'olefinic' and 'aromatic' compounds are differences of degree rather than of kind. It follows that, with the possible exception of extreme cases, it is impossible to describe such compounds as we have been discussing as purely 'aromatic' or 'non-aromatic'. Attempts to draw an arbitrary line between two such groups of compounds can be misleading; where such a line has been drawn has frequently depended on the predisposition of the particular line-drawer concerned. Rather it is better to recognise that different compounds have different degrees of aromatic character.

The various classes of compounds considered in succeeding chapters of this book all possess aromatic character in varying degrees. Because of this, and the fact that they have rings other than six-membered, they are known collectively as non-benzenoid aromatic compounds. Some of the commoner types of non-benzenoid aromatic compounds will be discussed in more detail in the following chapters.

FOR FURTHER READING

Craig, D. P. (1959). In *Non-benzenoid Aromatic Compounds*, edited by D. Ginsburg. Chapter I. Interscience.

Johnson, A. W. (1960). *J. Roy. Inst. Chem.*, 90.

Vol'pin, M. E. (1960). *Russian Chem. Rev.*, 129.

Peters, D. (1960). *J. Chem. Soc.*, 1274.

Baker, W. (1956). In *Perspectives in Organic Chemistry*, edited by A. Todd. Pages 28 ff. Interscience.

Baker, W. and McOmie, J. F. W. (1955). In *Progress in Organic Chemistry*, Vol. III, edited by J. W. Cook. Pages 44 ff. Butterworth.

Baker, W. and McOmie, J. F. W. (1959). In *Non-benzenoid Aromatic Compounds*, edited by D. Ginsburg. Chapter IX. Interscience.

X

AZULENES

THE first family of compounds to be recognised as non-benzenoid aromatic compounds were the azulenes, derivatives of *azulene* (I), $C_{10}H_{10}$.

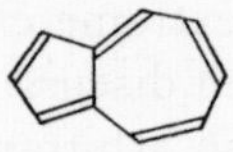

(I)

It has been known since the fifteenth century that blue colours develop in certain essential oils, e.g. camomile oil. The blue colours are due to azulene derivatives. It is now realised that reduced azulenes occur very widely in essential oils. They were not investigated chemically until 1915. Work on azulenes soon indicated that they had aromatic character for the following reasons:

(a) They could be formed by dehydrogenation reactions (from natural sesquiterpenes).

(b) They could be formed in pyrolytic reactions (e.g. in the low temperature distillation of lignite).

(c) They formed addition complexes with picric acid, trinitrobenzene, etc.

These facts were first explained in terms of benzenoid formulae, but the latter proved inadequate, and degradative work established the present formula for azulene, first put forward by St. Pfau and Plattner in 1936. Plattner and St. Pfau were also the first to synthesise an azulene derivative, as shown below. A later modification (Anderson, 1951) used to prepare azulene is also given.

(It is interesting to note that azulene was actually prepared, although not identified, by Wislicenus in 1893. He obtained it as a blue by-product in the preparation of cyclopentanone by distillation of calcium adipate, its formation possibly being assisted by impurities in the latter compound.)

112

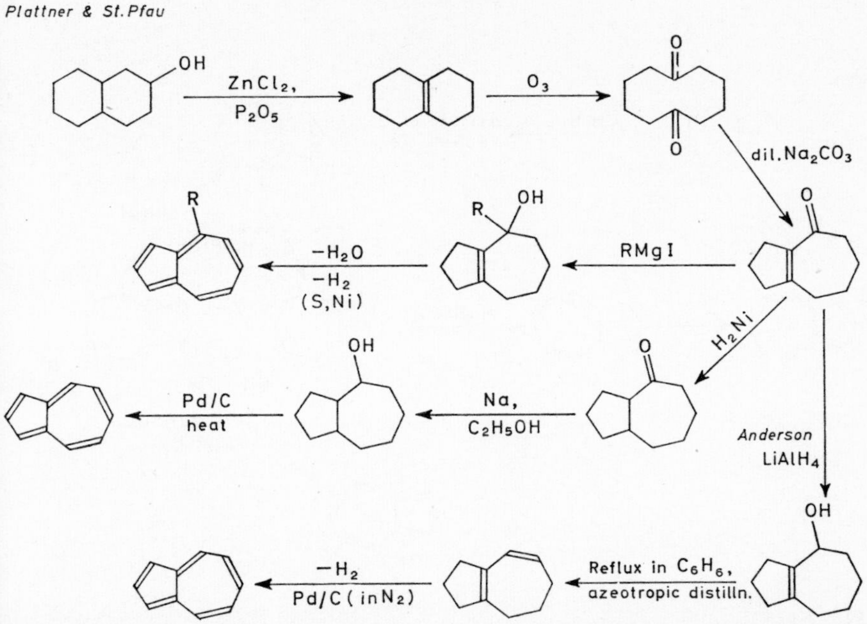

Plattner & St. Pfau

Many different syntheses have been carried out since then. Until recent years all required dehydrogenation as the last step. This is a big disadvantage, as yields are frequently low in such reactions; modern techniques have, however, raised the yields in these dehydrogenations to 60%, using molybdenum/nickel sulphide or palladium charcoal at 450° as catalysts.

These earlier syntheses inevitably involved two main types of approach:

(a) ring enlargement of an indane or indene derivative;
(b) closure of a five-membered ring on to a preformed seven-membered ring or (less frequently) vice versa.

A few examples of these earlier syntheses are now given.

Method (a)

(1)

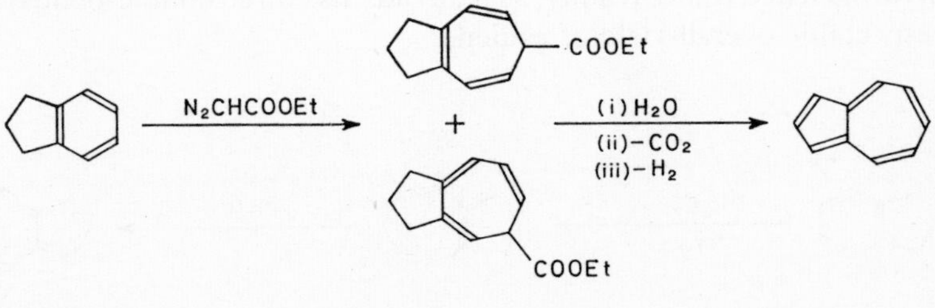

(2)

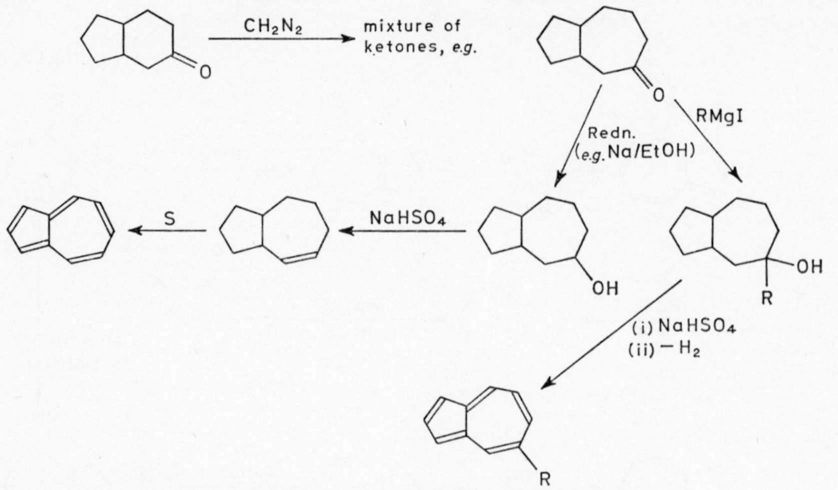

(3)

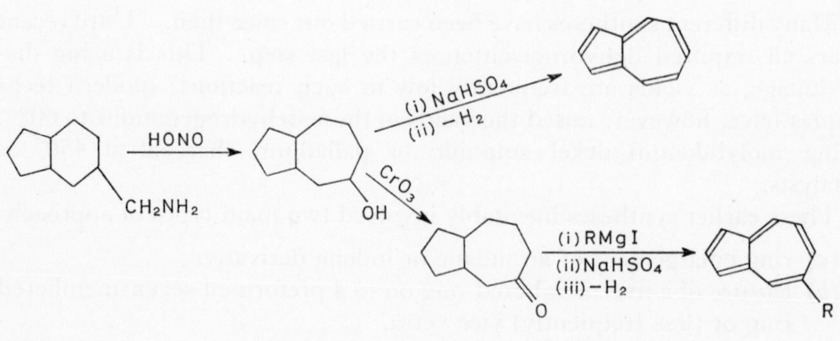

(4) A later use of this general method by Doering (1953) is elegant in its simplicity. A solution of diazomethane in indane (both readily accessible) was first irradiated with ultra-violet light and the product then dehydrogenated (more readily, as it already has three double-bonds) to give a respectable overall yield of azulene:

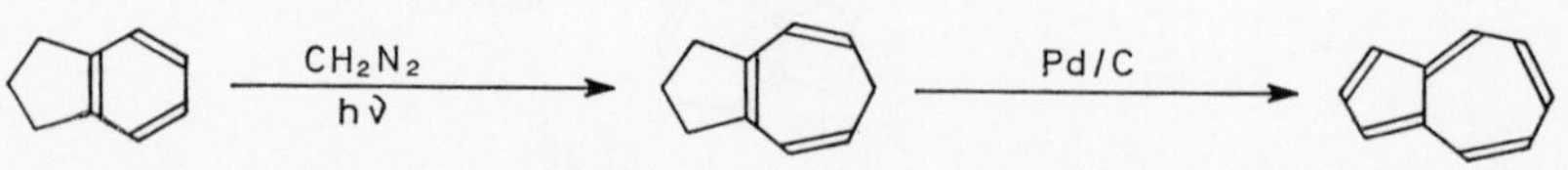

Method (b)

(1)

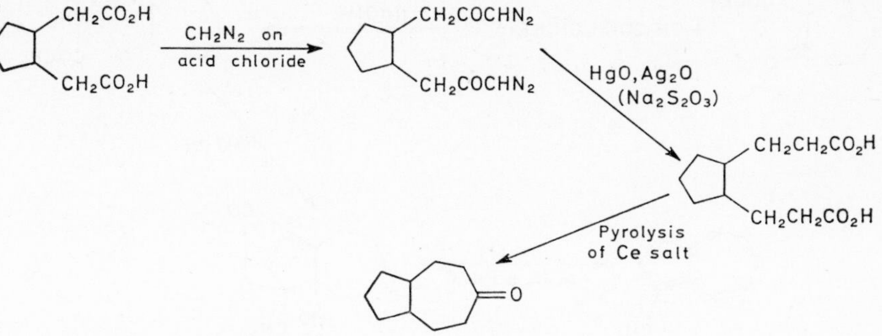

The ketone thus obtained is then converted to azulene or to 6-alkyl-azulenes as above.

(2)

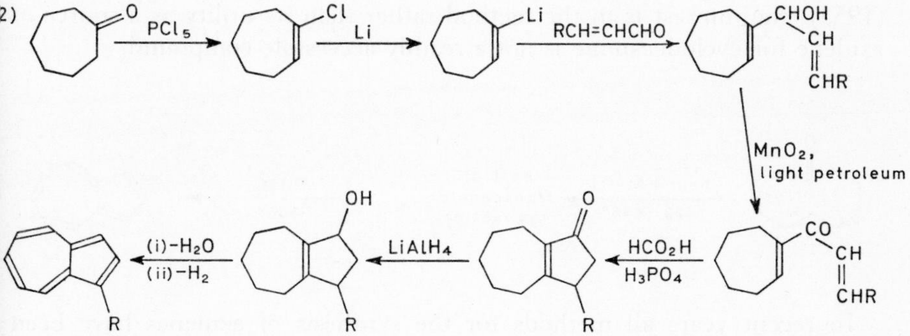

(3)

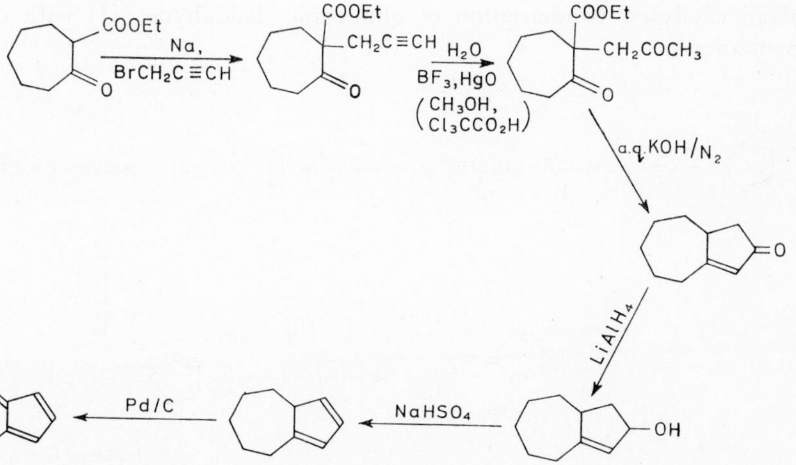

(4)

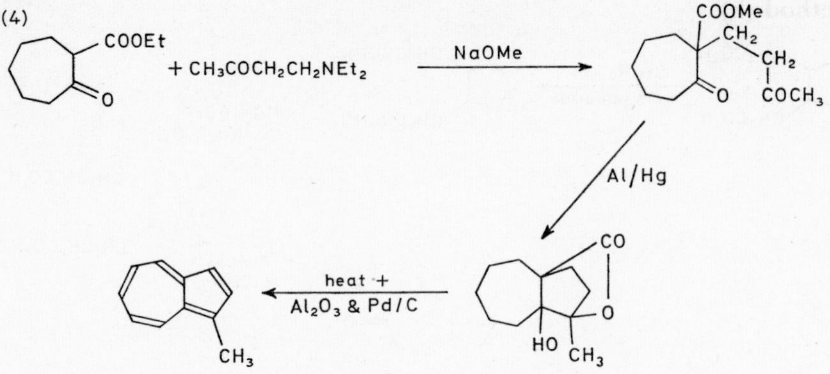

An interesting ring-closure method starting from cyclodecanone and involving a transannular cyclisation was carried out by Prelog and Schenker (1953); the interest is in the method rather than its utility as a source of azulene for cyclodecanone is not a readily accessible compound.

In recent years all methods for the synthesis of azulenes have been overshadowed and superseded by a most elegant series of methods which obviate the necessity of a dehydrogenation step. Basically they all use the alkali catalysed condensation of glutaconic dialdehyde (II) with cyclopentadiene:

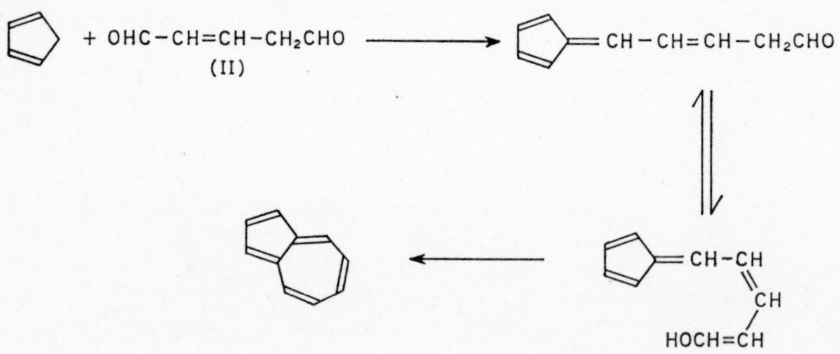

Glutaconic dialdehyde is itself unstable, however, but a di-*N*-methylaniline derivative is readily obtained from pyridine by the steps shown:

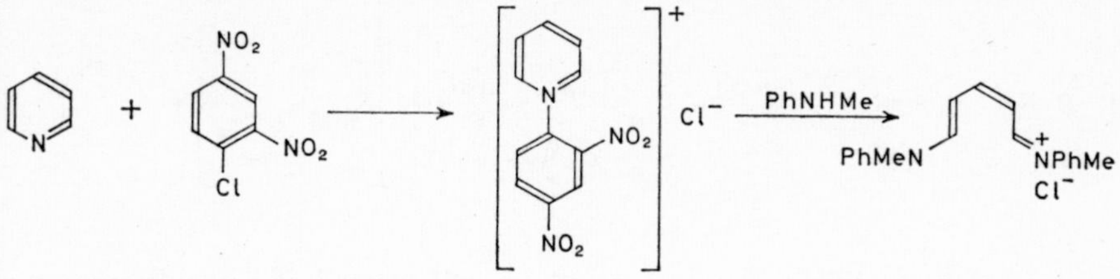

The first of the new syntheses of azulene (1955) by Rösler and König, and independently by Ziegler and Hafner, proceeded from the di-*N*-methylaniline derivative as follows:

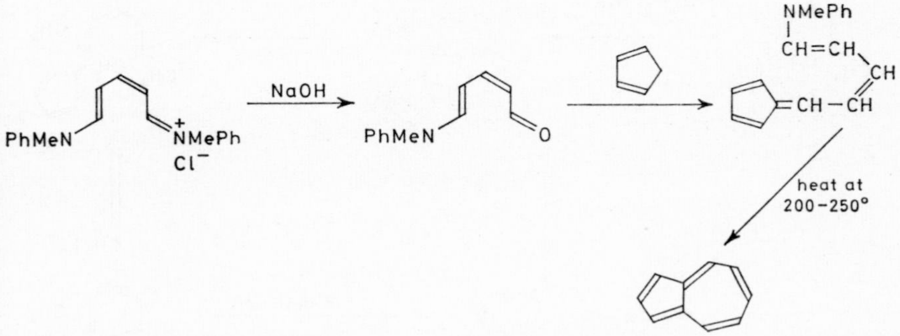

The method has been further developed by Hafner.   First he found that the di-*N*-methylanilino-compound would condense directly with cyclopentadiene in the presence of sodium ethoxide to give the required intermediate fulvene:

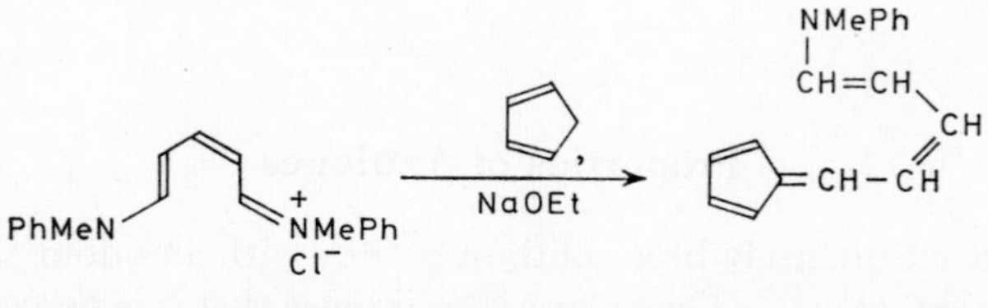

He similarly used the method to prepare 1-alkylazulenes from alkylcyclopentadienes.

An even simpler form of the reaction involves the treatment of an *N*-alkylpyridinium salt with the sodium derivative of cyclopentadiene.   A not very stable *N*-alkyl-2-cyclopentadienyl-1,2-dihydropyridine is formed, which on heating to *ca.* 200° in benzidine is converted directly into azulene:

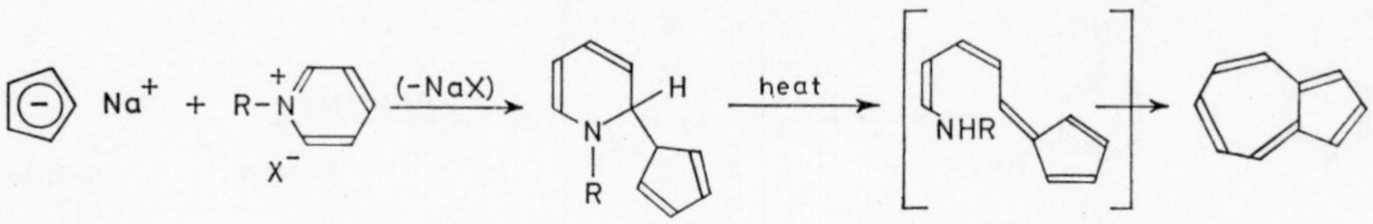

A further modification uses a pyrylium salt instead of a pyridinium one as starting point. For example 4,6,8-trimethylazulene was prepared from cyclopentadiene and 2,4,6-trimethylpyrylium perchlorate as follows:

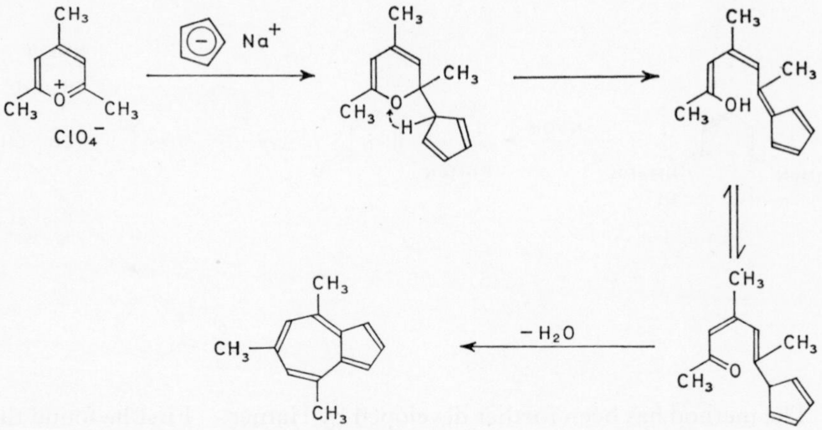

This reaction proceeds readily at room temperature; the intermediates can only be isolated by carrying out the reaction at −20°.

Properties of Azulenes

Azulene is an intensely blue solid, m.p. 99°, with an odour very similar to that of naphthalene. The colour is so intense that it is perceptible even at a dilution of 1 part in 10,000 (e.g. in light petroleum). It can be isomerised irreversibly to naphthalene on heating; this is in agreement with the fact that although azulene has a considerable resonance energy (46 kcal./mole), it is smaller than that of naphthalene (77 kcal./mole).

Reduction

Azulene can be reduced both chemically, by means of sodium and ethanol, and catalytically, in the presence of palladium.

Oxidation

The azulene nucleus can be oxidised by ozone or potassium permanganate. Some azulenes decompose on standing in air, especially if they are impure.

Action of alkali and acid

Azulenes are unaffected by strong alkali. They dissolve in strong acids, e.g. phosphoric, hydrochloric, sulphuric acids, to give yellow solutions, from which they are precipitated again on dilution. Solution has been shown to be due to the reversible formation of a 1-azulenium cation:

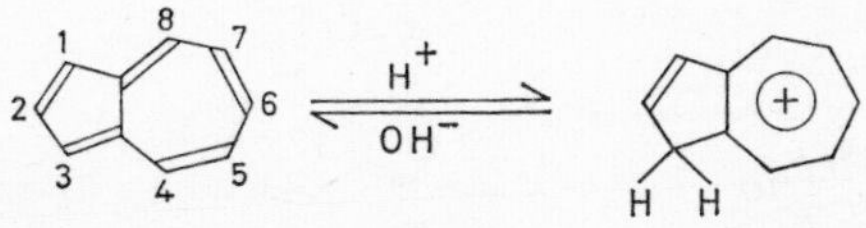

Stable azulenium salts have been isolated, e.g. the action of perchloric acid in acetic acid on 4,6,8-trimethylazulene gives the corresponding azulenium perchlorate as a light brown crystalline solid.

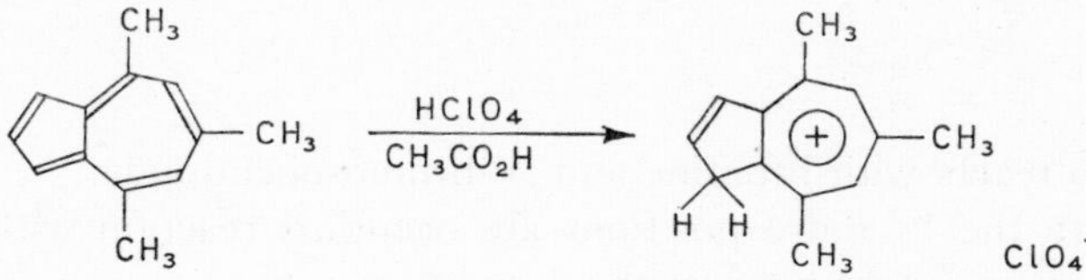

In forming the azulenium cation, a cycloheptatrienylium ion is in fact formed.

Reactions with electrophilic (cationoid) reagents

Electrophilic reagents substitute very readily in the five-membered ring of azulene, at the 1-(3-) position. Thus azulene can be nitrated with such mild reagents as copper nitrate in acetic anhydride or tetranitromethane, a reagent which only normally reacts in this way with powerfully activated benzenoid compounds. Friedel-Crafts acylation takes place without the

9—A.C.

catalyst normally necessary. Another example of electrophilic substitution in the azulene series is the condensation reaction with aromatic aldehydes in the presence of acid. Some of these reactions are shown schematically below.

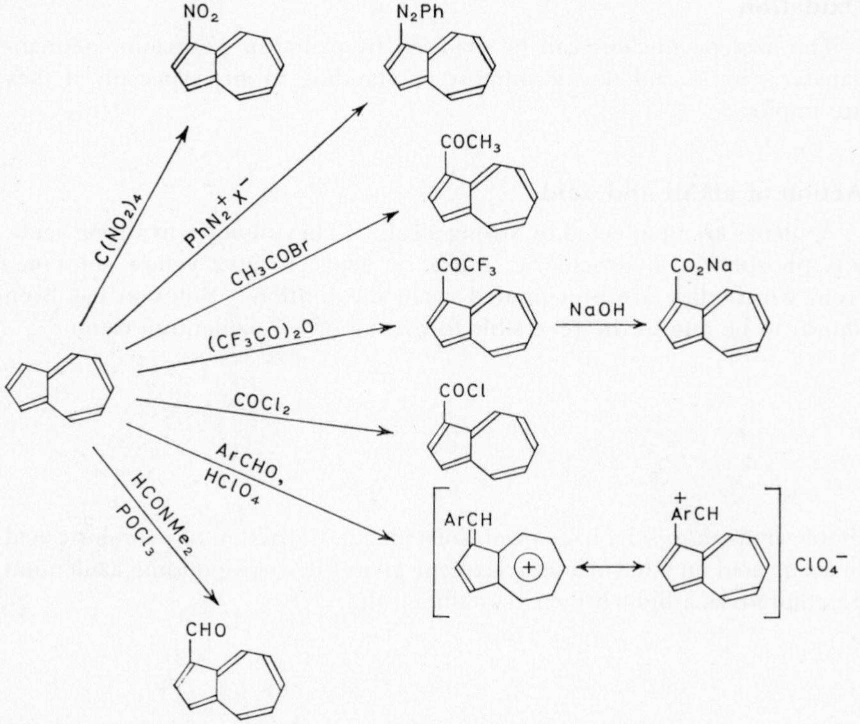

Azulene also reacts with bromine and *N*-bromosuccinimide.

When both the 1- and 3-positions are occupied reaction with electrophilic reagents may take place at the 5-position, e.g.

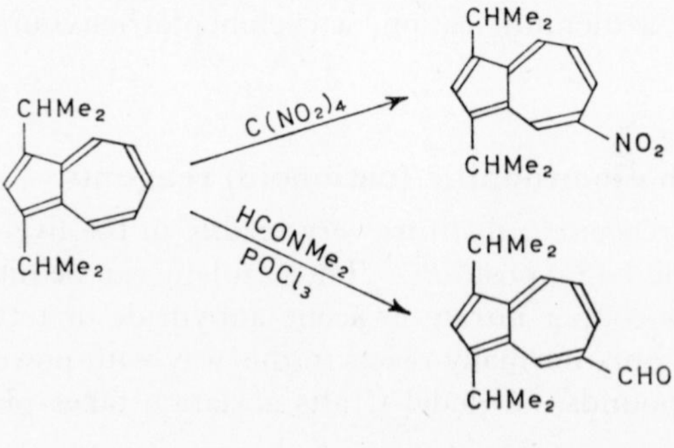

Reactions with nucleophilic (anionoid) reagents

Azulene reacts with nucleophilic reagents such as lithium alkyls or sodamide to give substitution in the seven-membered ring at the 4-(8-) position:

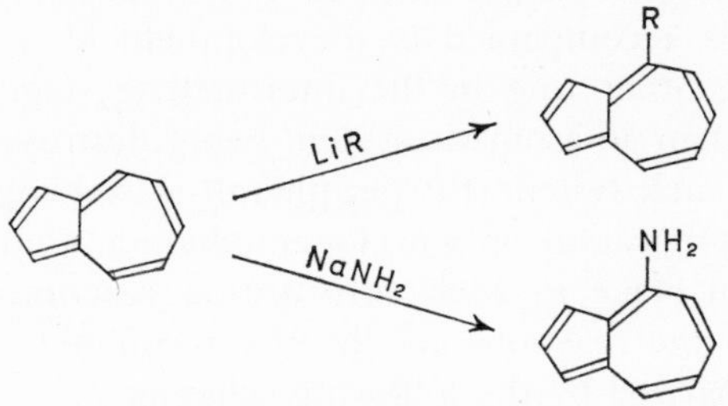

Of the reactions of azulene cited above some (e.g. hydrogenation, oxidation) resemble those of olefins, whereas others (e.g. complex formation, electrophilic substitution) are typical of aromatic compounds.

This apparent dichotomy need cause no trouble for, as discussed before, all aromatic compounds do not show the same degree of aromaticity. Naphthalene, which is normally considered as indisputably aromatic, can also be reduced by sodium and alcohol, to tetrahydronaphthalene.

Recent years have seen increasing attention paid to the detailed structure of azulene. Basically two main types of structure can be considered, a peripheral conjugated system with two Kekule forms, as in (I), or a charged structure (II), wherein both rings have a sextet of π-electrons, the five-membered ring gaining an electron from the seven-membered ring, and the two rings thereby becoming respectively negatively and positively charged.

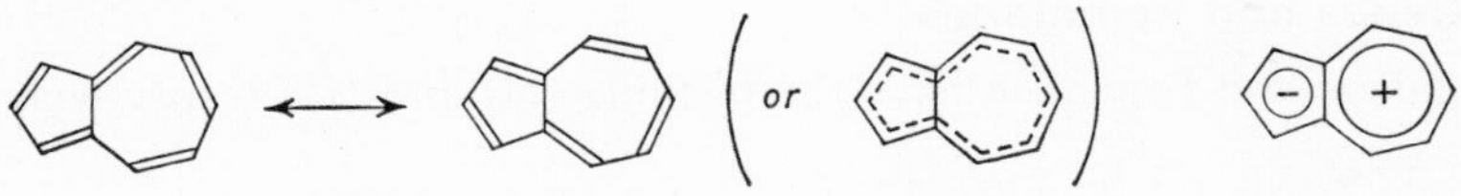

The dipole moment of azulene is only 1·0 D. Structure (II) cannot therefore contribute greatly to the ground state of azulene. It is now held that the stabilisation and aromatic character derive mainly from the delocalised system of 10 π-electrons around the periphery; this can be represented either as in (I A) or as a Kekule hybrid (I). In this structure the main function of the bridge bond is to hold the framework of carbon atoms rigidly planar, as required for resonance interaction. Thus azulene may be considered as essentially a C_{10} aromatic hydrocarbon in whose conjugated system the central bond plays no important part.

Because of the small but definite dipole moment there must be, however, a small contribution from structure (II). This dipolar form becomes particularly important in the course of reactions of azulene with electrophilic or nucleophilic reagents. Thanks to it, attack by a reagent on the appropriate ring is accompanied by development of a normal sextet of π-electrons in the other ring in the intermediate stage of the reaction. Rather therefore than an aromatic system being destroyed in the reaction intermediate, one such system (the peripheral) is exchanged for another (a cycloheptatrienylium cation or a cyclopentadienide anion). This means that the transition stage in such substitution reactions is energetically favoured and that the reactions are thereby facilitated. These reactions can thus be summarised by the following schemes.

Electrophilic substitution

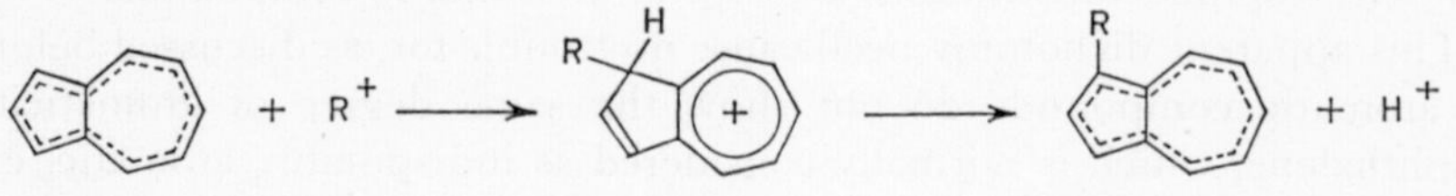

Nucleophilic substitution

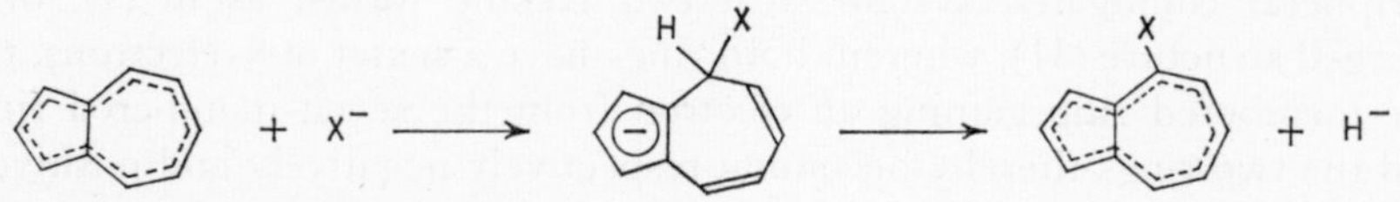

Pentalenes and heptalenes

Pentalene and heptalene have the formulae (I) and (II) respectively.

(I)   (II)

An amount of unsuccessful work has been devoted to attempted syntheses of these hydrocarbons. As they should have completely conjugated ring systems, it was at one time thought possible that they might have some aromatic character. More recent ideas, taking into account the Hückel

Rule, lend no support to such a possibility. No simple pentalene has yet been prepared but very recently a synthesis of heptalene has been described. The method of preparation was as follows:

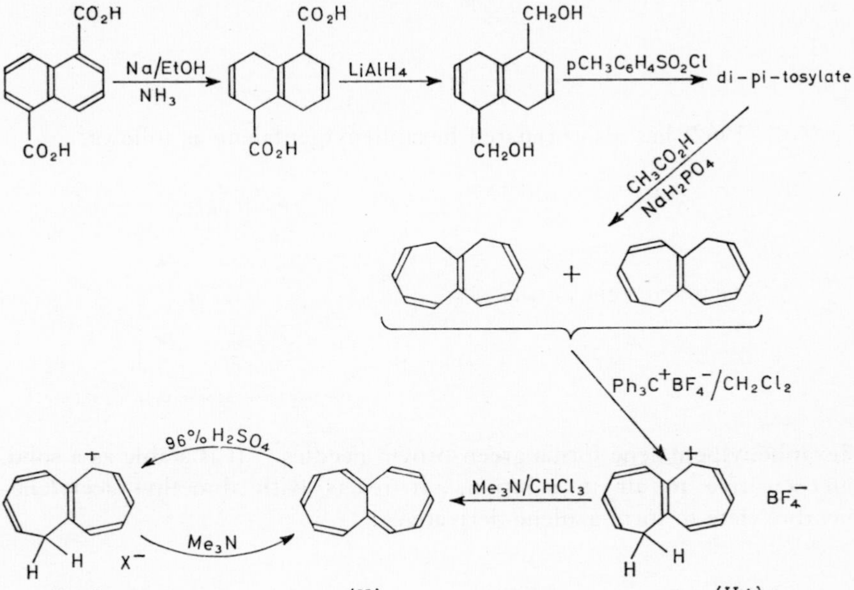

CO$_2$H CO$_2$H CH$_2$OH

$\xrightarrow[\text{NH}_3]{\text{Na/EtOH}}$ $\xrightarrow{\text{LiAlH}_4}$ $\xrightarrow{\text{pCH}_3\text{C}_6\text{H}_4\text{SO}_2\text{Cl}}$ di−pi−tosylate

CO$_2$H CO$_2$H CH$_2$OH

$\xrightarrow[\text{NaH}_2\text{PO}_4]{\text{CH}_3\text{CO}_2\text{H}}$

+

$\xrightarrow{\text{Ph}_3\text{C}^+\text{BF}_4^-/\text{CH}_2\text{Cl}_2}$

+

BF$_4^-$

$\xleftarrow{\text{Me}_3\text{N/CHCl}_3}$

(II A)

96% H$_2$SO$_4$

+

$\xrightarrow{\text{Me}_3\text{N}}$

H H X$^-$

(II B) (II)

Heptalene proved to be a yellowish- or reddish-brown liquid which is very sensitive to oxygen, readily polymerising in its presence. It can be reduced to bicyclo-[5,5,0]-dodecane. It forms tropylium type salts (see chapter XII) such as (II A) and (II B) above; the tetrafluoroborate is a yellow crystalline material.

Linstead (1952) synthesised the bronze coloured compound dibenz-pentalene (III), but it shows no aromatic character in its five-membered rings. It behaves like a conjugated diene and polymerises readily.

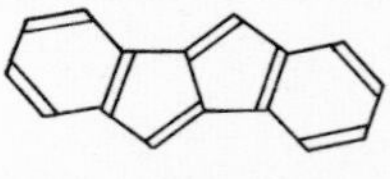

(III)

A monobenzopentalene (IV) has been prepared recently by Le Goff (1962). It is a green compound which is stable to heat, air, and moderately strong acid. It is slowly destroyed by stronger acids. It reacts readily with nucleophilic reagents.

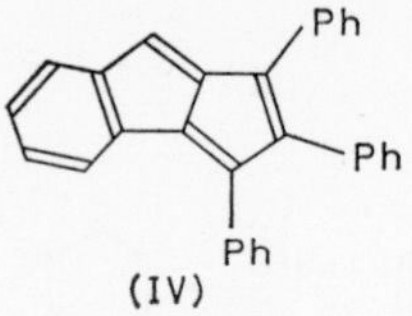

(IV)

Le Goff (1962) has also prepared hexaphenylpentalene as follows:

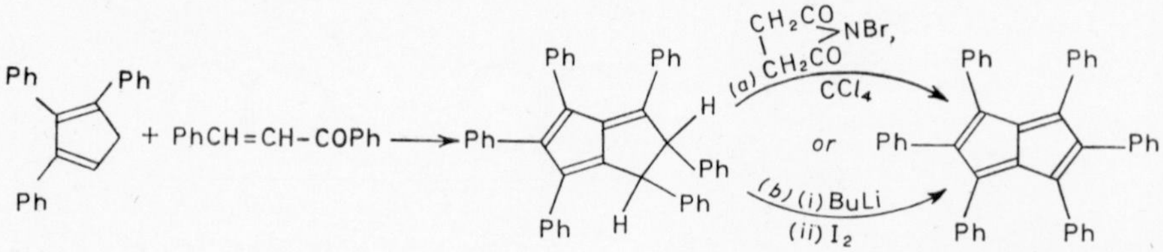

[method (b) is poorer than method (a)]

Hexaphenylpentalene forms green-brown needles. It is stable as a solid, but sensitive to air in solution. It reacts with dimethyl acetylene-dicarboxylate to form azulene derivatives:

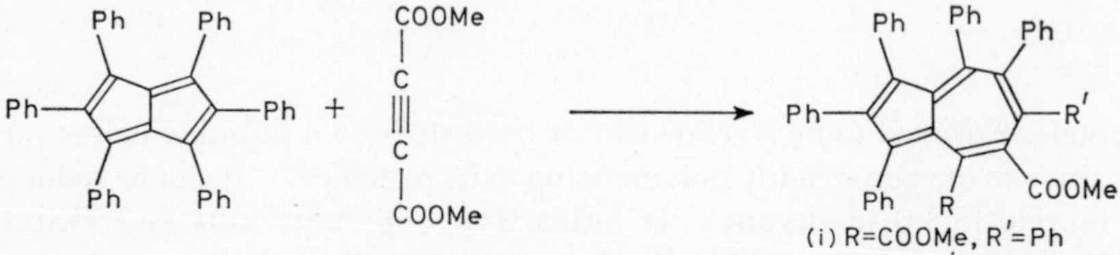

(i) R=COOMe, R'=Ph
(ii) R=Ph, R'=COOMe

Hafner (1958) prepared the heptalene derivative (V) as a stable red crystalline product which shows aromatic properties, but this is, of course, a rather special case as the accompanying five-membered ring can interact with the seven-membered rings as in azulenes. Compound (V) dissolves in organic solvents to give green solutions. Hafner also prepared the

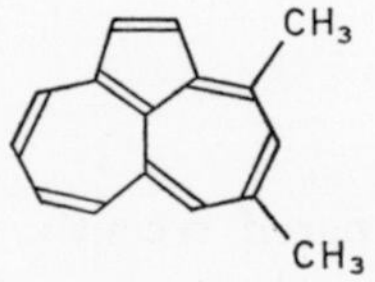

(V)

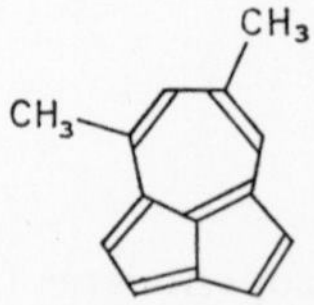

(VI)

yellow-brown pentalene derivative (VI), but this compound is very unstable, has no aromatic properties, and resembles Linstead's dibenzo-
pentalene.

A dianion derived from pentalene has also been prepared very recently
(see p. 154).

FOR FURTHER READING

Heilbronner, E.; Keller-Schierlien, W. and Heilbronner, E. (1959). In *Non-benzenoid Aromatic Compounds*, edited by D. Ginsburg. Chapters 5–6. Interscience.

Nozoe, T. and Ito, S. (1961). In *Progress in the Chemistry of Natural Products*, XIX, edited by L. Zechmeister. Pages 32 ff. Springer.

Reid, D. H. (1958). *Chem. Soc. Special Publications*, **12**, 69.

Hafner, K. (1958). *Angew. Chem.*, **70**, 419.

Gordon, M. (1952). *Chem. Rev.*, **50**, 127.

PENTALENES AND HEPTALENES

Bergmann, E. D. (1959). In *Non-benzenoid Aromatic Compounds*, edited by D. Ginsburg. Chapter 4. Interscience.

XI

AROMATIC SEVEN-MEMBERED RING COMPOUNDS

Tropones and tropolones

In 1942 a compound called stipitatic acid was isolated from a mould (*penicillium stipitatum* Thom); two other related acids, puberulic acid and puberulonic acid, were also isolated from other moulds.

The molecular formula of stipitatic acid was shown to be $C_8H_6O_5$, but despite the apparent simplicity no satisfactory structural formula could be advanced. Its chemical properties were as follows:

Of the five oxygen atoms, two were in a carboxyl group and two in enolic hydroxyl groups, one of which was more acidic than the other. The remaining oxygen atom appeared to be part of a 'masked' carbonyl group; although stipitatic acid itself was unresponsive to carbonyl reagents a normal carbonyl group appeared on hydrogenation.

Stipitatic acid reacted with three molecules of diazomethane to give *two* isomeric trimethyl derivatives, $C_7H_3O(OMe)_2CO_2Me$.

On fusion with alkali it was isomerised to 5-hydroxyisophthalic acid (I).

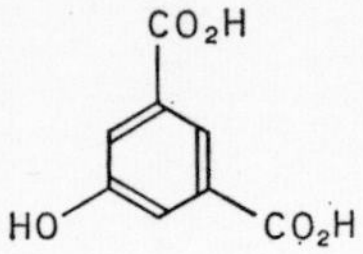

(I)	(II)	(III)

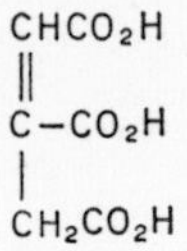

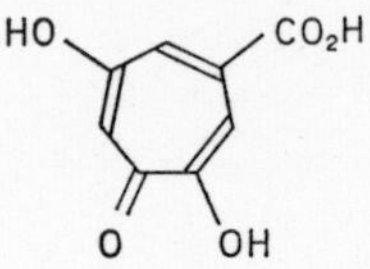

It did not behave as a normal olefin—thus with bromine in glacial acetic acid a bromo-substituted product was formed instead of any addition reaction taking place.

It dissolved in concentrated hydrochloric or nitric acids, and could be recovered unchanged on dilution of these acid solutions with water.

Oxidation gave a mixture of malonic acid and aconitic acid (II).

126

In 1945 M. J. S. Dewar suggested the formula (III) for stipitatic acid. He also suggested that the parent ring system (IV), which he called *tropolone* might possess aromatic character, ascribing this to resonance between such forms as (V) and (VI), and also the tautomers (VII) and (VIII). He also pointed out the resemblance between tropolone and an

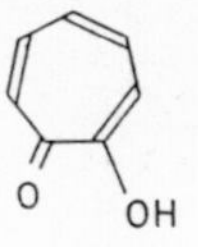

(IV) 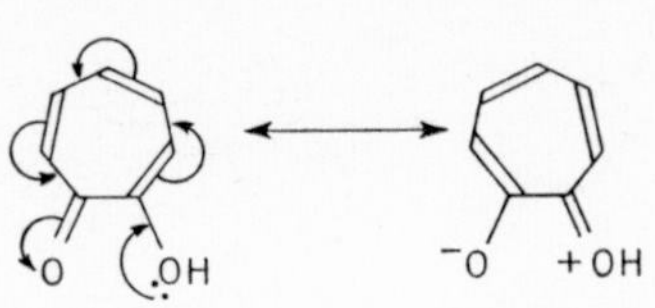　　　　(V)　　　　(VI) 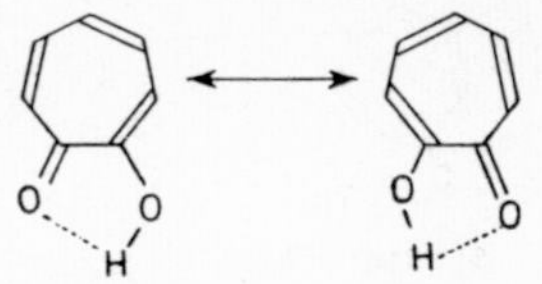　　　　(VII)　　　　(VIII)

extended carboxyl group:

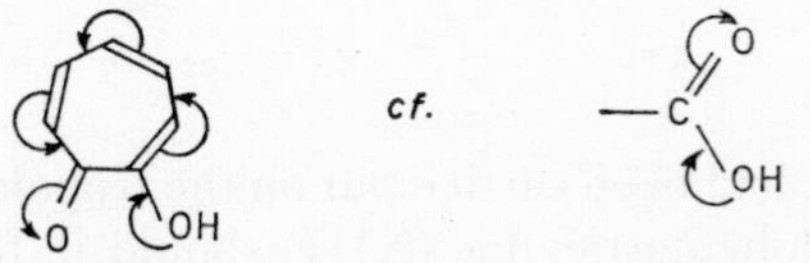

In conformity with these suggestions it was shown that no isomers of the type (IX) and (X) could be isolated. On the other hand the existence of two isomeric trimethyl derivatives of stipitatic acid was explained, i.e. (XI) and (XII), which cannot undergo tautomeric change in the way that (VII) and (VIII) (or (IX) and (X)) can.

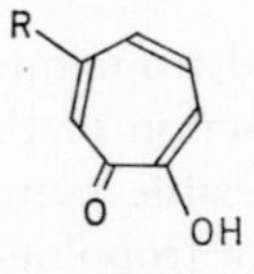

(IX) 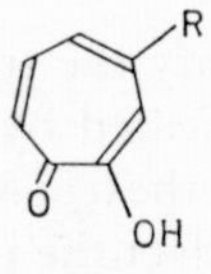　　　　(X) 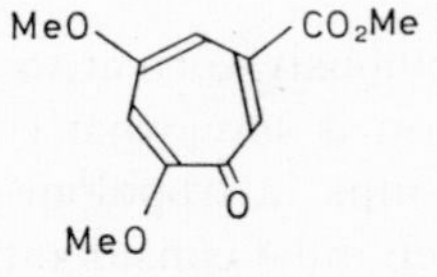　　　　(XI) 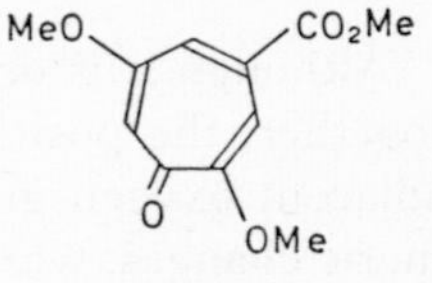　　　　(XII)

Formula (III) is now accepted as the correct one for stipitatic acid. Puberulic acid and puberulonic acid were also shown to be tropolone derivatives, as were α-, β-, and γ-thujaplicin, found in the heartwood of red cedar, and purpurogallin, formed by oxidation of pyrogallol. (See over.)

Since then numerous other tropolone derivatives have been found in nature.

Some years after Dewar's suggestions had been published it was found that workers in Japan, headed by Nozoe, had quite independently studied the structure of various tropolone derivatives from 1942 onwards, and had proposed the same solution to the problem of their structure.

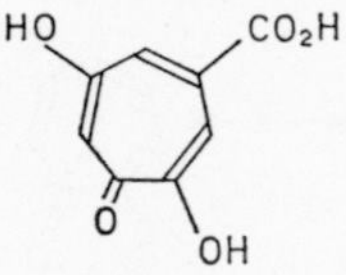

Stipitatic Acid 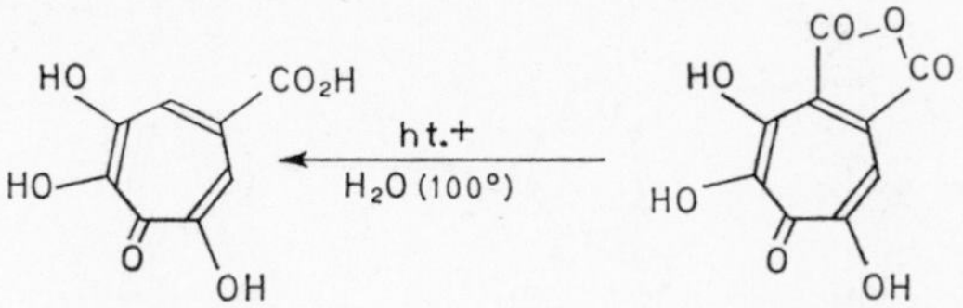   Puberulic Acid   Puberulonic Acid

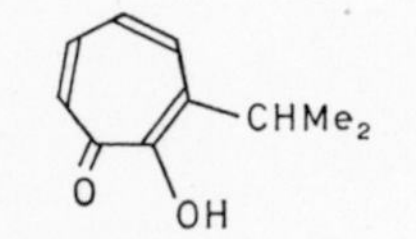

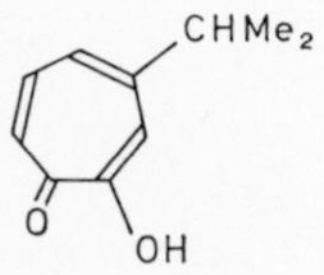

α–Thujaplicin   β–Thujaplicin   ɤ–Thujaplicin 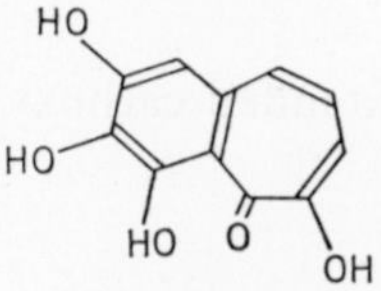   Purpurogallin

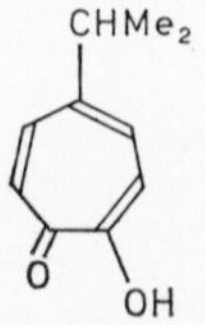

After much work had been carried out on the tropolones it was suggested that *tropone* or cycloheptatrienone (XIII) should in fact be more suitably regarded as the parent compound of this series of aromatic seven-membered ring compounds, and that tropolone might be thought of as a 'phenol' derived from tropone.   Tropone itself was first synthesised in 1951.

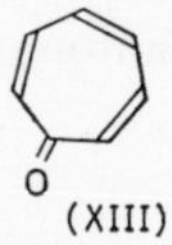

(XIII)

Although it is obviously correct to classify the tropones and tropolones together, the position is somewhat complicated by the interaction of the adjacent oxygen groups in tropolone and the consequent possible tautomeric changes, which must considerably affect the properties of tropolone. Aromatic character is in fact more fully developed in tropolone than in tropone.

Syntheses of tropolones

Tropolone syntheses may be grouped into three main classes, (*a*) syntheses starting from preformed seven-membered rings, (*b*) condensation reactions leading to a tropolone ring, (*c*) ring-expansion of benzene rings.   Examples of these methods are now given.

(a) Syntheses starting from preformed seven-membered rings

Cook, in Britain, and Nozoe, in Japan, and their co-workers developed the first syntheses of tropolones, from cycloheptane-1,2-dione as starting material.

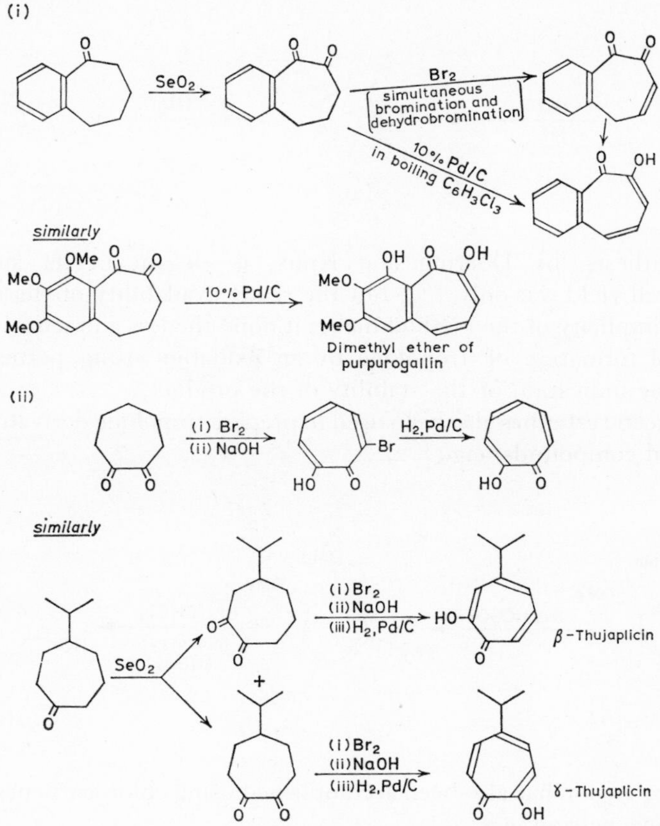

(i)

similarly

Dimethyl ether of purpurogallin

(ii)

similarly

β-Thujaplicin

γ-Thujaplicin

(b) Condensation reactions leading directly to a tropolone ring

Phthalaldehyde condenses with hydroxyacetone or its ethers to give βγ-benztropolone (or an ether).

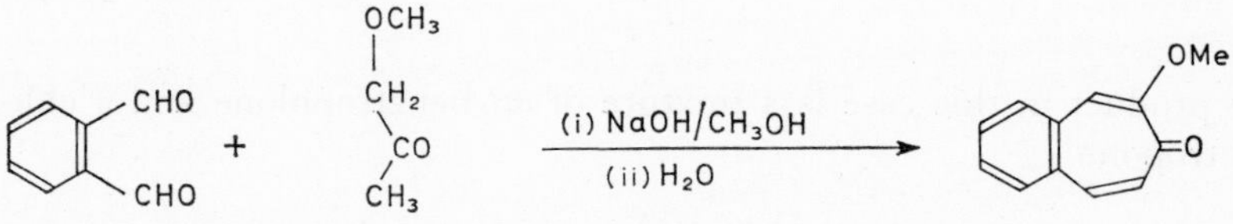

Attempts to use maleic dialdehyde in place of phthaldehyde have been unsuccessful.

(c) Ring expansion of benzene rings

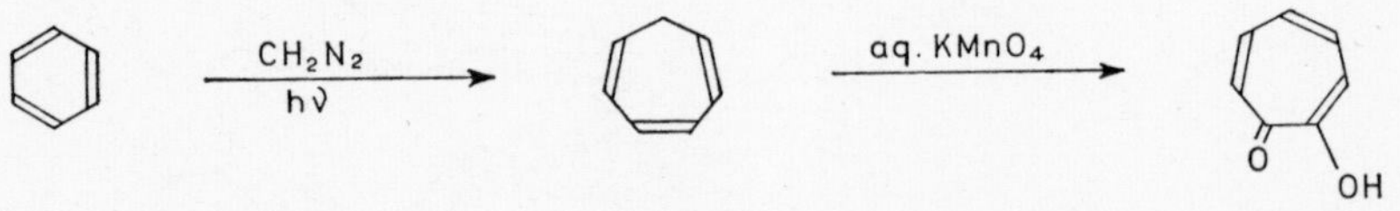

This synthesis, by Doering and Knox, is elegant in its simplicity. The overall yield was only 1%, but the ready availability of the reactants and the simplicity of the method makes it none the less a practical method. The final formation of tropolone by an oxidation using permanganate gives some indication of the stability of the product.

Diazoacetic ester has also been used to prepare tropolone derivatives from benzenoid compounds, e.g.

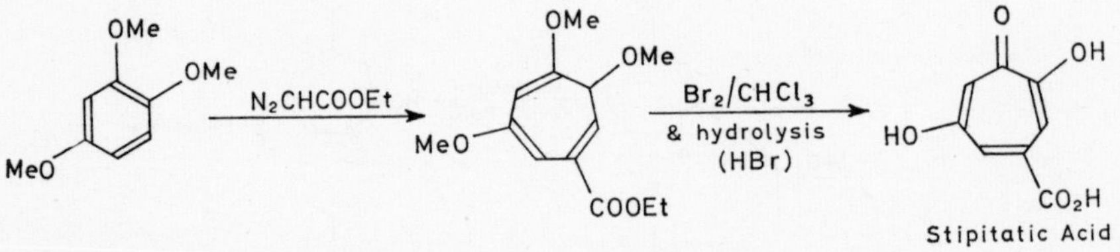

Ring expansion has also been accomplished using chlorocarbenes to react with a benzene ring, e.g.

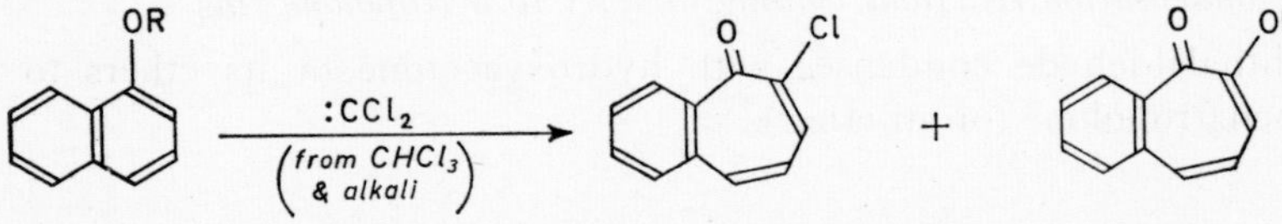

The product in this case is a mixture of $\alpha\beta$-benztropolone and a chloro-benztropone.

(d) Other syntheses of tropolones

Other recent syntheses of tropolones include the following interesting methods.

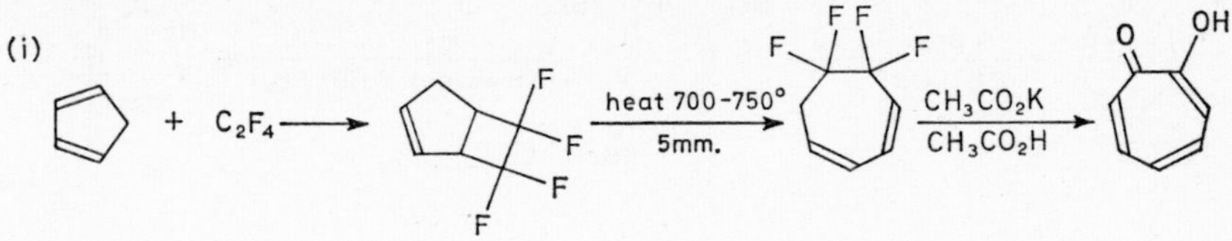

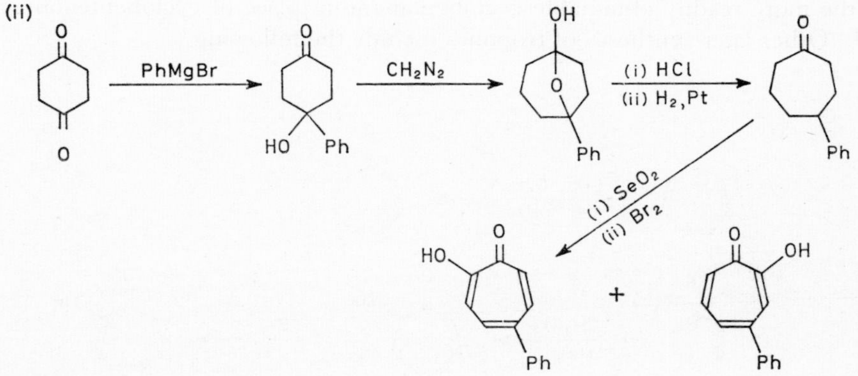

(i)

(ii)

Syntheses of tropones

Tropone was synthesized for the first time in 1951, independently and simultaneously by Dauben and Ringold and by Doering and Detert. Their respective methods were:

Doering and Detert

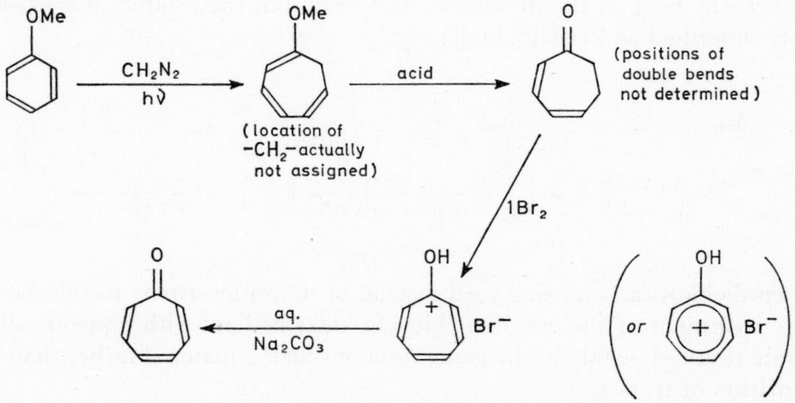

Dauben and Ringold

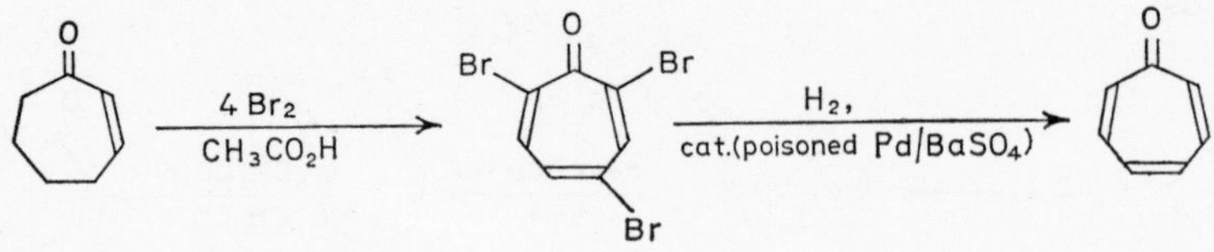

A year later Nozoe published a similar synthesis to that of Dauben but using the more readily obtainable cycloheptanone in place of cycloheptenone.

Other later syntheses of tropones include the following.

(i)

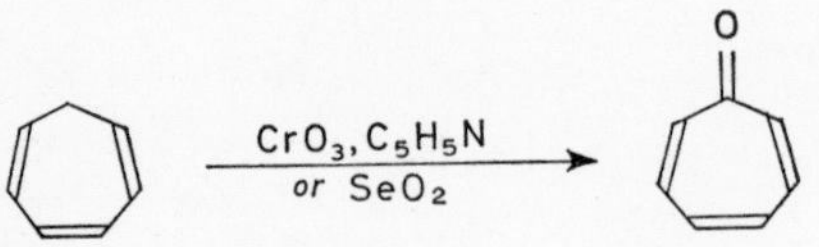

(ii)

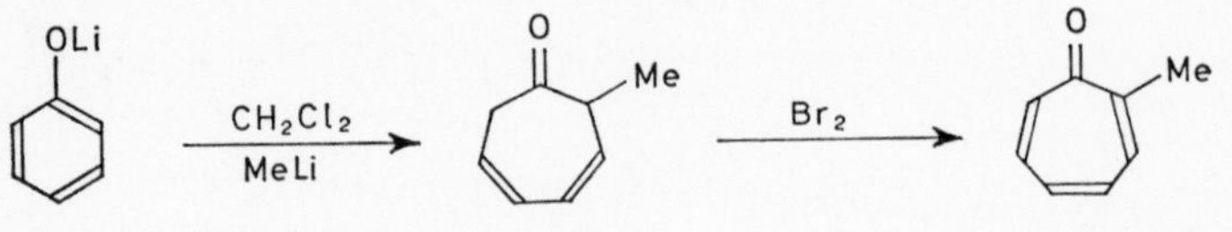

(iii)

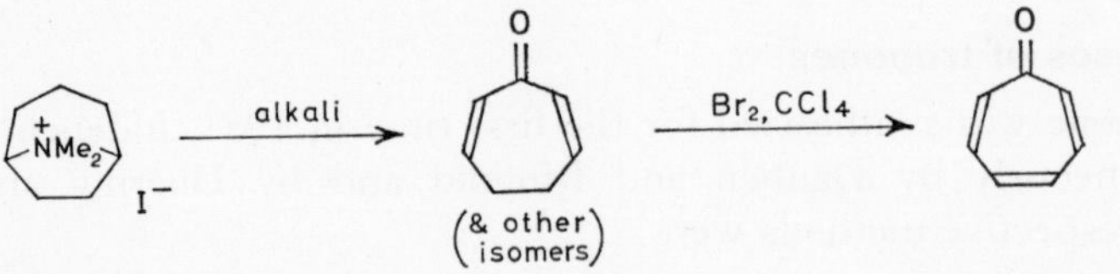

$\begin{pmatrix}\& \text{ other}\\ \text{isomers}\end{pmatrix}$

It is interesting to note that this last synthesis, from tropinone methiodide, has actually been in the literature since 1887, but the product was erroneously described as benzaldehyde.

(iv)

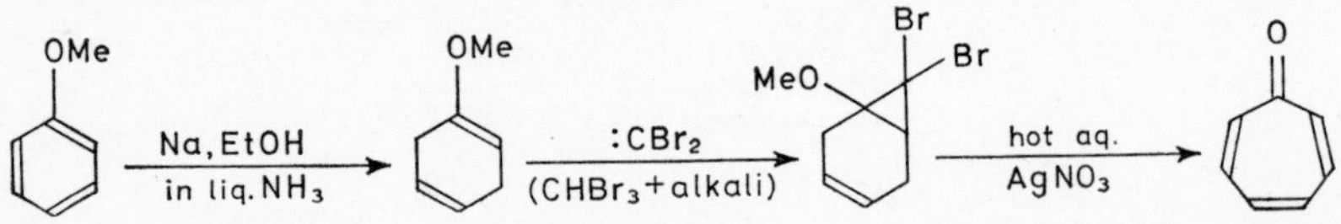

When dichlorocarbene was used instead of dibromocarbene in the second step, treatment of the resultant bicyclic intermediate with aqueous silver nitrate resulted mostly in the generation of starting material rather than the formation of tropone.

An interesting synthesis of 2,7-dimethyltropone from cycloheptanone is by conversion of the latter to a Mannich base followed by Hofmann degradation and dehydrogenation:

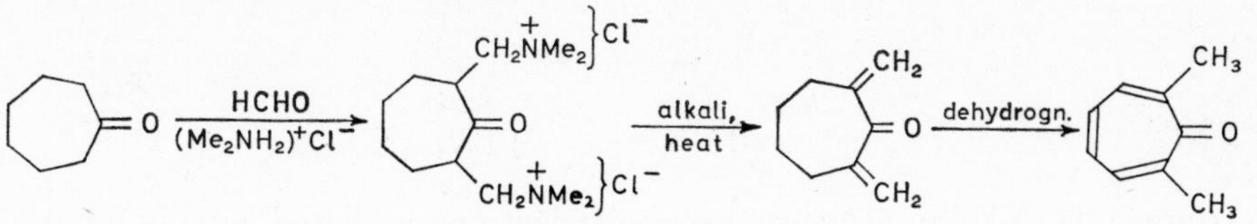

Interconversion of tropones and tropolones

Doering used the following methods to obtain tropolone from tropone and to convert tropolone into α-phenyltropone. (He also converted the latter into α-phenyltropolone.)

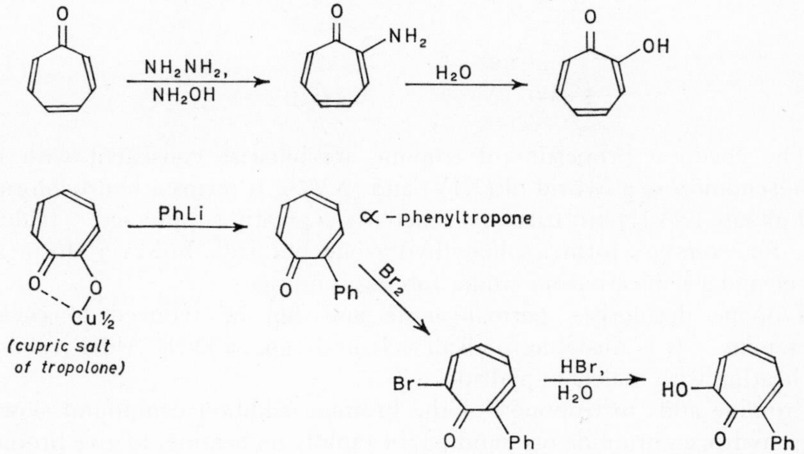

Other interconversions of tropones and tropolones are mentioned in the discussions of the properties of these compounds which follow.

Properties of tropones

Tropone is a colourless liquid completely miscible with water. It has a markedly higher boiling point (113°/15 mm.) than its isomer benzaldehyde (68°/15 mm.), an abnormal infra-red absorption peak for the carbonyl group (1638 cm.$^{-1}$; cf. cycloheptanone, 1702 cm.$^{-1}$), and a high dipole moment (4·3 D; cf. benzaldehyde, 2·97 D; and acetone, 2·8 D).

All these properties are consistent with tropone having a partially dipolar structure; it may be represented as a hybrid of (XIV) and (XV).

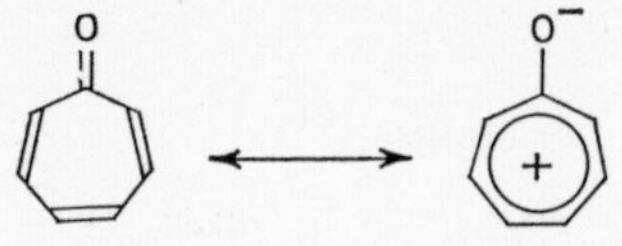

(XIV)   (XV)

In formula (XV) an aromatic sextet of electrons is shared equally among the seven ring carbon atoms. (See Chapter X, p. 107.)

Further confirmation of the dipolar character of tropone comes from the physical properties of tropone-γ-carboxylic acid, which chars at 250° without melting and probably exists as the zwitterion (XVI).

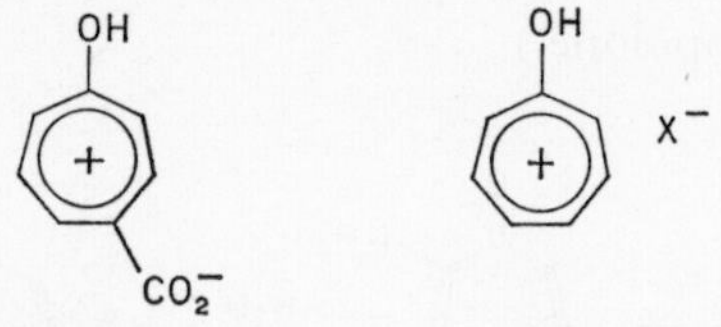

(XVI)   (XVII)

The chemical properties of tropone are likewise consistent with its representation as a hybrid of (XIV) and (XV). It forms a hydrochloride and picrate (XVII) but carbonyl reactivity is greatly suppressed. It does not, for example, form a phenylhydrazone but will, however, form an oxime and a semicarbazone under forcing conditions.

Tropone decolorises permanganate and can be reduced to cyclo-heptanone. It is unstable to alkali. It undergoes a Diels–Alder reaction on heating with maleic anhydride.

Bromine adds to tropone but the bromine addition compound slowly loses hydrogen bromide on standing, or rapidly on heating, to give bromo-substituted tropones. Benzene diazonium chloride also substitutes in the tropone ring, reacting at the α-position.

Tropone can be alkylated or arylated in the α-position by reaction with a Grignard reagent or lithium derivative followed by dehydrogenation:

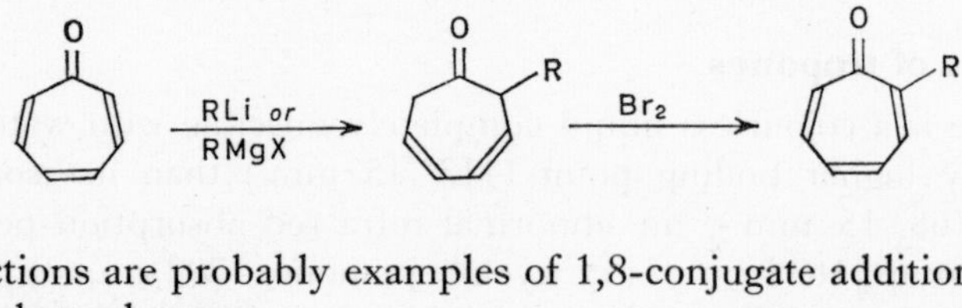

These reactions are probably examples of 1,8-conjugate addition followed by a enol→keto change.

The bromine atom in α-bromotropone is inert to silver nitrate but in the presence of acid catalysts it may be replaced by other groups of atoms, for example other halogens, cyano-, hydroxy-, methoxy- and amino-groups. α-Chlorotropone behaves similarly. This behaviour is reminiscent of that of halo-*p*-benzoquinones or *o*- or *p*-chloronitrobenzenes. α-Chlorotropone has thus been used as an intermediate in the preparation of tropolone from tropone, as follows:

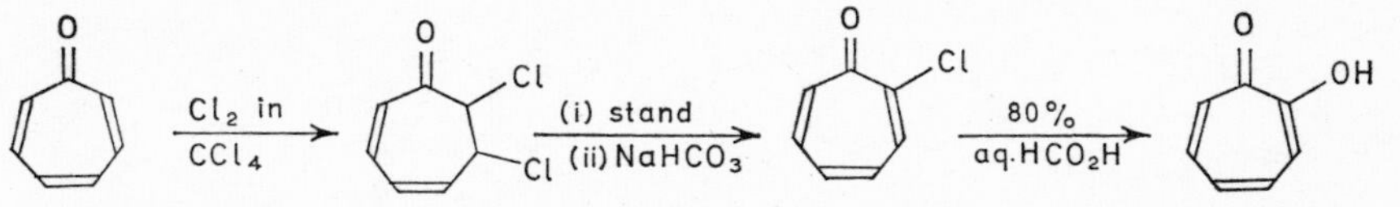

Alkaline hydrolysis converts α-halotropones into benzoic acid, possibly by a mechanism reminiscent of the benzil–benzilic acid type of rearrangement.

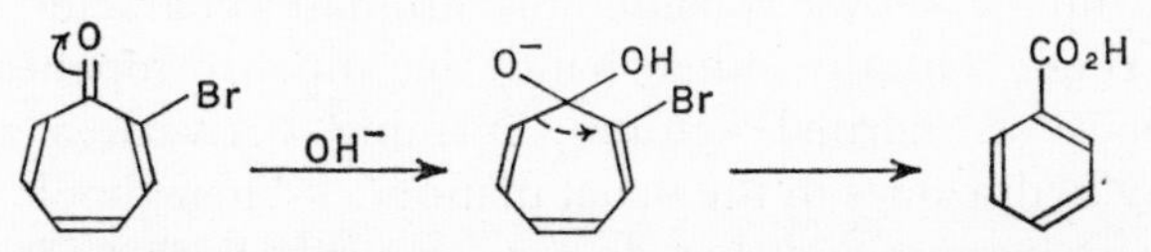

Most tropones rearrange to benzene derivatives in the presence of alkali, the ease with which this takes place being dependent on the substituent groups present, electron-attracting groups facilitating and electron-repelling groups hindering rearrangement. Thus whereas tropone-4-carboxylic acid rearranges in aqueous alkali at room temperature, 3-hydroxytropone is very resistant, even on fusion with solid potassium hydroxide.

The above properties, some of which resemble those of an aromatic compound, and others those of an olefin, are consistent with tropone being a hybrid of (XIV) and (XV); it may thus be compared with γ-pyrone (XVIII).

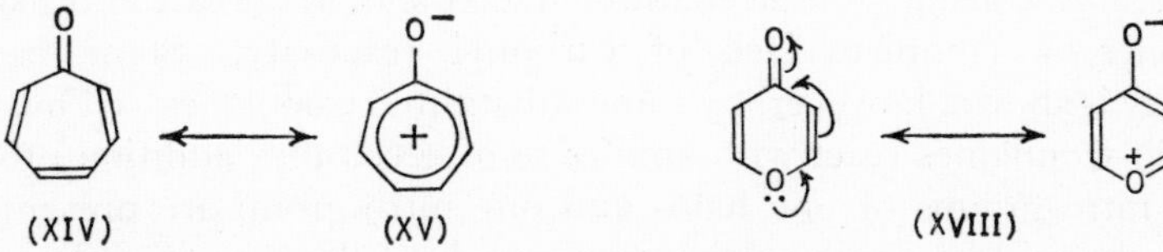

(XIV)　　　(XV)　　　　　　　(XVIII)

The formulation of tropone as (XV) implies that it should have aromatic stabilisation. Convincing evidence of high resonance energy in the tropone series comes from measurements of the heats of combustion and other properties of different 2,7-polymethylene-4,5-benzotropones (XIX). If *n* is small, the seven-membered ring must be non-planar and resonance is inhibited; this is not the case where *n* is large. This inhibition of resonance is shown by the diminished resonance energy ($=48.7$ kcal./mole) of the 2,7-pentamethylene compound (XIX, $n=5$) compared with the 2,7-dodecamethylene compound (XIX, $n=12$) or with 2,7-dimethyl-4,5-benzotropone, whose resonance energies are, respectively, 82·7 and 84·6 kcal./mole.

A 4,5-benzotropone (XX) was actually first described as long ago as 1910, by Thiele; he commented on its failure to form an oxime or phenylhydrazone.

$=O \quad (CH_2)_n$

(XIX)   (XX)   (XXI)   (XXII)

O

This benzotropone shows considerable aromatic character in its seven-membered ring. On the other hand the dibenzotropones (XXI) and (XXII) behave as normal ketones, forming derivatives such as 2,4-dinitrophenylhydrazones in the usual manner. Their dipole moments are also normal for ketones and they do not form salts with acids. Saturation of their non-benzenoid double bonds causes little significant change in their ultra-violet spectra, again indicating that there is little aromatic character in the seven-membered ring.

Tropolones

The tropolones are crystalline solids, monocyclic ones being colourless, and unsubstituted benzotropolones yellow, whilst purpurogallin is red. They dissolve more readily in hydroxylic solvents than in ether or hydrocarbons. They frequently sublime readily, a fact which has sometimes assisted in their purification.

They show considerable aromatic character and, in the case of the simpler tropolones, a complete lack of carbonyl reactivity. Some carbonyl reactivity is shown, however, by some substituted tropolones. Thus nitro- and halo-tropolones react with amines to give complex addition products. If two nitro-groups or one halo- and one nitro-group are present these complexes can lose water to give compounds of the type of anils. Other examples of carbonyl reactivity in substituted tropolones have been recorded.

Tropolones are fairly resistant to reducing agents. Catalytic hydrogenation does not proceed in the presence of palladium, but powerful catalysts (e.g. platinum) do bring about reduction, giving a variety of products. The relative resistance of tropolones to oxidation is shown by the method used for their synthesis by Doering and Knox. Per-acids in general do not affect tropolones, while selenium dioxide will oxidise side-chains attached to the tropolone ring without the ring being attacked. Oxidation under stronger conditions does, however, cause breakdown of the ring.

Electrophilic reagents take part in substitution reactions with the tropolone ring, in the α- and γ-, or 3, 5, and 7-positions. The γ- or 5-position is usually preferred (cf. o- and p-substitution in phenols). Thus tropolones may be nitrated, brominated, etc., and also couple with diazonium compounds. These reactions may be shown schematically:

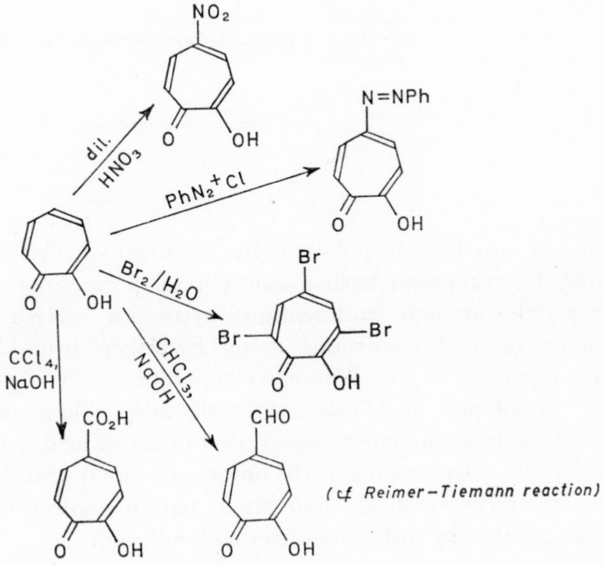

Such reactions cannot be carried out in strong acid solution for under these conditions tropolones exist as cations (XXIII) which are very stable and unreactive.

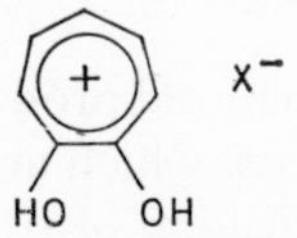

(XXIII)

In consequence tropolones are unaffected by fuming sulphuric acid at 100–150°! To effect sulphonation, sulphamic acid (NH_2SO_3H) is used. Similarly nitration does not occur if sulphuric acid is present.

Tropolone also forms a scarlet molecular complex, amphoteric in behaviour, with one molecule of bromine.

Interconversion of substituents occurs in a similar way as in the benzene series, e.g. 5-nitro- and 5-nitroso-tropolone are readily reduced to 5-aminotropolone, which may in turn be diazotised and substitutions effected by means of the Sandmeyer reaction. 3- and 4-aminotropolones behave anomalously with nitrous acid, 3-aminotropolone giving salicylic acid, and 4-aminotropolone giving 4-hydroxytropolone without formation of an intermediate diazonium compound. Other substitution reactions may sometimes lead to anomalous results, e.g.

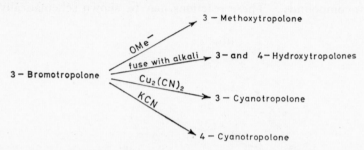

The formation of 4-hydroxytropolone in the alkaline hydrolysis of 3-bromo-tropolone may be compared with a commercial preparation of *m*-cresol from *o*- or *p*-chlorotoluene and sodium hydroxide. Hydrolysis of 3-bromotropolone in acid conditions using hydrogen bromide proceeds without rearrangement to give 3-hydroxytropolone.

As enols, tropolones give salts with alkalies. Their acidity (pK, tropolone, $= 7·0$) is intermediate between that of acetic acid (pK $= 4·8$) and phenol (pK $= 10·0$). Resonance in the anion so formed results in the salts being more strongly coloured than their parent molecules. Simpler tropolones are soluble in sodium bicarbonate solution.

Also as enols tropolones give coloured products with ferric chloride. They form ferric and cupric complexes which are soluble in chloroform and are sometimes of use for the purification of tropolones.

The hydroxyl group is readily alkylated, for example by methanol and hydrochloric acid, or by diazomethane, or by the action of an alkyl halide on the sodium or silver salt of the tropolone.

If one regards tropolone as an 'extended' acid, since interaction of its keto and enol groups through a conjugated chain is possible, then the process of alkylation of tropolone may be likened to the esterification of acids, and the products of the reaction to esters. Like esters too, these

O-alkyl tropolones may be hydrolysed to the free tropolone, take part in transesterification reactions, and react with ammonia to give α-amino-tropones (cf. amide formation). On the other hand only with difficulty may the hydroxyl group be acylated. The products in this case may be likened, on the carboxylic acid analogy, to acid anhydrides. The ease of alkylation and difficulty of acylation of tropolones and the ease of hydrolysis of the O-alkyltropolones is in marked contrast to the behaviour of phenols and phenol ethers.

Phosphorus tribromide and thionyl chloride respectively convert tropolone to α-bromo- and α-chloro-tropone. Again this contrasts with the reaction of phenol.

Allyl ethers of tropolone undergo Claisen rearrangements, the allyl group usually migrating to the 3- or 7-positions; occasionally migration takes place to the 5-position, e.g.

In the discussion of stipitatic acid it was mentioned that the tropolone ring rearranges in the presence of alkali to benzoic acid derivatives; tropones behave similarly. This reaction is general but requires varying conditions to bring it about for different compounds. Thus fusion of stipitatic acid with potassium hydroxide gives 5-hydroxyisophthalic acid, but tropolone itself requires a temperature of only 220° to be converted into benzoic acid. Tropolone methyl ethers rearrange much more easily than the free tropolones; for example tropolone methyl ether is converted into methyl benzoate by means of a boiling methanolic solution of sodium methoxide. It seems likely that the neutral alkyl ethers are less stable than the resonance stabilised tropolone salts. Nitrotropolones rearrange even more easily to benzenoid derivatives; 3,5-dinitro-6-isopropyltropolone

(5,7-dinitro-β-thujaplicin) rearranges to 2,4-dinitro-5-isopropylbenzoic acid merely on recrystallisation from alcohol:

Although simple tropolones show no carbonyl reactivity, some related benzotropolones such as (XXIV) do show some carbonyl reactivity, whilst the γ-tropolone (XXV) gives both an acetate and a monoxime. Its solutions are red.

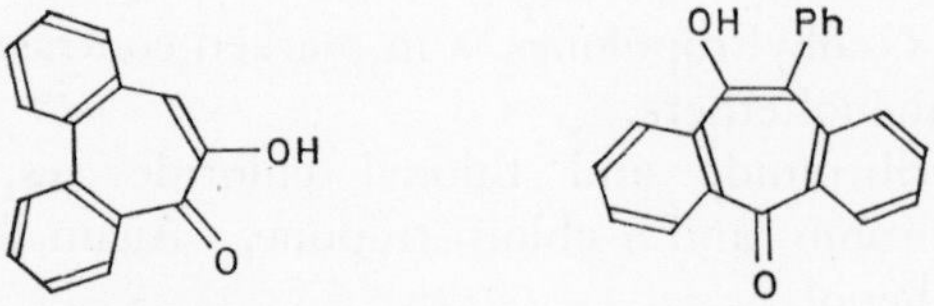

(XXIV) (XXV)

This loss of 'tropolone character' may be compared with the loss of tropone characteristics in dibenzotropones (cf. p. 136).

The fine detail of the structure of the tropolones has been studied very minutely. If 'Kekulé' structures such as (XXVI) and (XXVII) are alone considered, the 1,2-bond remains single throughout and does not contribute

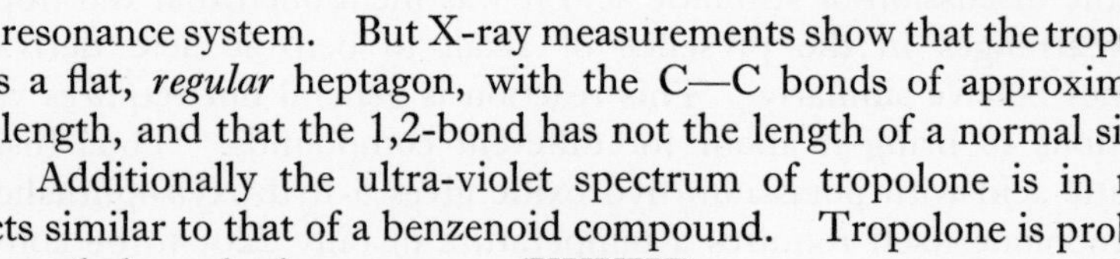

(XXVI) (XXVII)

to the resonance system. But X-ray measurements show that the tropolone ring is a flat, *regular* heptagon, with the C—C bonds of approximately equal length, and that the 1,2-bond has not the length of a normal single-bond. Additionally the ultra-violet spectrum of tropolone is in many respects similar to that of a benzenoid compound. Tropolone is probably best regarded as a hydroxytropone (XXVIII):

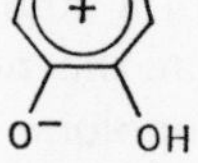

(XXVIII)

But interaction between the hydrogen of the hydroxyl and the 'carbonyl' oxygen undoubtedly contributes to the stability and properties of tropolone. This is demonstrated by its greater aromaticity and stability as compared to tropone, and by the fact that β- and γ-hydroxytropones show a number of differences in behaviour from tropolone, e.g. they are more acidic and less volatile (cf. the nitrophenols).

Some compounds related to tropolone

(a) 3- and 4-hydroxytropones

3- and 4-hydroxytropone, which are positional isomers of tropolone, have been prepared as follows.

(i)

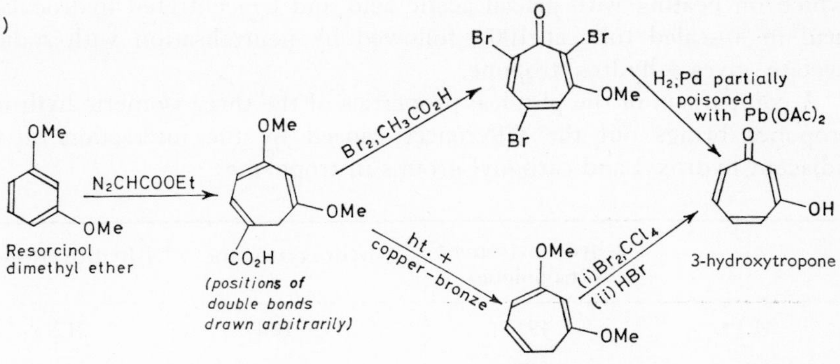

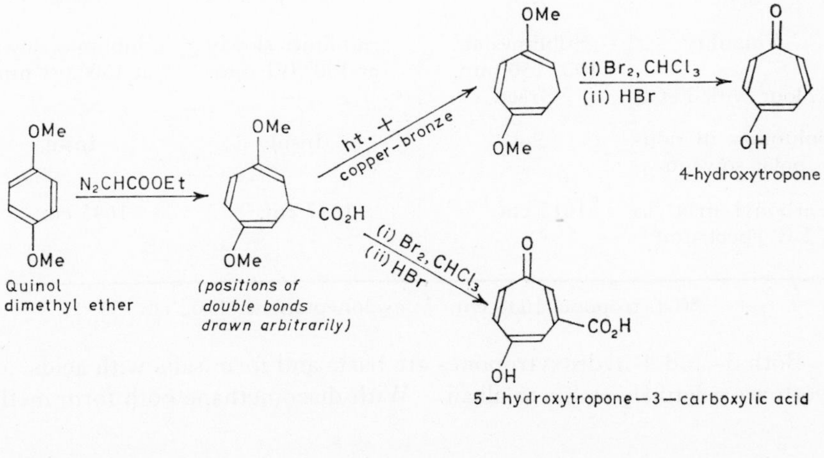

Resorcinol dimethyl ether

(positions of double bonds drawn arbitrarily)

3-hydroxytropone

Quinol dimethyl ether

(positions of double bonds drawn arbitrarily)

4-hydroxytropone

5 – hydroxytropone – 3 – carboxylic acid

(ii) ... reduction (2 stages) & tosylation ... C_5H_5N ... Br_2 ... 3-hydroxytropone

... reduction (2 stages) & tosylation ... C_5H_5N ... Br_2 ... 4-hydroxytropone

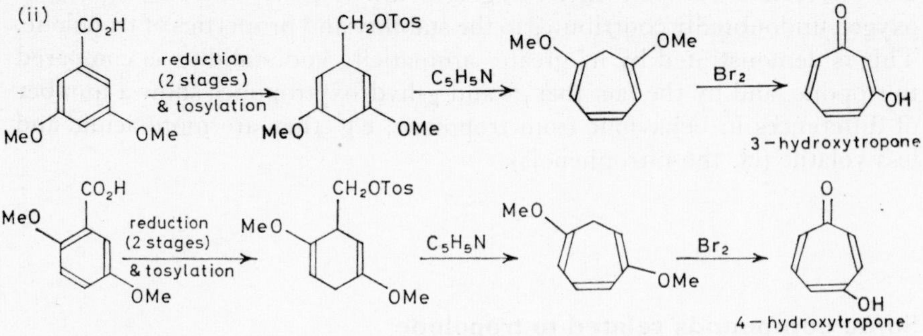

(iii) ... Na, EtOH in liq. NH_3 ... :CCl$_2$ (CHCl$_3$ + alkali) ... hot aq. $AgNO_3$ ... 3-hydroxytropone

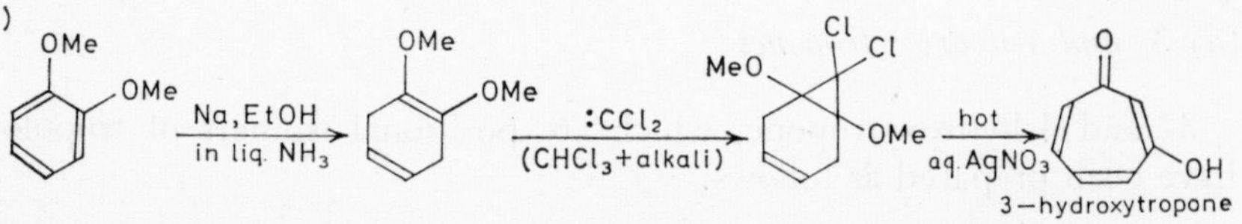

4-hydroxytropone has also been prepared from cycloheptanone. In bromination of the latter compound a minor product is 4-bromotropone, which on heating with glacial acetic acid and concentrated hydrochloric acid in a sealed tube at 100°, followed by neutralisation with sodium acetate, gives 4-hydroxytropone.

A comparison of the physical properties of the three isomeric hydroxytropones brings out the differences caused by the interaction of the adjacent hydroxyl and carbonyl groups in tropolone:

	2-hydroxytropone (tropolone)	3-hydroxytropone	4-hydroxytropone
M.Pt.	49°	179–180°	212°
pK$_a$	6·7	5·4	5·65
Volatility	Sublimes at 100°/150 mm.	Sublimes slowly at 130°/0·1 mm.	Sublimes slowly at 130°/0·1 mm.
Colour with FeCl$_3$	Green	—	—
Solubility in non-polar solvents	Sol.	Insol.	Insol.
Carbonyl max. in I.R. spectrum*	1615 cm.$^{-1}$	1647 cm.$^{-1}$	1645 cm.$^{-1}$

*(Cf. tropone, 1638 cm.$^{-1}$; cycloheptanone, 1702 cm.$^{-1}$)

Both 3- and 4-hydroxytropones are basic and form salts with acids, and both are relatively stable to alkali. With diazomethane both form methyl ethers which can be hydrolysed readily by acid or alkali.   (Like tropolone both can be represented as 'extended' acids:

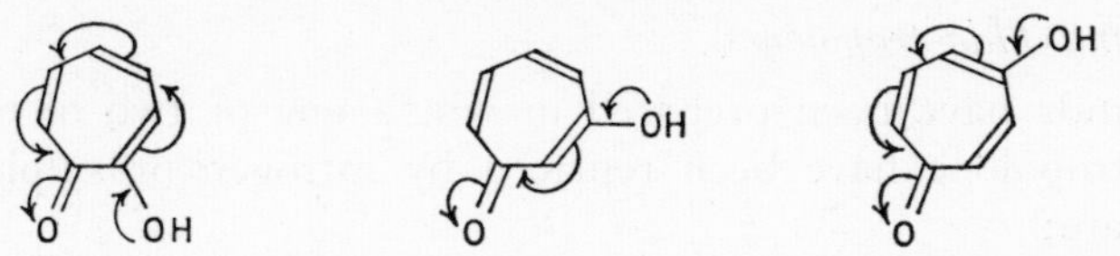

Their methyl ethers are thus comparable with esters, as discussed above in the case of tropolone methyl ether.)

Electrophilic substitution takes place in the 2-position of 3-hydroxy-tropone; it reacts thus with bromine, chlorine, a mixture of nitric and sulphuric acids, and diazonium compounds, giving 2-bromo-, 2-chloro-, 2-nitro- and 2-phenylazo- derivatives respectively.   2-nitro-3-hydroxy-tropone has been reduced catalytically to 2-amino-3-hydroxytropone and the latter compound diazotised.   The 2-halo-derivatives are rather unreactive but acid hydrolysis of 2-bromo-3-hydroxytropone gives 3-hydroxytropolone.

4-hydroxytropone gives a 2,5,7-tribromoderivative on bromination, and also couples with diazonium compounds.

Although differing from tropolone in a number of ways, both compounds have a stability and reactivity more comparable with the latter than with tropone.   Both isomers can be stabilized by resonance involving a number of canonical forms both in the form of neutral molecules, and especially as the anions:

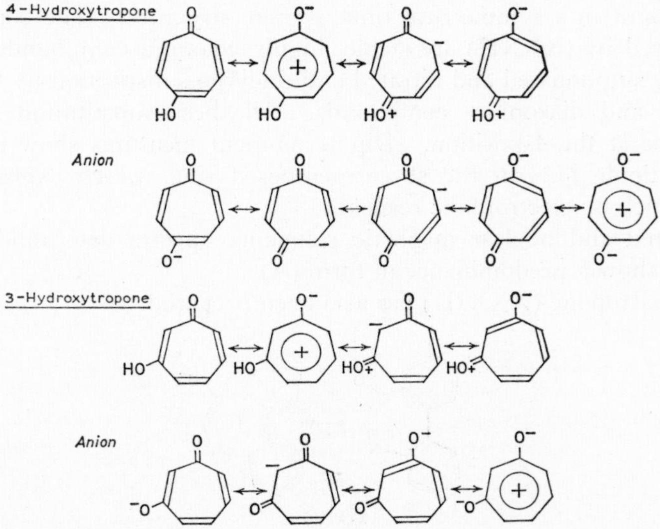

On the whole 4-hydroxytropone more closely resembles tropolone than 3-hydroxytropone does.

(b) Aza- and Thia-tropolones

Compounds have been prepared in which one or two of the oxygen atoms of tropolone have been replaced by nitrogen or sulphur atoms. Examples are:

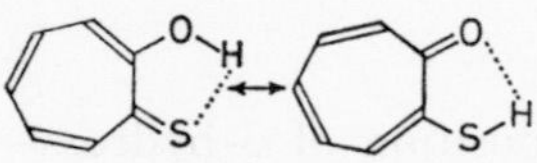

(XXIX) 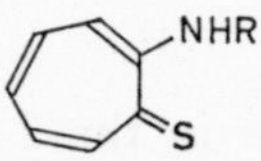   (XXX) 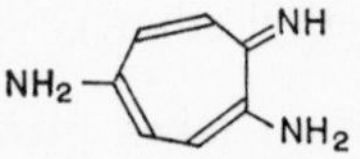   (XXXI) 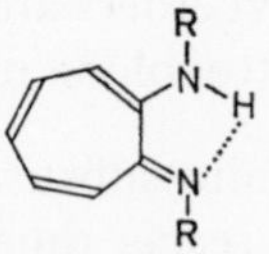   (XXXII) 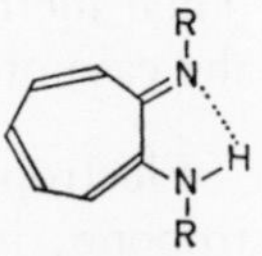   (XXXIIA)

The spectrum, and especially the nuclear magnetic resonance spectrum, of (XXXII) shows that this molecule is symmetrical and that its two nitrogen atoms are completely equivalent. In consequence it has been represented as:

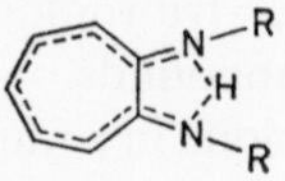

In the molecule ten electrons are shared among the atoms linked by a dotted line, producing a complete peripheral conjugation (cf. azulene). On the other hand, this evidence could equally well be explained by assuming a rapid tautomeric change between (XXXII) and (XXXII A), which would result in a symmetrical time average structure. The compounds represented by (XXXII) are stable, highly coloured compounds. They are easily sulphonated and nitrated and undergo substitution by bromine, chlorine, and diazonium compounds. All these substitution reactions take place at the 4-position. Dipole moment measures show that they have a dipole *towards* the seven-membered ring, which explains their ready attack by electrophilic reagents.

Infra-red and nuclear magnetic resonance spectra determinations on (XXIX) show a predominance of form (A).

The azatropone (XXXIII) has also been prepared.

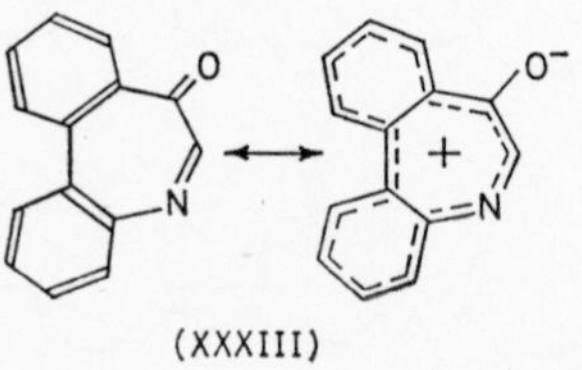

(XXXIII)

This azatropone has a carbonyl peak in its infra-red spectrum at 1613 cm.$^{-1}$, lower than any other tropone hitherto recorded.   It is resistant to catalytic hydrogenation at ordinary pressures, and forms no 2,4-dinitrophenylhydrazone.   With acids it forms purple salts.

Tropylium salts

The concept of the aromaticity of the positively charged seven-membered ring and the use of this concept in explaining the properties of tropones and tropolones was finally justified by Doering's synthesis in 1954 of cycloheptatrienylium bromide or *tropylium bromide* (I).

$$\left(+ \right) \quad Br^-$$

(I)

This compound had actually been prepared by Merling in 1891, but not recognised.   It was obtained as follows:

$$\xrightarrow[\text{derivative}]{Br_2 \quad \text{dibromo}} \xrightarrow{\text{heat}} \left(+ \right) \quad Br^-$$

Tropylium bromide is a deliquescent solid with salt-like properties.   It is soluble in water—being the only simple carbonium ion stable to water—and insoluble in organic solvents.   On addition of silver nitrate to an aqueous solution silver bromide is immediately precipitated.

In 1955 M. J. S. Dewar prepared a similar tropylium salt as follows:

$$\xrightarrow{N_2CHCOOEt} EtOOC - \xrightarrow[\text{reduced pressure}]{Br_2; \text{ heat under}} HO_2C - \left(+ \right) \quad Br^-$$

II

Compound (II) is soluble in water and alcohol, but insoluble in benzene and light petroleum.   It has no melting point and is a strong acid.   With silver nitrate solution silver bromide is precipitated.   Compound (II) can be reduced to cycloheptanecarboxylic acid.

Various other syntheses of tropylium salts have been carried out since 1955.   They may be classified according to the starting compound.

(a) Syntheses starting from cycloheptatriene

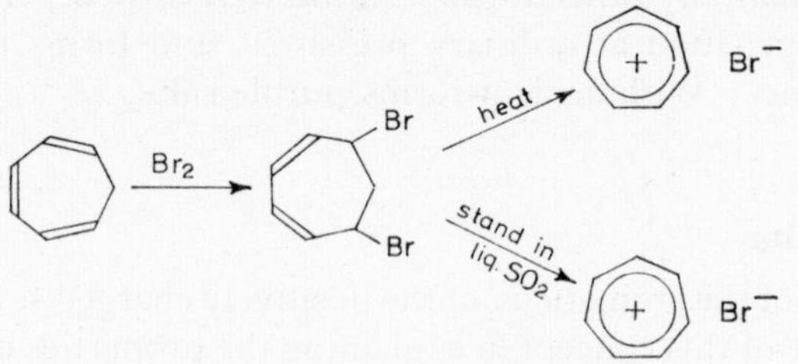

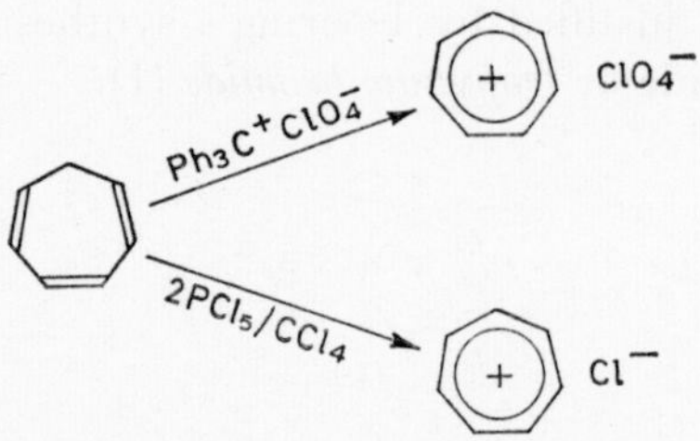

The two latter methods both give tropylium salts in quantitative yield; excellent yields can also be obtained by the action of perchloric or fluoroboric acids in acetic acid, and in the presence of oxygen, on cycloheptatriene. Oxidation of cycloheptatriene by many other reagents, e.g. chromium trioxide, selenium dioxide, sulphuryl chloride, stannic chloride, boron tribromide, concentrated sulphuric acid, concentrated nitric acid, and by electrolytic oxidation, gives tropylium salts, although in lower yields. Cycloheptatriene is also converted into tropylium salts in excellent yield by the action of quinones, especially those of higher redox potential, such as tetrachloro-1,2-benzoquinone and 2,3-dichloro-5,6-dicyano-1,4-benzoquinone.

(b) From cycloheptatrienecarboxylic acid

Various reagents, e.g. potassium permanganate, periodic acid, potassium persulphate, lead tetraacetate, ceric ammonium sulphate, oxidise cycloheptatrienecarboxylic acid to tropylium salts. The reaction between the acid or acid chloride and acetyl fluoroborate produces tropylium fluoroborate; silver perchlorate converts the acid chloride and also cyanocycloheptatriene into tropylium perchlorate.

(c) From cyclooctatetraene

A remarkable oxidation reaction giving tropylium salts, although only in 5% yield, is by the action of permanganate on cyclooctatetraene. This undoubtedly proceeds through cycloheptatrienecarboxylic acid as an intermediate.

(d) From tropyl compounds

Some tropyl (cycloheptatrienyl) compounds can be converted into tropylium salts, e.g.

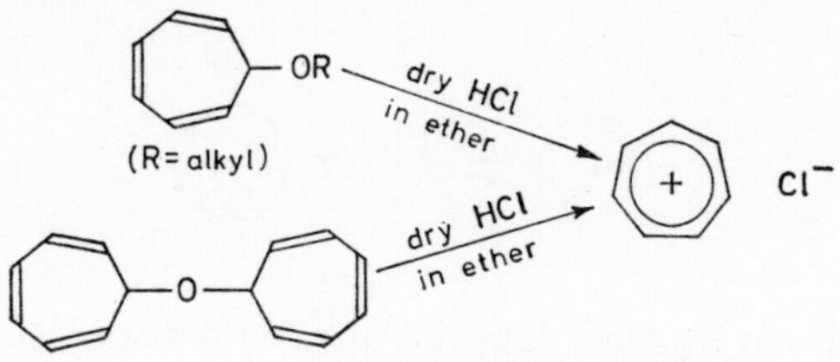

(e) From benzene

Tropylium chloride is obtained, albeit in only 1% yield, by the action of methylene chloride and potassium tert.-butoxide on benzene.

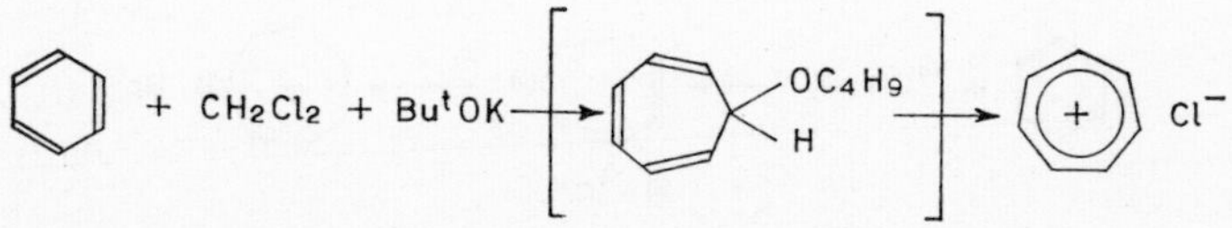

It should be noted that the syntheses of tropylium salts from cycloheptatrienecarboxylic acid and its derivatives are in fact syntheses starting from benzene, since the acid (or nitrile) is obtained from benzene by the action of diazoacetic ester (or diazoacetonitrile).

(f) Preparation of benzotropylium salts from benzotropones

Reduction of benzotropones by means of lithium aluminium hydride gives a benzotropyl alcohol from which the benzotropylium salts can be obtained.

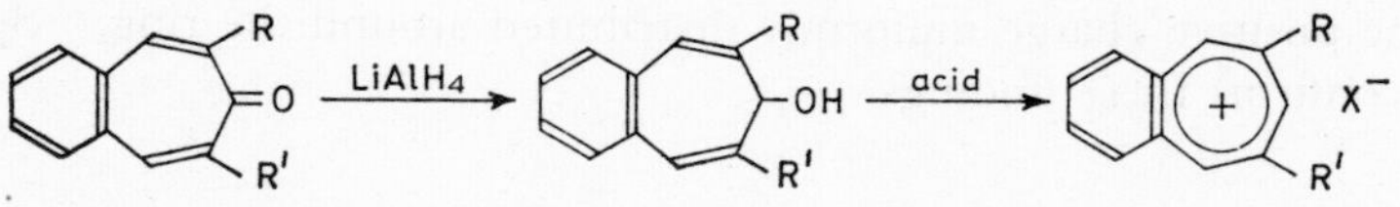

Properties of tropylium salts

Tropylium salts have high melting-points. They are insoluble in non-polar solvents, but dissolve in hot acetonitrile and nitromethane and can be recrystallised from these solvents.   On solution in, or on heating with, alcohols, tropylium salts are partly converted into alkyl ethers. Tropylium bromide and chloride are deliquescent and freely soluble in water but tropylium perchlorate and fluoroborate are only sparingly soluble.   In aqueous solution there is an equilibrium:

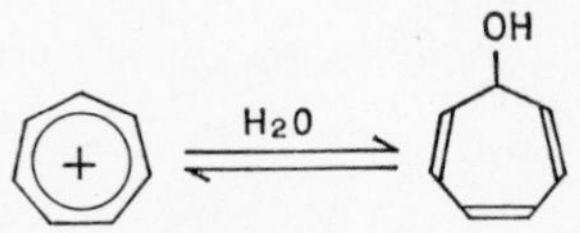

This has been shown by recording the ultra-violet spectrum in solutions of different pH; the acidity is comparable to that of acetic acid.   The perchlorate may explode on heating.

Vol'pin, Kursanov *et al.* have demonstrated that the tropylium ion is symmetrical.   They prepared a sample having one of its seven carbon atoms labelled by a ^{14}C atom:

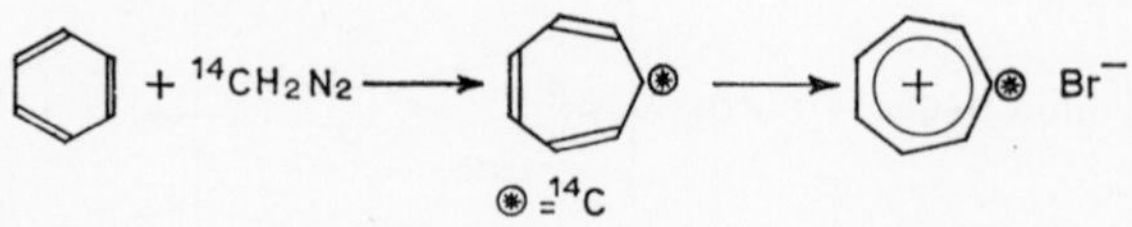

This labelled sample was then reacted with phenyl magnesium bromide to give phenylcycloheptatriene.   On oxidation of the latter with permanganate the benzoic acid formed had a specific radioactivity just one-seventh of the original tropylium bromide.

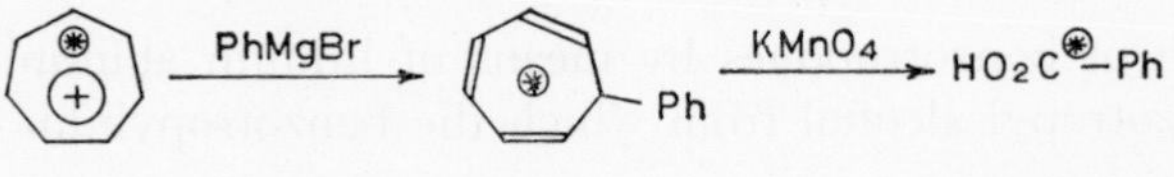

Hence all the carbon–carbon bonds in the tropylium ion must be equivalent and the positive charge uniformly distributed around the ring.   Spectral work confirms these findings.

Chemical reactions of tropylium salts

(a) Reduction

Catalytic reduction of tropylium salts produces cycloheptane; bi-molecular reduction is brought about by zinc and alkali.   Cycloheptatriene

is formed by the action of lithium aluminium hydride or sodium borohydride on tropylium salts.

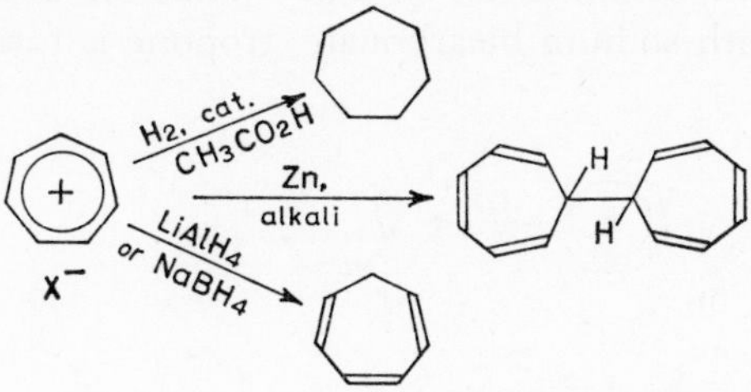

The action of *N*-bromosuccinimide on the bimolecular reduction product
produces the interesting, but unstable, red hydrocarbon heptafulvalene:

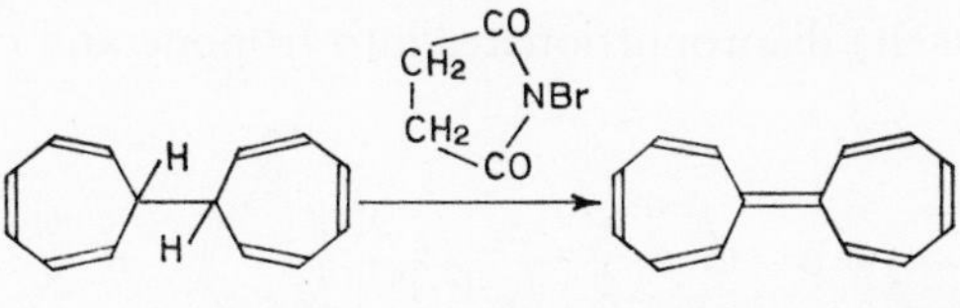

(b) Oxidation

The oxidation of tropylium salts by chromic oxide in pyridine gives
tropone, but most oxidising agents cause ring-contraction and formation of
benzaldehyde and thence benzoic acid.

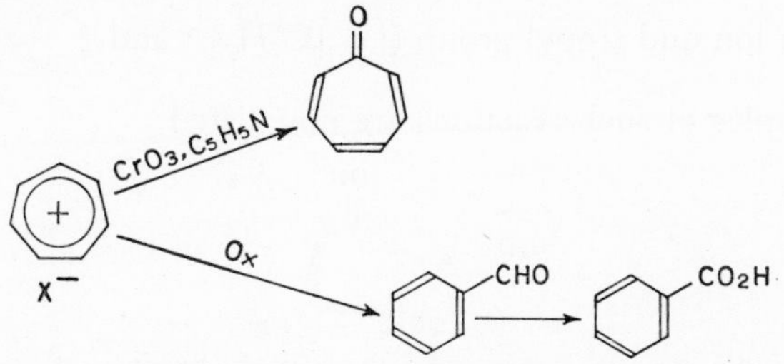

Ox. = neutral $KMnO_4$; CrO_3 in acetic acid; Ag_2O; *etc.*

Aqueous hydrogen peroxide converts tropylium salts into benzene, formic
acid and carbon monoxide, with a little phenol as by-product.

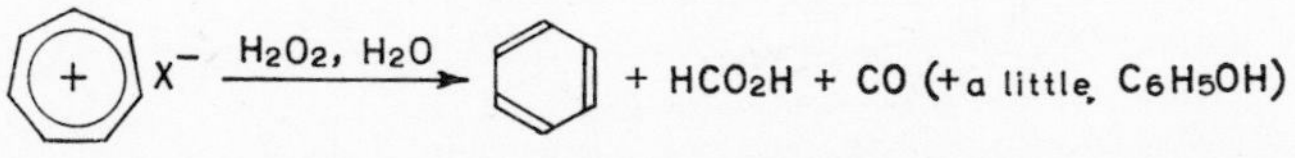

Tropylium salts react with bromine in ethanol to form a yellow adduct,
which on treatment with water is also converted into benzaldehyde.

(c) Disproportionation

Tropylium ions can extract hydride ions from easily oxidisable compounds, though the action is not strong. Thus on slow neutralisation of tropylium salts with sodium bicarbonate, tropone is formed as follows:

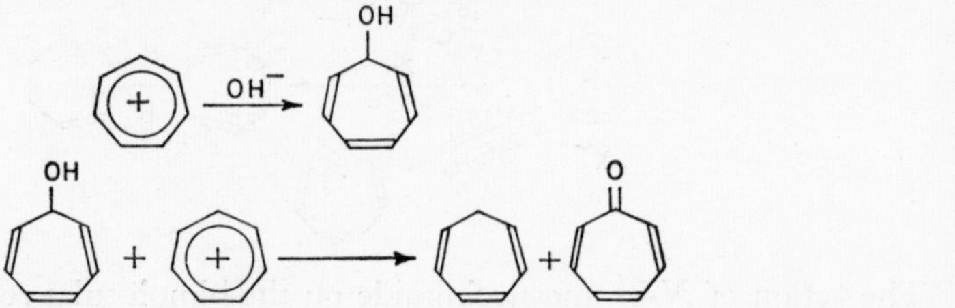

Similarly ditropyl ether on standing with tropylium ions or with a very little hydrochloric acid (which causes some formation of tropylium ions from the ether itself) disproportionates into tropone and cycloheptatriene:

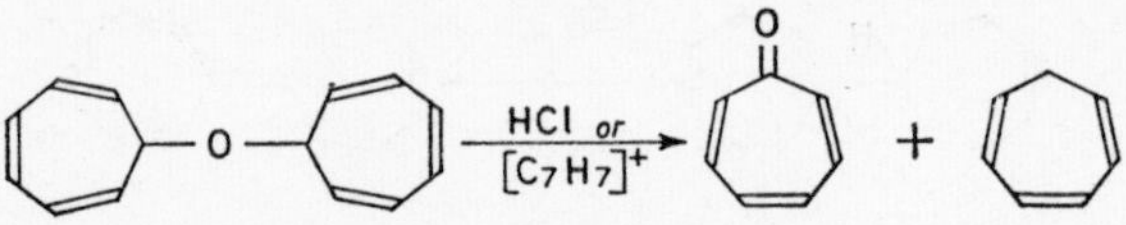

(d) Reactions with nucleophilic (anionoid) reagents

Although the tropylium ion is a very stable carbonium ion, it naturally reacts readily with nucleophilic reagents, owing to its having a positive charge. Many of these reactions are dominated by the balance between the tropylium ion and tropyl group (i.e. $[C_7H_7]^+$ and 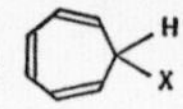).

Some examples of such reactions are now listed:

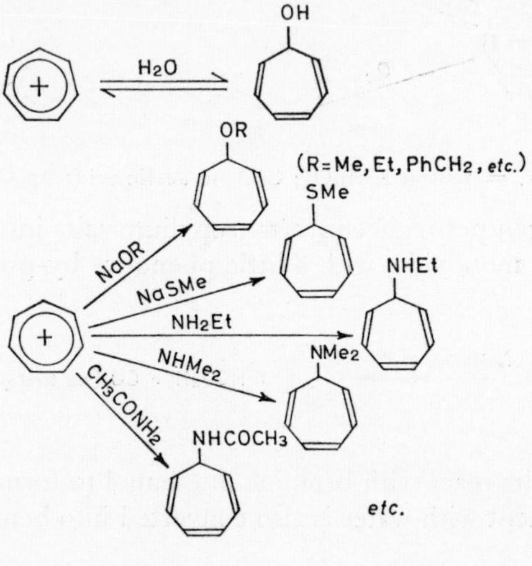

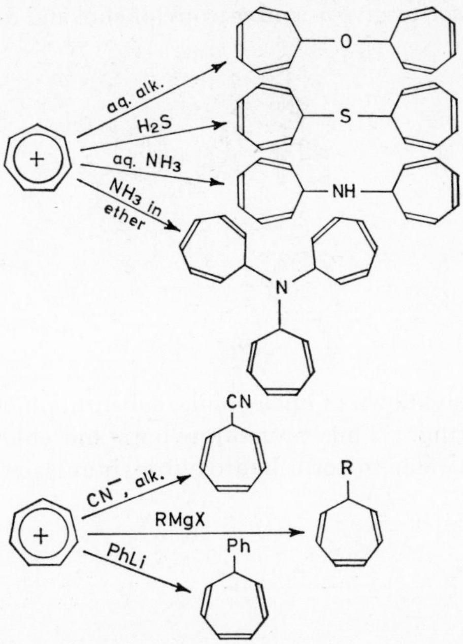

Tropylium salts react with carbanions derived from carboxylic acids, esters, aldehydes, ketones and nitroalkanes, e.g.

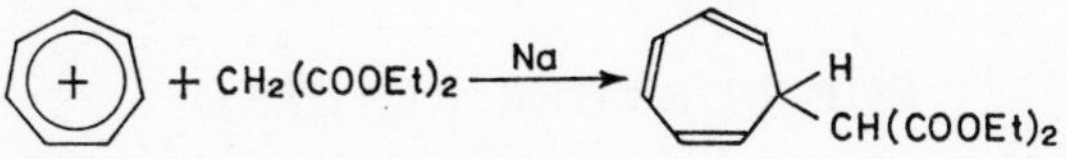

Similarly with alkyl cyanides, ethyl cyanoacetate, and malononitrile products such as (A) or (B) are formed.

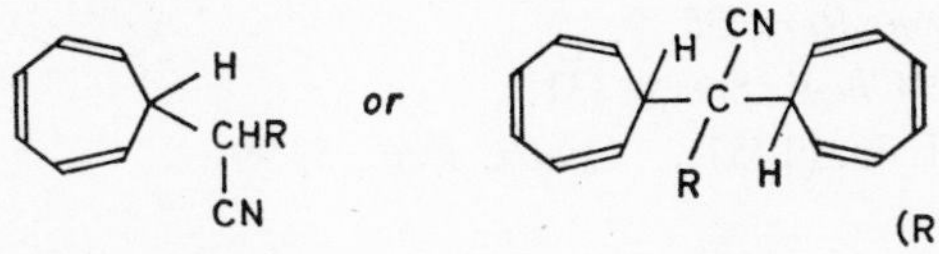

(R=CN, COOEt or alkyl)

The reactions involving compounds such as β-ketoesters or β-diketones, which have highly reactive methylene groups, proceed very readily in the cold.   With alkali metal phenoxides and with alkali metal salts of tropolone tropylium salts react to give *o*- and *p*-tropylphenol and 3- and 5-tropyltropolone respectively.

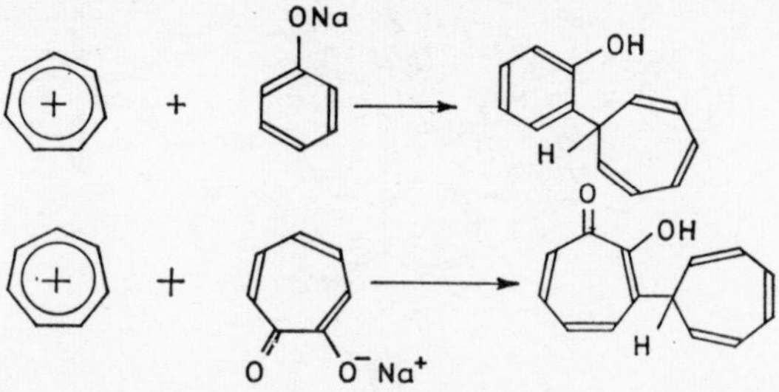

Examples are also known of nucleophilic substitution of groups attached to the tropylium ring. Thus bromotropylium and chlorotropylium salts readily react with water to form hydroxytropylium salts:

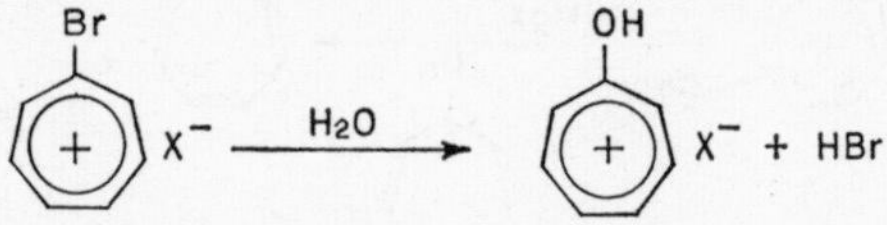

Not surprisingly tropylium salts are extremely inert towards electrophilic reagents, and it has not yet proved possible to carry out any of the electrophilic substitution reactions such as nitration, sulphonation, Friedel-Crafts reaction, which are characteristic of benzenoid aromatic compounds.

FOR FURTHER READING

Nozoe, T. (1959). In *Non-benzenoid Aromatic Compounds*, edited by D. Ginsburg. Chapter 7. Interscience.

Nozoe, T. (1961). In *Progress in Organic Chemistry*, Vol. V, edited by J. W. Cook. Pages 132 ff. Butterworth.

Nozoe, T. (1956). In *Progress in the Chemistry of Natural Products*, XIII, edited by L. Zechmeister. Pages 232ff. Springer.

Pauson, P. L. (1955). *Chem. Rev.*, **55**, 9.

Johnson, A. W. (1954). *J. Chem. Soc.*, 1331.

Cook, J. W. and Loudon, J. D. (1951). *Quart. Rev.*, **5**, 99.

XII

AROMATIC FIVE-MEMBERED RING COMPOUNDS

Cyclopentadienide derivatives

UNLIKE the tropylium ion, the cyclopentadienide ion was recognised and prepared many years ago. Thiele, in 1901, prepared potassium cyclopentadienide by the action of potassium on cyclopentadiene:

This salt is extremely reactive and quickly inflames in air, but the mere fact that such a salt could be isolated is notable. It is to be expected that a negatively charged molecule would be very susceptible to oxidation. It is, however, stable in non-hydroxylic solvents and in an inert atmosphere. In recent years the sodium and lithium salts of cyclopentadiene have been utilised frequently in synthetic work.

The full significance of the existence of cyclopentadienide salts was not at first recognised, and it was left to Robinson, in 1925, to point out that the anion would be stabilised by its aromatic sextet.

Since Thiele's work other substituted cyclopentadienides have been prepared which are perfectly stable in air. Thus Hale, in 1912, prepared the salt (I) from nitromalondialdehyde, although, like Thiele, he did not comment on the nature of his sodium salt.

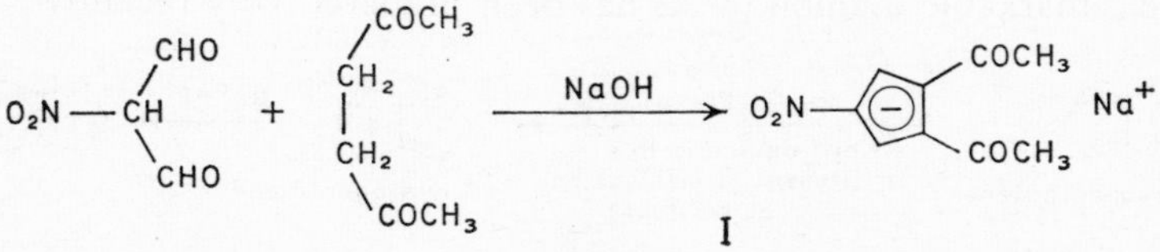

153

Recently Peters has prepared the anion (II) as follows:

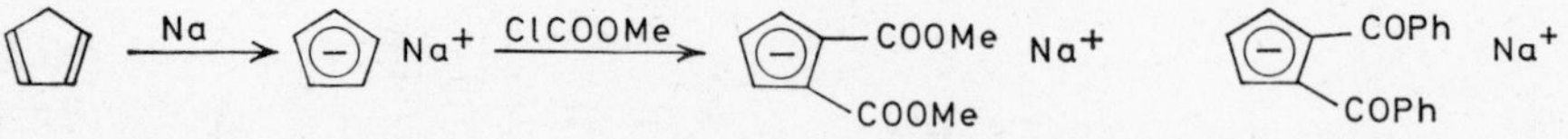

Another known stable cyclopentadienide derivative is compound (III). In all the three latter examples the cyclopentadienide ions gain extra stability and resistance to oxidation from the electron-attracting groups attached to the carbon ring.   All of them are coloured solids.

Hafner (1959) has prepared a most interesting cyclopentadiene derivative (IV) by the action of N,N-dimethylformamide on cyclopentadiene:

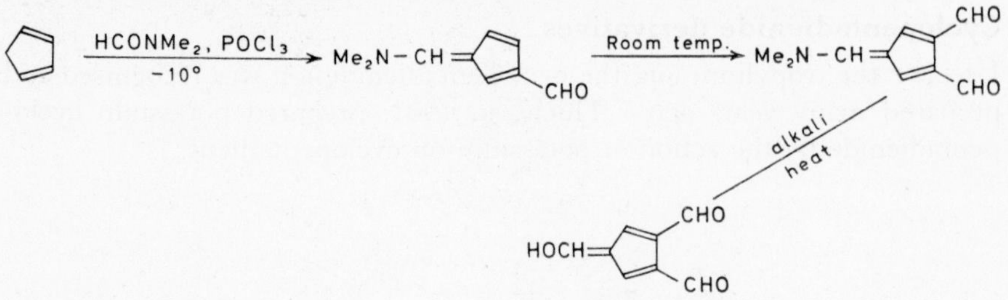

Compound (IV) is a strong acid, no doubt owing to the stabilisation of the anion derived from it:

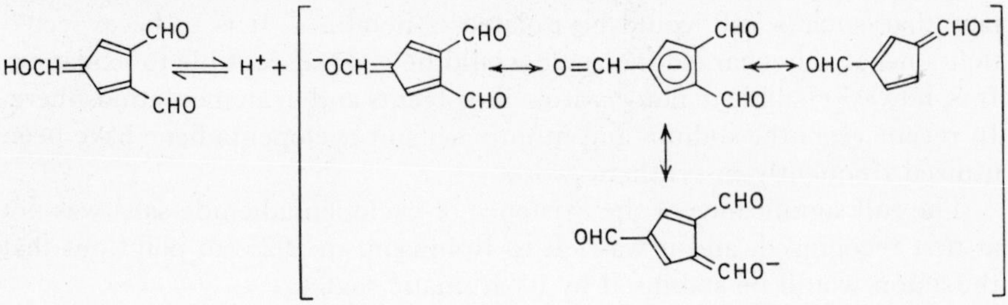

The anion (V) is also stable.

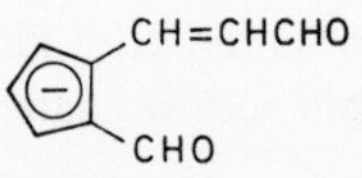

The remarkable dianion (V A) has been prepared very recently:

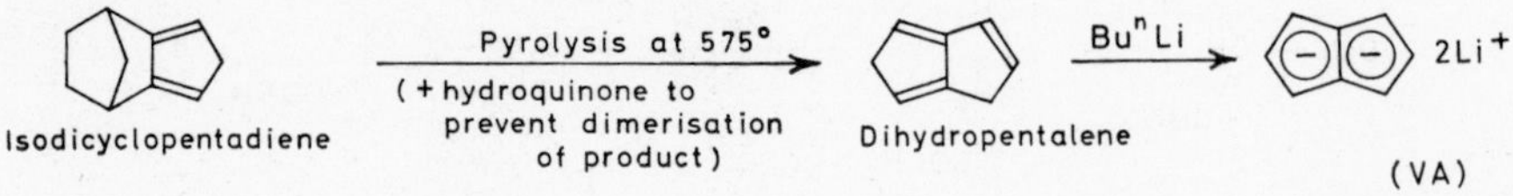

It is a white crystalline compound, which is stable in solution in tetrahydro-furan at room temperature.

Simple cyclopentadienide rings stabilised by positively charged exocyclic groups were not prepared until recent years, but some such compounds derived from fluorene, e.g. 9-diazofluorene (VI), and 9-trimethylsulpho-nium fluorenylide (VII) had been prepared at earlier dates. The latter compound was shown to possess a large dipole moment, as might be expected.

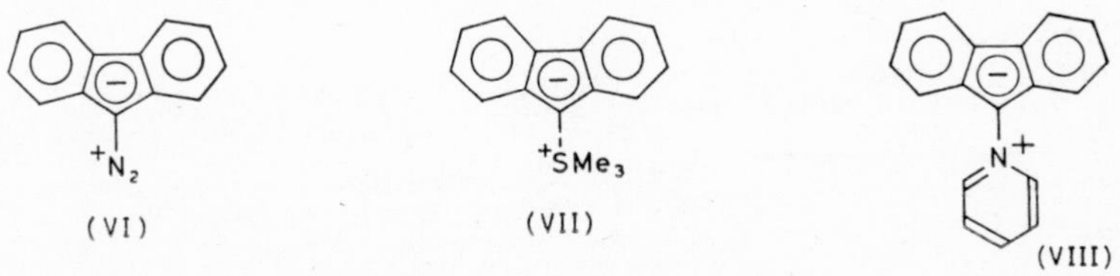

(VI)   (VII)   (VIII)

Compound (VI) was prepared first by Staudinger in 1911 and is a stable red crystalline solid. Compound (VII), and the related pyridinium fluorenylide (VIII) were on the other hand rather unstable, and quickly decomposed. Introduction of an electron-attracting nitro-group into the fluorene part of the molecule increases the stability of the resulting fluorenylide.

With the recognition of tropolone and tropone, and the consequent interest in non-benzenoid aromatic compounds, compounds similar to (VI)–(VIII), but derived from cyclopentadiene itself, were sought.

In 1953 Doering prepared diazocyclopentadiene (IX) by the following method:

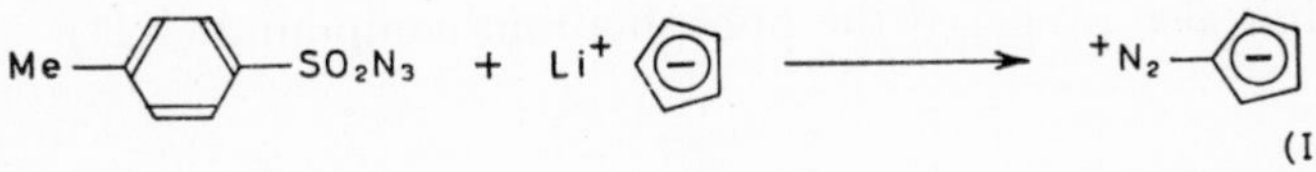

(IX)

This compound was a red oil which could be reduced catalytically to cyclopentanone hydrazone. Cram (1963) has shown that it undergoes electrophilic substitution reactions such as nitration, mercuration and coupling with diazonium salts.

In 1955 Lloyd and Sneezum prepared pyridinium cyclopentadienylide (X) as follows:

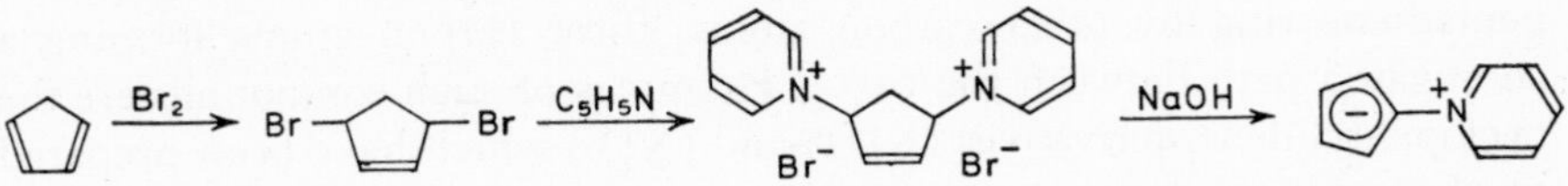

(X)

This compound is a coppery-red solid, soluble in acid and reprecipitated by alkali, and almost insoluble in non-polar organic solvents. It can be reduced to cyclopentylpiperidine, although some alkyl-pyridinium analogues appear to be resistant to catalytic hydrogenation. Kursanov has shown that it is possible to substitute the hydrogen atoms of the five-membered ring by deuterium and bromine (the latter by means of potassium hypobromite). Lloyd and Sneezum also prepared a pyridinium tetraphenylcyclopentadienylide:

One striking property of the pyridinium cyclopentadienylides is the variation in colour of their solutions, depending on the polarity of the solvent. Thus compound (X) gives an orange solution in alcohol, red in acetone or chloroform and blueish-purple in light petroleum. Similarly its tetraphenyl derivative, which is a deep-blue solid, dissolves in ethanol giving a red solution, but in benzene or ether giving a blue solution. These cyclopentadienylides have high dipole moments (13·5 D).

Ramirez and Levy have prepared a triphenylphosphonium cyclo-pentadienylide (XI) by the same method, but using triphenylphosphine instead of pyridine. This phosphonium compound is a stable yellow solid. It has been shown to couple with aromatic diazonium compounds. Ramirez has also prepared the phosphonium compound (XII).

In a cyclopentadienylide the hetero-atom bearing the positive charge is attached directly to the cyclopentadiene ring but it is possible to have similar compounds in which the hetero-atom is separated from the cyclo-pentadiene ring by other carbon atoms, these carbon atoms forming a conjugated path between the two. Examples of such compounds are the cyclopentylidene derivatives (XIII) and (XIV) which have been prepared by the methods shown.

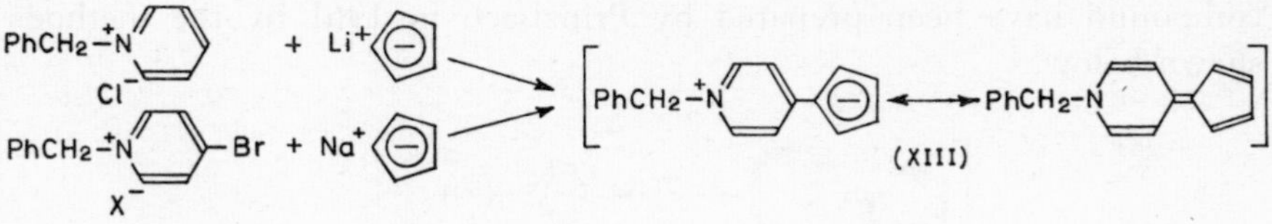

Both of these compounds are yellow-orange crystalline compounds of high melting point, having spectra which are in accord with a dipolar structure.   Other similar compounds have also been prepared.

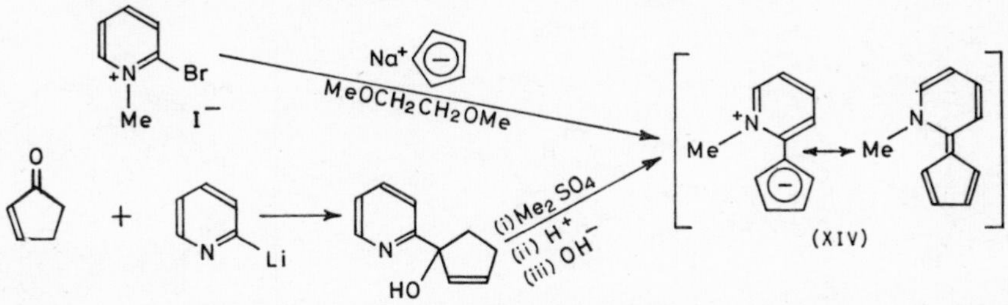

Part of the relative stability of many fulvenes (see Chapter IX) derives from stabilisation due to resonance between forms such as (XV A) and (XV B).

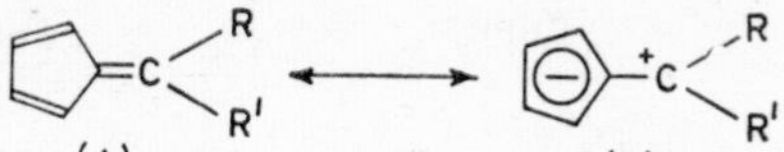

That a dipolar form does contribute to the structure is confirmed by the fact that fulvenes have dipole moments (*ca.* 1·5 D), the ring being negative and the exocyclic carbon atom positive.

The contribution of the polar form is increased if the aldehyde from which the fulvene is prepared has a hetero-atom which can readily accommodate the positive charge.   Thus the fulvenes (XVI) and (XVII) from furfural and from thiophene-2-aldehyde are fairly stable fulvenes.   They can be represented as hybrids as shown:

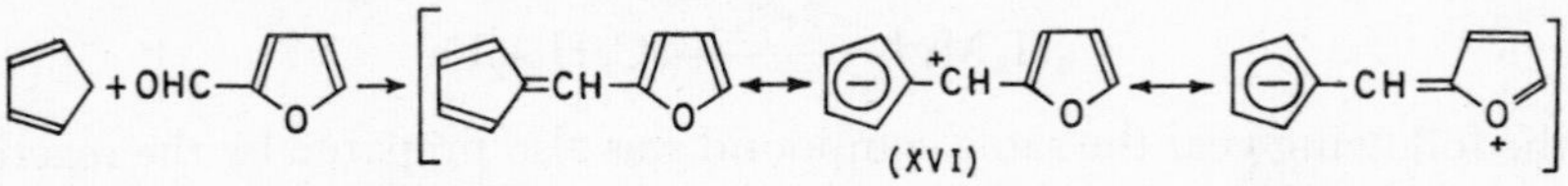

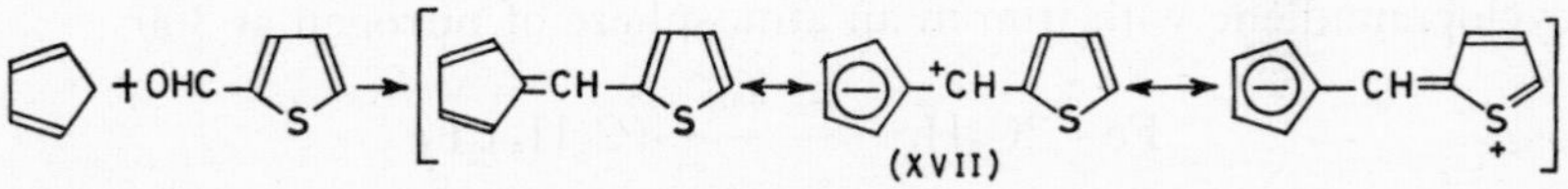

A compound which quite obviously would be of the utmost interest to prepare is tropylium cyclopentadienylide (XVIII).   Derivatives of this compound have been prepared by Prinzbach in 1961 by the methods shown below.

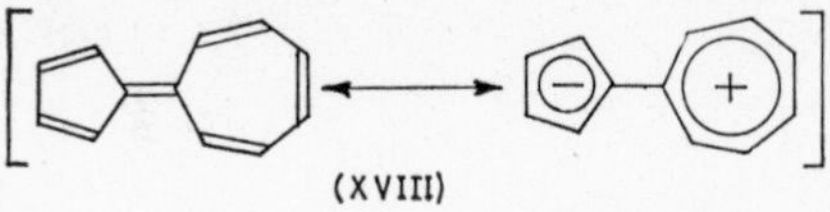

(XVIII)

(i)

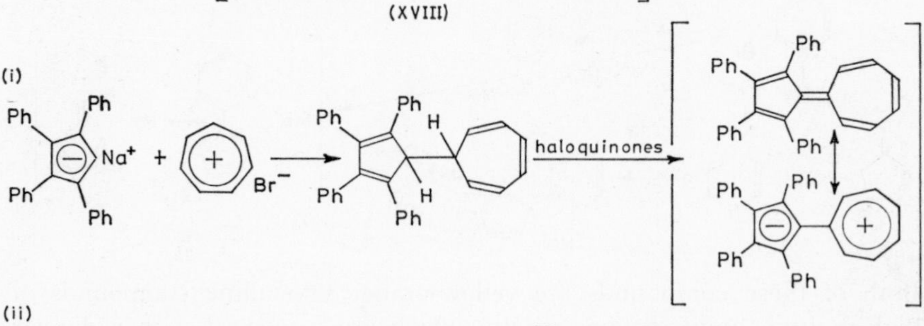

(ii)

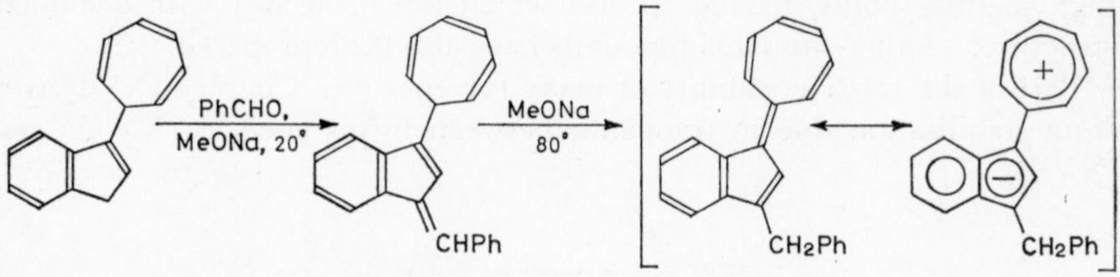

Ferrocene, etc.

A most remarkable type of cyclopentadiene derivative was discovered, accidentally, in 1951. Pauson was attempting to prepare the as yet unknown fulvalene (I), by the action of ferric chloride on cyclopentadienyl magnesium iodide, but obtained instead a compound $(C_5H_5)_2Fe$:

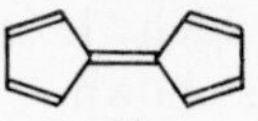

(I)

$$C_5H_5MgI \xrightarrow{FeCl_3} (C_5H_5)_2Fe$$

In the following year the same compound was also prepared by the reaction of cyclopentadiene with iron in an atmosphere of nitrogen at 300°:

$$Fe + 2C_5H_6 \xrightarrow{N_2, \ 300°} (C_5H_5)_2Fe$$

This compound, *ferrocene*, was originally attributed the structure (II), but Woodward (1952) suggested the 'sandwich' structure (III), in which each of the ten carbon atoms was equidistant from the central iron atom, the linkage with the iron atom being equally shared among them.   All the carbon–carbon bonds are equivalent, as are all the hydrogen atoms.

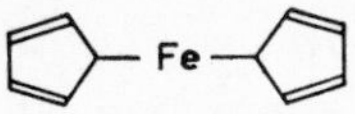

(II) 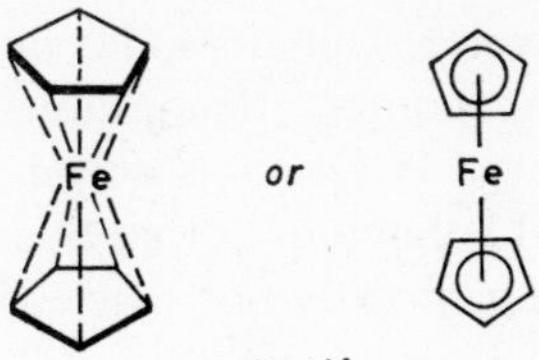   (III)

This structure has been confirmed by X-ray analysis; the symmetry of the molecule is also evident from such data as the infra-red spectrum (there is a single C—H stretching bond at 2075 cm.$^{-1}$), dipole moment, etc.

Ferrocene was the first compound to be prepared containing carbon, hydrogen and iron only.   More important it proved to be the first member of a whole new series of aromatic compounds of general formula (IV), wherein M represents a metal atom, and in which the π-electrons of the cyclopentadienide rings interact with this central metal atom.

(IV)

Two other preparative methods for ferrocene which have been developed are:

(i) $FeCl_3 + Fe \longrightarrow FeCl_2$

        $FeCl_2 + [C_5H_5]^- Na^+ \longrightarrow (C_5H_5)_2Fe$

(ii)

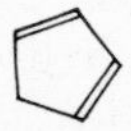

$+ FeCl_2 \xrightarrow{Et_2 NH} (C_5H_5)_2Fe$

A modification of the second method involves the formation of ferrous chloride from iron by the action of the hydrochloride of the amine eventually used to effect the condensation:

$$Fe + 2R_3NH^+Cl^- \longrightarrow FeCl_2 + 2R_3N + H_2$$
$$FeCl_2 + 2C_5H_6 + 2R_3N \longrightarrow (C_5H_5)_2Fe + 2R_3NH^+Cl^-$$

The net reaction is thus

$$Fe + 2C_5H_6 \longrightarrow (C_5H_5)_2Fe + H_2$$

Properties of ferrocene

Ferrocene is an orange crystalline compound which can be recrystallised from organic solvents. It is remarkably stable; it is insoluble in, and unaffected by, water, caustic soda, or concentrated hydrochloric acid, even at their boiling points. It sublimes at 100° and is volatile in steam and alcohol vapour. It resists pyrolysis, even at 470°.

Its chemical behaviour is that of an aromatic compound rather than that of an olefin, e.g. it does not react with maleic anhydride in a Diels–Alder reaction.

It is not reduced catalytically except under extreme conditions; thus at near 350° and in the presence of Raney nickel it is converted into cyclopentane and iron. It is notable that benzene rings can be reduced preferentially. Lithium in ethylamine reduces ferrocene to cyclopentadiene and iron

$$(C_5H_5)_2Fe \xrightarrow{\text{Li, } C_2H_5NH_2} 2 \;\bigcirc\!\!\!\!\!\!\bigtriangleup + Fe$$

Similar reductions by lithium, applied to substituted ferrocene derivatives, have been useful in the orientation of the substituent groups.

On oxidation a blue *ferricinium* cation $[(C_5H_5)_2Fe]^+$ is obtained. Attempts to carry out bromination, nitration or sulphonation under the conditions normally used for benzenoid compounds similarly result in oxidation of ferrocene to this ferricinium cation, which renders electrophilic substitution virtually impossible. Sulphonation, however, can be achieved by using acetic anhydride as solvent; mono- and di-substitution products are obtained.

To obtain nitroferrocene, ferrocene is metalated with butyl lithium, forming a lithium derivative. The latter, on treatment with propyl nitrate gives nitroferrocene. The lithium derivative of ferrocene also reacts with carbon dioxide and with hydroxylamine to give, respectively, ferrocene carboxylic acid and aminoferrocene. The latter compound may also be got by reduction of nitroferrocene with tin and hydrochloric acid.

$$(C_5H_5)_2Fe \xrightarrow{\text{BuLi}} \begin{array}{l}\text{Lithium}\\\text{Derivative}\end{array}$$

$$\xrightarrow{CH_3CH_2CH_2ONO_2} (C_5H_5)Fe(C_5H_4NO_2) \xrightarrow{\text{Sn, HCl}} (C_5H_5)Fe(C_5H_4NH_2)$$

$$\xrightarrow{NH_2OH} (C_5H_5)Fe(C_5H_4NH_2)$$

$$\xrightarrow{CO_2} (C_5H_5)Fe(C_5H_4CO_2H)$$

Aminoferrocene cannot be diazotised owing to its susceptibility to oxidation; it is very susceptible to air and light.

Ferrocene can be acylated by means of a Friedel-Crafts reaction. Very mild conditions suffice; thus monoacetylferrocene is formed by the action of acetic anhydride in the presence of phosphoric acid. The acetyl group deactivates the whole molecule, and further substitution, even in the ring to which the acetyl group is not directly attached, does not occur under these mild conditions. Acetyl chloride and aluminium chloride react with ferrocene to give a diacetyl derivative. This consists almost entirely of the 1,1′-isomer, i.e. the isomer having one acetyl group substituted in each ring. A very small amount of 1,2-diacetylferrocene is also obtained but none of the 1,3-isomer.

1,1′-diacetylferrocene can be oxidised to the corresponding 1,1′-ferrocenedicarboxylic acid.

Direct alkylation of ferrocene by the Friedel-Crafts method has met with only moderate success, and alkyl derivatives are usually obtained by Clemmensen or catalytic reduction of the appropriate acyl derivative.

Diazonium salts react readily and smoothly with ferrocene to give mono- and di-(1,1′)-aryl derivatives.

$$(C_5H_5)_2Fe + ArN_2^+ \longrightarrow N_2 + (C_5H_5)Fe(C_5H_4Ar)$$

Ferrocene can be formylated by reaction with N-methylformanilide and phosphorus oxychloride. In the presence of amines formaldehyde and ferrocene give Mannich bases. The latter have been utilised to prepare ferrocene carbinol and methyl ferrocene:

Halogen atoms directly attached to a ferrocene ring are very inert to substitution reactions.

Stereochemistry of ferrocene

No two different *heteroannular* disubstituted (1,1') ferrocenes have ever been isolated, suggesting that there must be free rotation of the two rings.

If, on the other hand, in a *homoannular* disubstituted ferrocene, $(C_5H_5)Fe(C_5H_3XY)$, the two substituent groups are different, then optical isomers are possible.   (See Va and Vb.)   This has been demonstrated in the case of the ferrocene derivative (VI).

Analogues of ferrocene

The ability to form compounds analogous in structure to ferrocene is common to the transition elements which have two vacant or singly occupied *d*-orbitals available for bonding.

In the first transition series the analogues of all the elements from titanium to nickel (inclusive) are known.   Most of them are isomorphous and even have the same melting point (173°).   In the second and third transition series only elements in the same group as iron (ruthenium, osmium) have yielded compounds of this type.

Other 'sandwich' compounds

Since the discovery of ferrocene other 'sandwich' type compounds, with a metal atom between two hydrocarbon rings, have been recognised, and in recent years a proliferation of such compounds has been prepared. The hydrocarbon rings involved have included benzene, non-benzenoid aromatic, and olefinic rings (e.g. cyclopentadiene and cycloheptatriene). No doubt in all these cases it is the π-electron systems which are responsible for the bonding.

Sandwich compounds derived from chromium and benzene had in fact been prepared many years ago, but their true structure had not been realised.   They are prepared as follows:

Dibenzenechromium is a dark-brown solid, soluble in benzene and very stable. It sublimes *in vacuo*; on heating strongly it does not decompose until 300°, when it decomposes into chromium and benzene. Attempts to carry out typical aromatic substitution reactions on dibenzenechromium lead to disruption of the molecule.

Other metal complexes may be 'mixed' sandwiches with two different rings attached to the central metal atom, e.g. (VII) and (VIII).

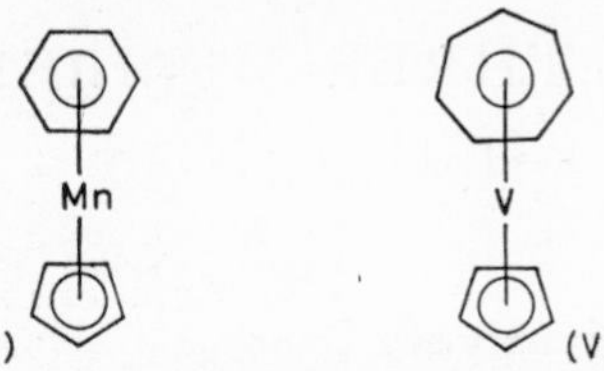

(VII)   (VIII)

There are also complexes involving only one carbocyclic ring attached to a metal atom, for example cycloocta-1,5-diene forms a palladium complex $C_8H_{12}PdCl_2$ which is stable up to more than 200°. Many of these mono-cyclic complex compounds also have carbonyl groups attached to the metal atom. Interesting examples of this type of complex are the cyclo-heptatriene and tropylium complexes of molybdenum, which have been prepared as follows:

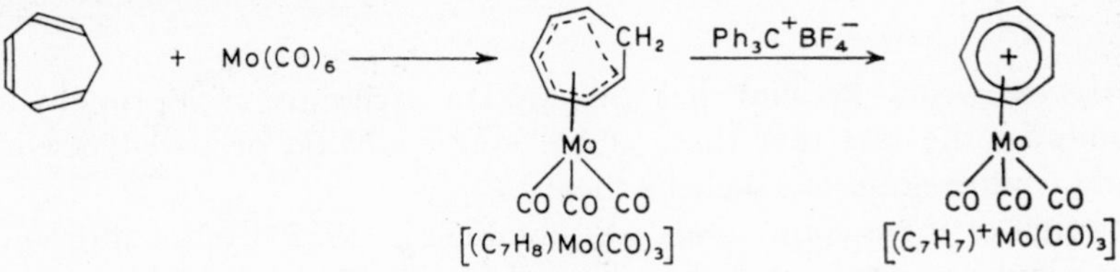

FOR FURTHER READING

Pauson, P. L. (1959). In *Non-benzenoid Aromatic Compounds*, edited by D. Ginsburg. Chapter 3. Interscience.

FERROCENE

Pauson, P. L. (1955). *Quart. Rev.*, **9**, 391
Pauson, P. L. (1955). *J. Roy. Inst. Chem.*, **79**, 363.
Plesske, K. (1962). *Angew. Chem.*, **74**, 301, 347.

FOR REFERENCES ON CYCLOPENTADIENYLIDES, ETC.

Lloyd, D. and Sneezum, J. S. (1958). *Tetrahedron*, **3**, 334.

XIII

AROMATIC THREE-MEMBERED RING COMPOUNDS

Cyclopropenylium derivatives

On Hückel's theory, cyclopropenylium derivatives (I) should be aromatic in character, as they have $(4n+2)$ electrons $(n=0)$ shared among three equivalent carbon atoms.

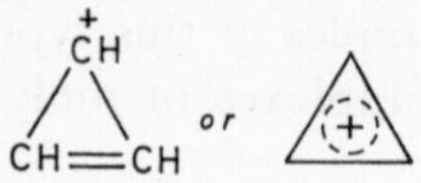

+
CH
CH═CH
or
+

(I)

In recent years Breslow has prepared a series of cyclopropenylium compounds; the fact that these stable ions could be prepared provided striking confirmation of Hückel's theory.

The first of these compounds was obtained in 1957, by the addition of diazophenylacetonitrile to diphenyl acetylene giving a cyclopropene derivative, which was then converted into a cyclopropenylium salt by means of boron trifluoride:

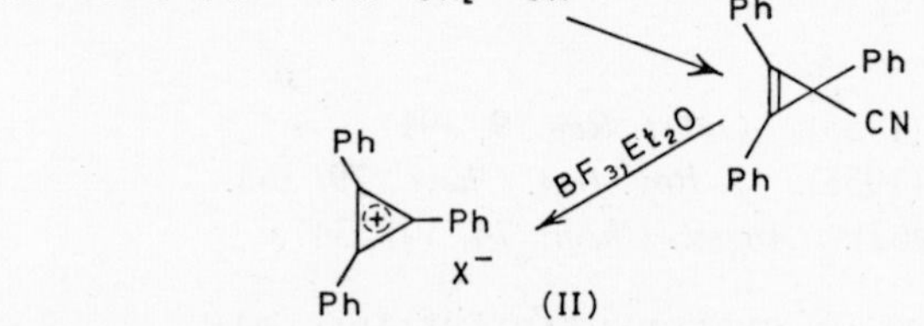

Ph−C≡C−Ph + Ph−CN₂−CN
Ph
Ph
CN
Ph
BF₃,Et₂O
Ph
Ph
X⁻
Ph

(II)

The anion of (II) was mostly BF_4^-, with some $[BF_3OH]^-$. Compound (II) was insoluble in ether, benzene or chloroform, but was soluble in methanol. It melted at 300° with decomposition and gave a stable picrate.

Some reactions of (II) are summarised below:

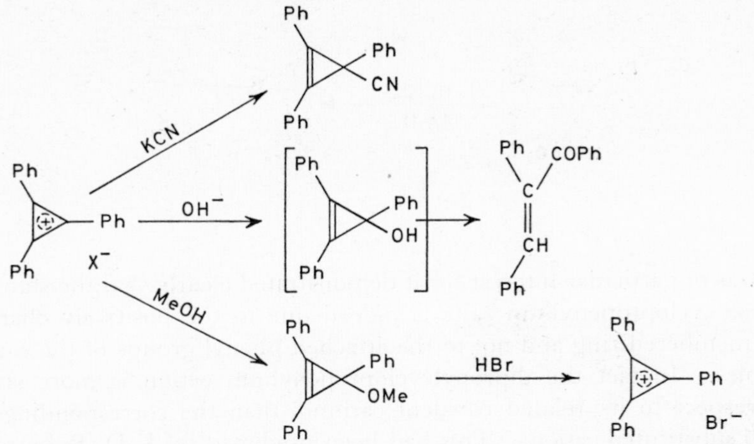

The bromide (III) is completely ionic, in contrast with triphenylmethyl bromide, Ph_3CBr, which is largely covalent. With zinc (III) gives the dimer (IV), which on heating passes into hexaphenylbenzene.

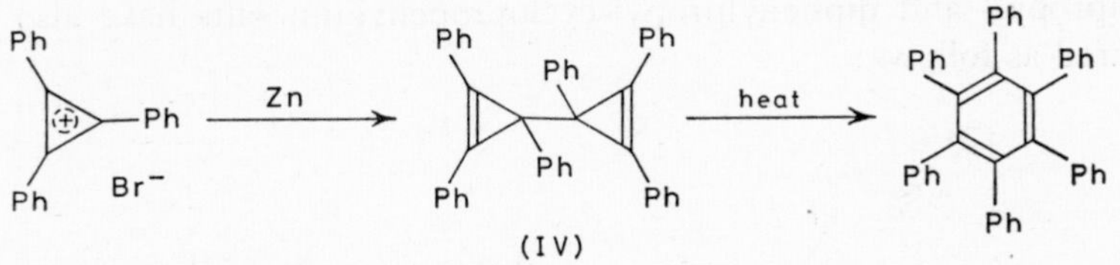

Diphenylcyclopropenylium salts have been prepared by carbene addition reactions to phenyl- and diphenyl-acetylenes, e.g.

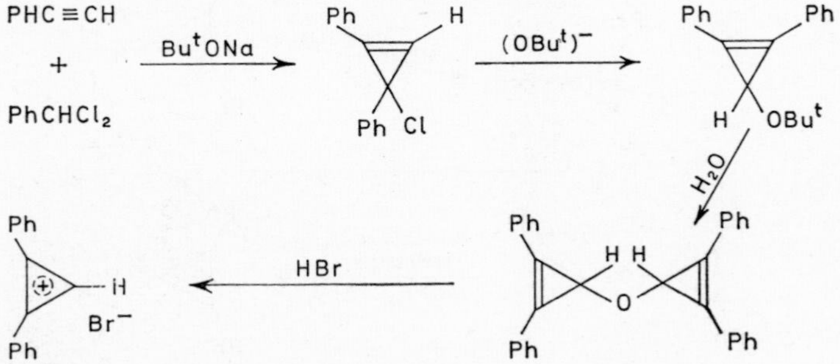

In 1960 Breslow prepared a di-n-propylcyclopropenylium salt (V) by the action of acetyl perchlorate on a di-n-propylcyclopropenecarboxylic acid:

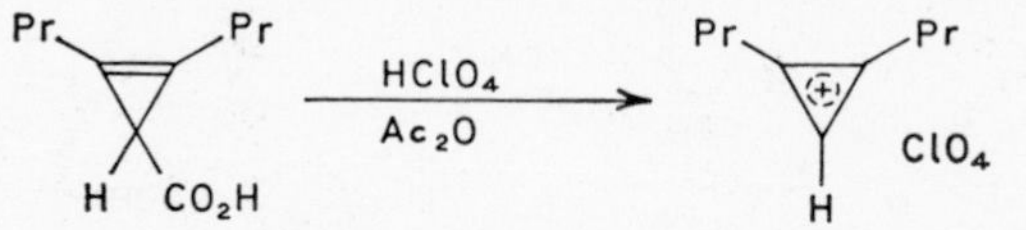

This was of particular interest for it demonstrated clearly that the stability of these cyclopropenylium salts is indeed due to the positively charged three-membered ring and not to the attached phenyl groups of the earlier examples. In fact the dipropylcyclopropenylium cation is more stable with respect to its related covalent carbinol than the corresponding di-phenyl substituted cation. This had been predicted by J. D. Roberts on the grounds that interaction between the two phenyl groups and the con-jugated double bond in the corresponding diphenylcyclopropene carbinol would stabilise the latter molecule relatively to the cation, a situation which would not arise in the case of a dialkylcyclopropene. The salt (V) is, as would be expected, insoluble in ether, hexane, etc., but soluble in polar solvents such as acetone.

Tripropyl- and diphenylpropyl-cyclopropenylium salts have also been prepared as follows:

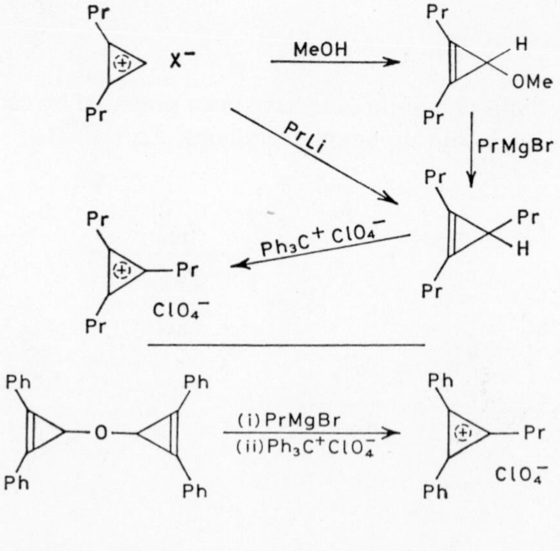

The ketone cyclopropenone (VI) should bear the same relationship to the cyclopropenylium cation as does tropone to the tropylium ion.

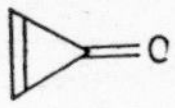

(VI)

Breslow and Vol'pin have prepared diphenylcyclopropenone as follows:

Breslow

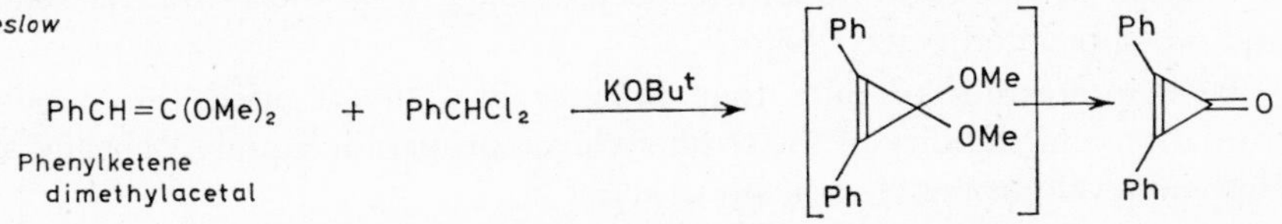

PhCH=C(OMe)$_2$ + PhCHCl$_2$ $\xrightarrow{\text{KOBu}^t}$

Phenylketene
dimethylacetal

Vol'pin

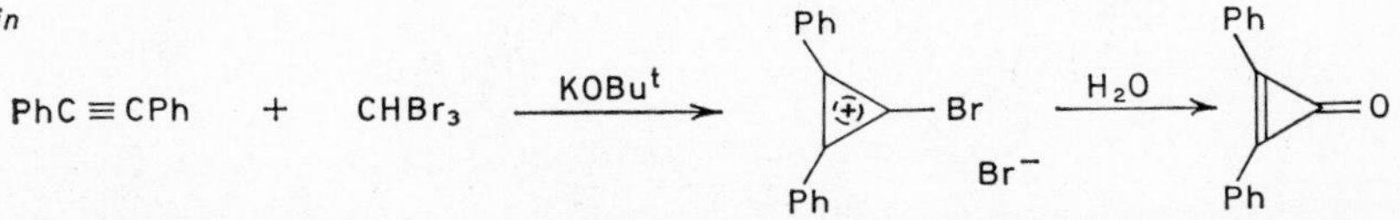

PhC≡CPh + CHBr$_3$ $\xrightarrow{\text{KOBu}^t}$

Diphenylcyclopropenone has a remarkably high dipole moment (5·08 D), higher even than that of tropone. It reacts with gaseous hydrogen bromide or hydrogen chloride to form salts:

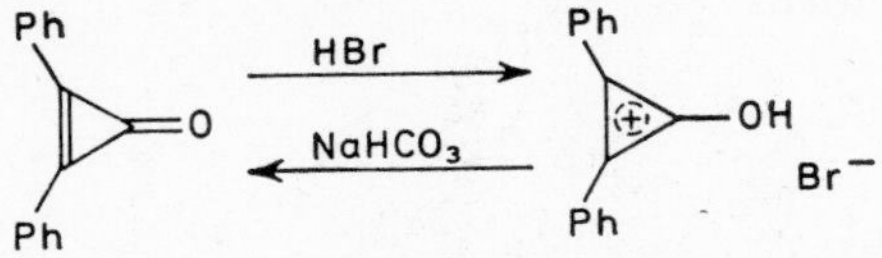

In view of the considerable angle strain involved in the molecule the stability of this cyclopropenone is remarkable; only at temperatures above 130° does it decompose, giving diphenylacetylene and carbon monoxide. The three-membered ring is also opened by heating with alkali:

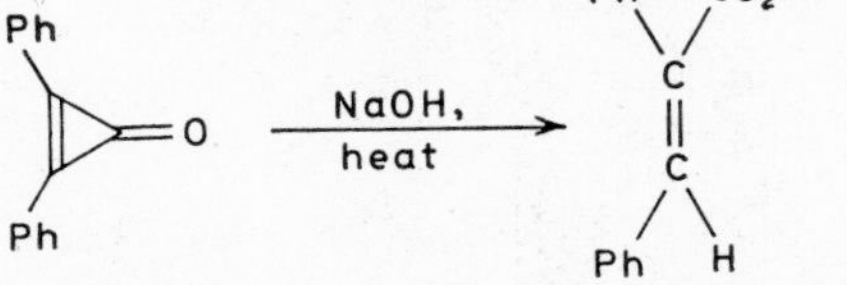

Lithium aluminium hydride reduces the double bond as well as the carbonyl group, even at −70°, presumably owing to the high polarity of the molecule.

Breslow has also prepared di-n-propylcyclopropenone as follows:

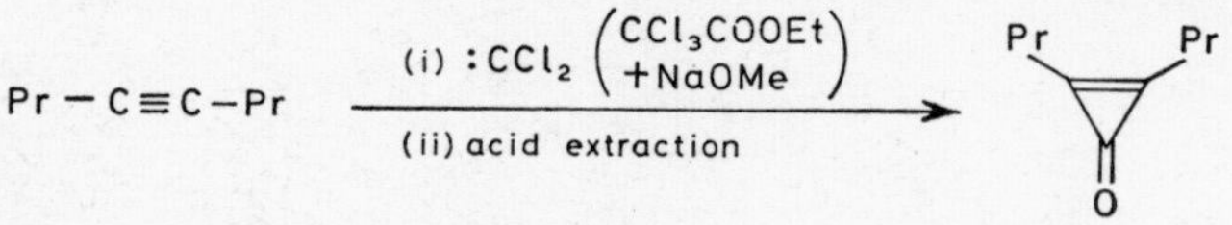

$$Pr-C\equiv C-Pr \xrightarrow[\text{(ii) acid extraction}]{\text{(i) }:CCl_2 \left(\begin{array}{c}CCl_3COOEt \\ +NaOMe\end{array}\right)}$$

It is moderately sensitive to oxygen but is otherwise stable. Di-n-butyl-cyclopropenone and diphenylcyclopropenone have also been prepared by the action of triethylamine on, respectively, $\alpha\alpha'$-dibromodi-n-amyl ketone and $\alpha\alpha'$-dibromodibenzyl ketone.

It is interesting to note that Breslow also investigated the possible formation and stability of the triphenylcyclopropenide anion (VII) and the triphenylcyclopropenyl radical (VIII).

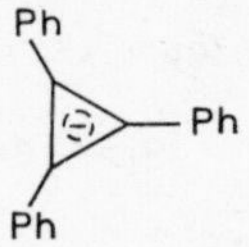

(VII) 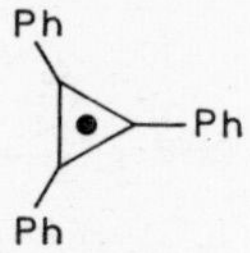   (VIII)

He showed that both could only exist as transient intermediates and not as stable entities. This provides further confirmation for Hückel's theory, for neither of them would have the requisite number of π-electrons to confer stability on them.

INDEX

Figures in bold type indicate the more important references of any particular entry